RING-FORMING POLYMERIZATIONS

PART A: CARBOCYCLIC AND METALLORGANIC RINGS

ORGANIC CHEMISTRY

A SERIES OF MONOGRAPHS

Edited by

ALFRED T. BLOMQUIST

Department of Chemistry, Cornell University, Ithaca, New York

1. Wolfgang Kirmse. CARBENE CHEMISTRY, 1964

2. Brandes H. Smith. BRIDGED AROMATIC COMPOUNDS, 1964

3. Michael Hanack. CONFORMATION THEORY, 1965

4. Donald J. Cram. FUNDAMENTAL OF CARBANION CHEMISTRY, 1965

5. Kenneth B. Wiberg (Editor). OXIDATION IN ORGANIC CHEMISTRY, PART A, 1965; PART B, *In preparation*

6. R. F. Hudson. STRUCTURE AND MECHANISM IN ORGANO-PHOSPHORUS CHEMISTRY, 1965

7. A. William Johnson. YLID CHEMISTRY, 1966

8. Jan Hamer (Editor). 1,4-CYCLOADDITION REACTIONS, 1967

9. Henri Ulrich. CYCLOADDITION REACTIONS OF HETEROCUMULENES, 1967

10. M. P. Cava and M. J. Mitchell. CYCLOBUTADIENE AND RELATED COMPOUNDS, 1967

11. Reinhard W. Hoffman. DEHYDROBENZENE AND CYCLOALKYNES, 1967

12. Stanley R. Sandler and Wolf Karo. ORGANIC FUNCTIONAL GROUP PREPARATIONS, 1968

13. Robert J. Cotter and Markus Matzner. RING-FORMING POLYMERIZATIONS, PART A, 1969; PART B, *In preparation*

RING-FORMING POLYMERIZATIONS

ROBERT J. COTTER and MARKUS MATZNER

RESEARCH AND DEVELOPMENT DEPARTMENT
CHEMICALS AND PLASTICS OPERATIONS DIVISION
UNION CARBIDE CORPORATION
BOUND BROOK, NEW JERSEY

PART A
Carbocyclic and Metallorganic Rings

1969

ACADEMIC PRESS   New York and London

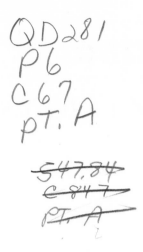

ACADEMIC PRESS, INC.
111 Fifth Avenue, New York, New York 10003

United Kingdom Edition published by
ACADEMIC PRESS, INC. (LONDON) LTD.
Berkeley Square House, London W.1

LIBRARY OF CONGRESS CATALOG CARD NUMBER: 68-26633

PRINTED IN THE UNITED STATES OF AMERICA

To our wives, Barbara and Debora, and children, Patricia, Robert, Jr., Katherine, and Stella. Their patient understanding, interest, and encouragement have contributed immeasurably to the writing of this book.

Preface

The primary purpose of this work is to provide organic and polymer chemists with a comprehensive review and compilation of those polymerizations that proceed with ring formation. It represents an attempt to collect and classify in one location polymerizations that result in the formation of linear polymers containing a new ring structure. Though primarily designed for those chemists who are charged with synthesizing new and unique polymeric repeat units, it is also intended to serve others as a ready reference work to the literature. This monograph, since it discusses polymers possessing a wide variety of organic structures that are only rarely mentioned in polymer chemistry textbooks, should also be useful to organic chemists who are about to begin research in polymer chemistry. Hopefully, this exposure will serve to foster the realization that organic polymer chemistry is as varied and limitless as organic monomer chemistry.

Ring-forming polymerizations comprise a field of polymer chemistry that has undergone a tremendous growth in research effort. The wide scope of this group of polymerizations has been obscured in the past because emphasis has been placed on the polymer class being produced, or on the property being sought from a particular polymer. While most chemists are aware of research being done on intra–intermolecular polymerizations, heterocyclic polymers, chelate polymerizations, thermally stable polymers, etc., few may have realized that work in these fields is interrelated by virtue of the fact that a ring structure is formed during the polymerization. Overall, the research in this field has resulted in the synthesis of some of the most complex and unique polymeric repeat units known to the present time.

This work is comprised of two volumes, Parts A and B; it is organized according to the type of ring that is formed in a particular polymerization. Part A covers polymerizations that form carbocyclic rings and those that lead to metallorganic ring-containing structures. Part B will cover polymerization reactions that yield polymers containing heterocyclic rings. The criterion that was used for inclusion of a polymerization was quite simple. Those that answer the question "Is a ring formed during the actual polymerization reaction?" in the affirmative are included. Thus, while this is not a comprehensive work on ring-containing polymers, it is intended to be comprehensive and complete for those polymers with a ring formed during polymerization. (The alert reader will find a few exceptions to this rule, but they only occur when omission would have seriously detracted from the usefulness of the reported data.) The tables of polymers that have been assembled and presented stand alone as a handy index to polymers that have been prepared by ring-forming polymerizations. In most instances, they are complete bibliographies for the individual polymers, since many have not been prepared by other routes. The monomers from which the polymers in the tables have been prepared are also listed in the Subject Index. Quickly locating a reference wherein the polymerization of a particular monomer has been studied can be a time-saver for those faced with choosing one synthetic path from among many to that monomer. Knowing that other workers have found that a particular synthetic route yields "polymerization grade" monomers should prove extremely valuable.

Searching the literature for the information was a lengthy endeavor since no other work or review has unified the material in this way. The usual information-retrieval techniques, including page by page searching of a large number of polymer journals, were employed. Special emphasis was placed on complete coverage of Russian and patent literature. Although our cross-checking tests do indicate a high degree of success in achieving comprehensive coverage, we hope the omissions that undoubtedly have occurred are not major ones.

As is the case with most endeavors of this type, many people have helped to make it possible. We wish to acknowledge this fact and extend our sincere appreciation to them. Over the last dozen years, the many scientists at Union Carbide who have investigated ring-forming polymerizations have served to stimulate our interest and enhance our knowledge. Among them are Eugene Kraiman, who pioneered research on Diels-Alder polymerizations (Chapter III) in the mid-1950's, and Rudolph W. Kluiber and Joseph Lewis, who achieved the synthesis of the first linear, soluble, high molecular weight chelate polymer (Chapter IX). Others who have contributed include Anthony A. D'Onofrio, S. W. Chow, and Carol K. Sauers. Philip E. Pratt, Eugene W. Beste, J. P. Schroeder, John Wynstra, and R. G. Tonkyn are also colleagues who have been associated with these and similar programs. We also wish to express our appreciation to members of the Technology Committee of the Union Carbide Corporation for their permission to publish this work. Invaluable expressions of interest and encouragement during this project were provided by Leon Shechter, Richard W. Quarles, and John M. Whelan. The early interest and advice of Professor Donald J. Cram is gratefully acknowledged. Others who have read and provided critiques of various parts of the manuscript include Walter T. Reichle, Y. L. Fan, James E. McGrath, Neil J. McCarthy, Jr., and Van Zandt Williams, Jr. Special thanks are extended to Miss Helene Kuhn for her diligent attention to our typing requests and her enthusiastic interest in our book. The aid of Alice Bair who prepared the Subject Index is sincerely appreciated. Others who cheerfully participated in the secretarial chores are Margaret Fischer, Mary Gallo, Dolores Knauber, Barbara Cochilla, Carol Harcarik, Grace Stevens, Patricia LaSasso, Joan Minichino, and Rita Matts.

ROBERT J. COTTER
MARKUS MATZNER

January, 1969
Bound Brook, New Jersey

Contents

xi

Tentative Contents of Part B

Part B: RING–FORMING POLYMERIZATIONS

Introduction

The last decade has witnessed an enormous increase in the number of organic and metallorganic structures that have been incorporated into linear polymers. A surprisingly high number of these new materials have been synthesized by ring-forming polymerization reactions. A ring-forming polymerization produces a polymer that contains a ring structure that is not present in any of the monomers. In most cases, the ring structure appears to be formed during the propagation step, simultaneous with the increase in molecular weight. It is this type of polymerization reaction that is covered in this book. However, detailed mechanistic studies that pinpoint exactly when the ring is formed are not available for most cases. Examples are known in which rings are definitely formed in polymers by postcyclization reactions on a precursor polymer. A few examples of this route to ring-containing polymers are discussed in this book, but comprehensive coverage of this type was not attempted.

History

The beginnings of modern, synthetic polymer chemistry can be traced to the pioneering research of Wallace H. Carothers which was carried out in the early nineteen thirties (27). (Others, of course, such as Baekeland and Staudinger also made important fundamental contributions to polymer synthesis.) One important concept that evolved from Carothers' work is that of monomer *functionality*, i.e., the average number of reactive functional groups per monomer molecule (8, 16). Monofunctional monomers give low molecular weight compounds as shown schematically in Eq. (Int.-1). If the reacting molecules are difunctional, linear, thermoplastic, high molecular weight polymers are formed, Eq. (Int.-2). If at least one of the reactants has a functionality of three or higher and the reaction is driven to completion, a three-dimensional, cross-linked polymer is obtained, Eq. (Int.-3). These considerations were formulated into laws that describe the effect of monomer functionality on product structure. However, examples of polyfunctional reactants that polymerize to linear polymers have been appearing with increasing frequency. In most cases, a ring is formed.

$$RA + R'B \longrightarrow RABR' \qquad \text{(Int.-1)}$$
$$\quad [1] \quad\ [2] \qquad\qquad\ \ [3]$$

$$n-A- \ +\ n-B- \ \longrightarrow\ -A\!\left[B-A\right]_n\!B- \qquad \text{(Int.-2)}$$
$$\quad [4] \qquad\qquad [5] \qquad\qquad\qquad [6]$$

$$\qquad\qquad\qquad\qquad\qquad \text{(Int.-3)}$$

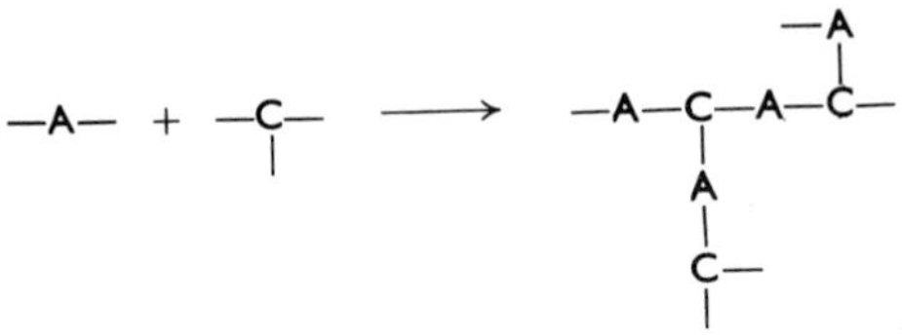

$$\quad [7] \qquad\ \ [8] \qquad\qquad\qquad [9]$$

Ring-forming polymerizations that lead to linear polymers require that the monomers possess functionalities of greater than two. At least one of the functions is necessary to form the ring. Equation (Int.-4) schematically depicts the polymerization of a trifunctional monomer with a difunctional monomer to yield a linear product. This can occur because one B function in [10] reacts with the newly formed –BA– linkage. Its proximity to the –BA– linkage allows it to react in a different manner than the other B functions in [10]. A specific example of the type depicted in Eq. (Int.-4) might be that shown in Eq. (Int.-5).

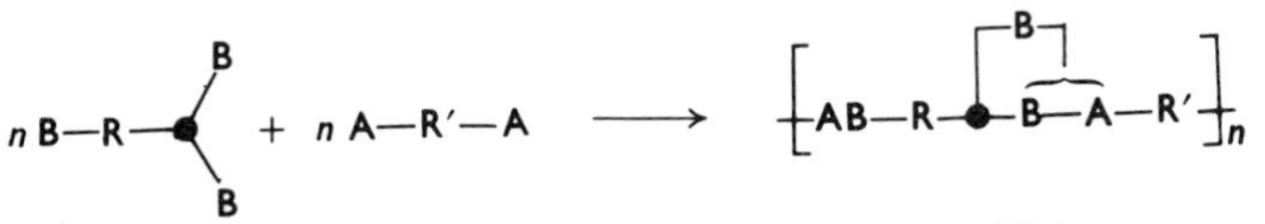

$$\qquad\qquad\qquad\qquad\qquad\qquad\qquad\qquad\qquad \text{(Int.-4)}$$

$$\quad [10] \qquad\qquad [11] \qquad\qquad\qquad\qquad [12]$$

$$n\,HOOC-\!\!\!\bigcirc\!\!\!-COOH \ +\ n\,H_2N(CH_2)_2NH_2 \longrightarrow$$

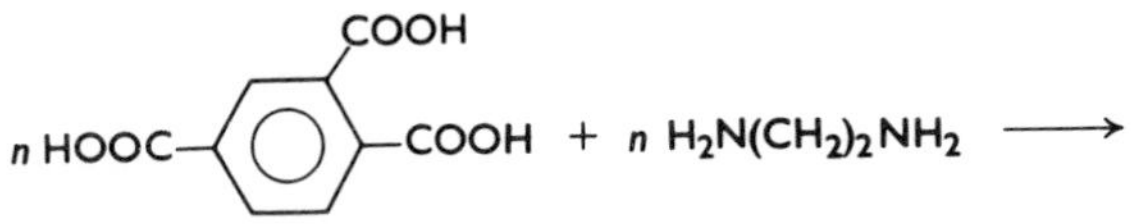

$$\qquad [13] \qquad\qquad\qquad\qquad [14]$$

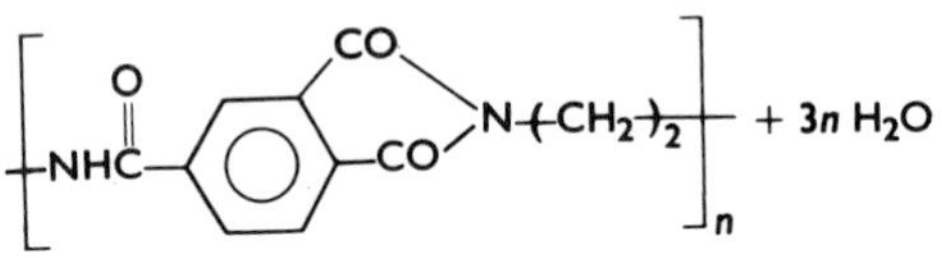

$$\qquad\qquad\qquad\qquad\qquad\qquad\qquad + 3n\,H_2O \qquad \text{(Int.-5)}$$

$$\qquad\qquad\qquad [15]$$

The remarkable intra–intermolecular polymerization in which a monomer with a functionality of four gives linear, soluble, high molecular weight polymer is shown schematically in Eq. (Int.-6). In both reactions, Eqs. (Int.-5) and (Int.-6), the polyfunctionality of the monomers that might lead to cross-linked products is not operative because other factors prevailing in the monomers determine a different reaction course. That this situation can occur with many different types of polyfunctional reactants is amply illustrated by the examples in this book.

$$n \quad \begin{array}{cc} CH_2 & CH_2 \\ \| & \| \\ CH & CH \\ \diagdown R \diagup \end{array} \quad \longrightarrow \quad \left[CH_2 \diagdown \underset{\diagdown R \diagup}{CH} \diagup CH \right]_n \qquad (Int.\ 6)$$

[16]   [17]

It is interesting to speculate whether Carothers' work, being so basic and all-encompassing, served to inhibit subsequent creativity in synthetic polymer chemistry. Frequently, when rapid, broad studies are made in a field of scientific endeavor, they can serve as unintentional barriers to further advances. While the successes of Carothers' researches were well utilized commercially, his failures were apparently well noted by researchers. Many new polyamides were prepared in attempts to find another nylon, but few new classes of polymers and fewer really new synthetic methods were developed. The polymer classes that he had found to possess properties inferior to the polyamides were scarcely investigated in the following years. More than 20 years passed after these reports before polycarbonates, polyethers, and polyesters were reinvestigated and the commercial products of today were developed. The wide scope that is only now emerging for ring-forming polymerizations of polyfunctional monomers to linear polymers is indeed remarkable. Its appearance may well have been delayed by the functionality laws of polymer science.

PERSPECTIVES

This book is organized according to the specific ring structure that is formed in a ring-forming polymerization. Chapters I–IV of this volume cover the polymerizations that form homocyclic carbon rings. Chapters V–XI cover polymerizations that form rings containing metal or metallike atoms. Part B will deal with polymerizations that form heterocyclic rings. This arrangement was chosen to be of maximum aid to the synthetic polymer chemists who are interested in tailormaking polymer repeat units. By classifying his proposed new repeat unit according to the types of rings present in it, he will be able to consult this book to ascertain whether any ring-forming polymerizations are of interest to him. Each chapter is further arranged according to polymer type and the various methods that have been used to prepare that type. The emphasis is on synthetic methods, with the numbers assigned to the methods also being used in the tables to indicate how the tabulated polymers were made. Although the considerations that result in a number being assigned to a method may seem arbitrary at times, they were often necessary to aid in the codification of the data.

Although the term polymer can mean different things to many people, this book is about linear polymers that were made intentionally. Tars, distillation residues, or glops from reactions that "went bad" (unintentional polymerizations) are not included. Ring-forming polymerizations that were planned to be such by their experimenters are what have been considered. The qualitative description of the molecular weight of a polymer can also be ambiguous. In this book, the term "high molecular weight" is used to mean that a level has been attained that imparts mechanical properties to the polymer. That is, it is either film- or fiber-forming and mechanical property evaluation is possible. Another way to look at our use of this term is that the polymer is high enough in molecular weight so that further increases do not appreciably change its mechanical properties. "Low molecular weight" is used to designate oligomers and "moderate molecular weight" describes polymer samples with molecular weights up to the threshold level for property appearance (30, 34). Since definite molecular weight numbers associated with these various criteria differ from class to class, and moreover, are generally not available anyway, these qualitative terms were found to be useful and meaningful.

Whether or not a high molecular weight, linear polymer was obtainable from a particular ring-forming polymerization was used as the main criterion for judging the merits of the method. The data in the tables were also selected to indicate at a glance if the polymer was obtained at a high molecular weight. However, being well aware of how fickle polymerizations can be with respect to whether high, moderately high, or low molecular weight products are obtained, all ring-forming polymerizations that were found have been included. No exclusions were made for any reason. Too many examples exist in the authors' experiences of "unsuccessful" polymerizations that were made to work when greater attention was paid to experimental techniques, monomer purification procedures, or other details. Finally, a word of warning is in order to those who may be uninitiated in the difficulties attendant to proving the structure of a polymer. The structures reported for the polymers described in this book are those suggested by the workers whose research is cited. In many cases, particularly in the area of chelate polymerization, the evidence presented for the assigned structures hinged mainly on the reactants employed and an elemental analysis of the intractable product. Of course, where evidence was found that disputed an assigned structure, it is included and discussed. The newer, nondestructive, spectrophotometric methods for structure determination have been used on many ring-containing polymers and their wider use is to be encouraged. In any event, we hope this alert will serve those who may not be aware of this problem.

CHAPTER OUTLINE

Chapters I–IV of this volume describe ring-forming polymerizations that lead to the formation of homocyclic carbon-containing rings. Carbon–carbon double bonds can be considered to be "two-membered rings." As such, polymerization reactions that propagate by double-bond formation fall within the scope of this book and are covered in Chapter I. Perhaps more importantly, the *pi* electrons of the double bond could be available for cross-linking reactions, and hence, a polyfunctionality is present that is similar to that in other ring-forming polymerizations. Chapter II describes those intra–intermolecular polymerizations that form homocyclic carbon rings. In this instance, diolefins with a functionality of four polymerize to linear polymers. Diels-Alder polymerizations are discussed in Chapter III and a wide variety of polymerization reactions that form all carbon rings are included in Chapter IV. This chapter also discusses certain diisopropenyl monomers that can polymerize to yield high molecular weight polyindanes. Reviews on "ladder" or "double-strand" polymers were useful sources of information (*14, 36*).

Ring-forming polymerizations that yield metallorganic ring-containing polymers are described in Chapters V–XI. Chapter V is an introduction to polymers from metals and unsaturated carbon compounds. This type of polymer has been called a "natural coordination polymer", because the polymeric structure exists primarily in the crystalline state. A review of this type of material is available (*9*); another review discusses metal–olefin and olefinlike substances (*15*). Chapters VI–X deal with metallorganic ring polymers formed by chelation and are arranged according to the elements in the ligand that are effecting chelation. Thus, Chapter VI covers chelation by ligands containing nitrogen atoms; Chapter VII, by nitrogen and oxygen atoms; Chapter VIII, by nitrogen and sulfur atoms; Chapter IX, by oxygen atoms; and Chapter X, by sulfur chelating ligands. Only those polymerizations that proceed by ring formation are included in these chapters. This choice does, of course, omit the other routes to chelate polymers, i.e., polymerization of a chelate through a pendant polymerizable function or postchelation on a polymer possessing suitable ligand sites. Chapter XI covers ring-forming polymerizations that yield polysiloxanes, polysilazanes, and certain poly-metalloxanes.

Polymerization reactions that form metallorganic rings straddle organic and inorganic chemistry. For this reason, information about this type of polymerization can be found under many classifications in the literature.

Reviews containing substantial amounts of data on metallorganic ring-forming polymerizations were found under chelate polymers (7, 18, 23, 31, 33); coordination polymers (5, 6, 9–12, 19, 20, 22, 24, 32, 35); metallorganic polymers (3, 17, 25); and high-temperature polymers (1, 2, 4, 26, 28). Reviews and books on inorganic polymers were also useful.

Polymerizations that form metal-containing rings are usually chelation reactions. Polymers that possess properties equalling the sum of their organic and inorganic structural components were a frequent goal. The metal was expected to contribute thermal stability and electrical and thermal conductivity, whereas the organic structure would supply the plasticity, toughness, and fabricability properties necessary for practical utility. The fact that there existed examples of the stabilization of organic compounds against thermal or chemical attack by chelation with a metal ion stimulated efforts in this direction. An oft-quoted example was the fact that copper phthalocyanine [18] could be sublimed "at about 500°C at low pressure in an atmosphere of nitrogen and carbon dioxide" and resists the action of molten potash and of boiling hydrochloric acid (13). Similarly, ethylenediaminobisacetylacetone is not exceptionally thermally stable, but its copper chelate [19] is only slowly decomposed at red heat (29). The tris (N-hydroxyethylethylenediamine) cobalt (III) ion [20] has been reported to be stable to nitric acid, and aqua regia

[18]

[19]

(Int.-7)

[20]

and thermally stable to 245°–250°C (*21*). The degree of success that has been achieved to date in the synthesis of useful materials with the desired properties has been quite variable. Nevertheless, a wide variety of polymeric structures have been prepared by chelation. This fact in itself is indeed intriguing and could serve as a fertile source of ideas for the synthesis of new and useful polymers in the future.

EXPLANATION OF TABLES AND ABBREVIATIONS

The tables of polymers that have been assembled and presented in this book stand alone as a handy index to polymers that have been prepared by ring-forming polymerizations. In most instances, they are complete bibliographies for the individual polymers, since many have not been prepared by other routes. The general guidelines that were used in assembling these tables from the literature data are given below. Abbreviations that are used in the tables and text are also explained.

Number

The first column in every table contains an arabic number that has been assigned to each polymer or entry in the table. The first entry in a table is No. 1, with the following ones being numbered consecutively.

Structure

The tables in Chapters I, II, and V–XI have the structure of the repeating unit of the polymer in the second column. Within a table, the polymers are arranged according to increasing complexity and/or empirical formula of the repeat unit. Generally, the aliphatic and cycloaliphatic structures are listed first, followed by those containing an increasing number of aromatic rings. Para-disubstituted benzene ring-containing polymers generally precede meta-disubstituted rings. Copolymers are listed under the homopolymers to which they are most closely related. In some instances, the name of the monomer from which the polymer was prepared is given under the repeat unit structure. If a structure has been presented in the text preceding the table, only a reference to that page and structure number may be listed. Abbreviations that are used in the structural formulas are always explained under the structure. The symbol $-\left[\left(\quad\right)_x\left(\quad\right)_y\right]_n$ denotes a copolymer, not a block copolymer.

Monomers

The second column in the tables of Chapters III and IV lists the names of the monomers that were polymerized. Order of arrangement follows the guidelines described above for structure. In every instance, the actual repeat unit of the polymer reported has been adequately described in the text preceding these tables.

Metal

The tables in Chapters V–XI (metallorganic ring-forming polymerizations) contain a column that lists the metals that were incorporated with the polymers and their oxidation number. They are designated as "M" in the structure of the repeat unit in the adjacent column.

Method

The tables in Chapters I–XI all contain a Method column which contains at least one number for each entry. This number refers to the synthetic method described in the preceding text of that chapter that was used to prepare the polymer. Since some polymers have been prepared by more than one method, one entry can have more than one method number. Data that are subsequently reported on the same line as the method number were obtained on a polymer sample that was prepared by the indicated method.

Color

Chapter V–XI tables contain a column in which the reported color of the polymer is listed. In the tables of Chapters I–IV, this information is reported under the Remarks and Property Data column.

Solubility

All of the tables contain a column relating solubility information. This column generally lists the solvents that have been reported for the polymer. If nothing was said about the solubility of the polymer in the original article, this column is left blank. If a polymer was described as being "insoluble," this has been reported in the table. If data reported in the Molecular Weight column were obtained by solution methods, the first solvent listed under Solubility is the solvent that was used.

Molecular Weight

Chapters I–IV and VI–XI contain a column that is entitled "Molecular Weight." The data listed herein can be of several types and are what the original article said about the molecular weight of the polymer that was obtained. If a range of molecular weight data was reported, only the highest values are listed. Abbreviations for the various types of viscosities are as follows: η, unspecified; $[\eta]$, intrinsic; η_{red}, reduced; η_{sp}, specific; η_{inh}, inherent; $z\eta$ viscosity number (8). Actual molecular weights are also reported in this column with the method used following in parentheses. Other abbreviations that appear in this column are $\bar{M}_n$, number average molecular weight; $\bar{M}_w$, weight average molecular weight; DP, degree of polymerization; and VPO, vapor-phase osmometry. The first solvent that is listed under Solubility is generally the one that was used to obtain molecular weight data by a solution method.

T_g $(°C)$

This is the glass or second-order transition temperature. These data were only infrequently available and are sometimes reported under the Remarks and Property Data column. The Russian literature reports a "temperature of maximum dimensional change" that could be a guide to the T_g. It is also listed when available under Remarks and Property Data.

Melting Point, T_m $(°C)$

This is the melting point of the polymer, but since this term is still used loosely in the polymer literature, the reported data are not always true melting points. When the presence or absence of crystallinity has been determined, the result has also been recorded, sometimes under Remarks and Property Data. Thus, when a material is noted as being crystalline, the reported melting point is quite apt to be a true crystalline melting point. When the method of determining the "melting point" has been reported it has been recorded in the Table. Some abbreviations used in this column are d, decomposition; PMT, polymer melt temperature; TGA, thermogravimetric analysis; and DTA, differential thermal analysis.

Remarks and Property Data

Most tables contain this column to record other pertinent data that give a more complete picture of the particular polymer. Abbreviations that can be found in these columns include psi, pounds per square inch; IR, infrared, EPR, electron paramagnetic resonance; NMR, nuclear magnetic resonance; and some of the ones already defined previously.

References

The reference numbers listed are those where preparation of the particular polymer entry has been described or where the polymer is mentioned. They refer only to the list at the end of the chapter in which they appear.

ABBREVIATIONS

AIBN	azobis(isobutyronitrile)
DMAC	dimethylacetamide
DMF	dimethylformamide
DMSO	dimethyl sulfoxide
TCNE	tetracyanoethylene
THF	tetrahydrofuran

REFERENCES

1. Aitken, I. D., Sheldon, R., and Stapleton, G. B., *Brit. Plastics* **34**, 662 (1961).
2. Aitken, I. D., Sheldon, R., and Stapleton, G. B., *Brit. Plastics* **35**, 39 (1962).
3. Andrianov, K. A., "Metalorganic Polymers." Wiley (Interscience), New York, 1965.
4. Atlas, S. M., and Mark, H. F., *Angew. Chem.* **72**, 249 (1960).
5. Bailar, J. C., Jr., *Chem. Soc. (London), Spec. Publ.* **15**, 51 (1961).
6. Bailar, J. C., Jr., Martin, K. V., Judd, M. L., and McLean, J. A., Jr., WADC Tech. Rep. No. 57-391, Part I (1957).
7. Berlin, A. A., and Matveeva, N. G., *Usp. Khim.* **29**, 277 (1960); *Russ. Chem. Rev. (English Transl.)* p. 119 (1960).
8. Billmeyer, F. W., "Textbook of Polymer Science," Chapters 8-12. Wiley (Interscience), New York, 1966.
9. Block, B. P., *in* "Inorganic Polymers" (F. G. A. Stone and W. A. G. Graham, eds.), p. 447. Academic Press, New York, 1962.
10. Block, B. P., *Encycl. Polymer Sci. Technol.* **4**, 150 (1966); *Chem. Abstr.* **65**, 17056 (1966).
11. Block, B., *Double Liaison* **105**, 109 (1964); *Chem. Abstr.* **66**, 4431, 46601u (1967).
12. Block, B. P., *Am. Chem. Soc., Div. Polymer Chem., Preprints* **8**, 303 (1967).
13. Dent, C. E., and Linstead, R. P., *J. Chem. Soc.* p. 1027 (1934).
14. DeWinter, W., *Rev. Macromol. Chem.* **1**, 329 (1966); *Chem. Abstr.* **66**, 5285, 55758w (1967).
15. Douglas, B. E., *in* "The Chemistry of Coordination Compounds" (J. C. Bailar, Jr., ed.), Chapter 15, p. 487. Reinhold, New York, 1956.
16. Flory, P. J., "Principles of Polymer Chemistry." Cornell Univ. Press, Ithaca, New York, 1953.
17. Haslam, J. H., *Advan. Chem. Ser.* **23**, 272 (1959); *Chem. Abstr.* **54**, 4347 (1960).
18. Hatano, M., *Yuki Gosei Kagaku Kyokai Shi* **24**, 453 (1966); *Chem. Abstr.* **65**, 4035 (1966).
19. Huggins, M. L., *Am. Chem. Soc., Div. Polymer Chem., Preprints* **8**, 306 (1967).
20. Huggins, M. L., *Proc. 8th Intern. Conf. Coord. Chem., Vienna, 1964* p. 253; *Chem. Abstr.* **67**, 2131, 22201b (1967).
21. Keller, R. N., and Edwards, L. J., *J. Am. Chem. Soc.* **74**, 215 (1952).
22. Kenney, C. N., *Chem. & Ind. (London)* p. 880 (1960).
23. Kenney, C. N., *in* "Developments in Inorganic Polymer Chemistry" (M. F. Lappert and G. J. Leigh, eds.), p. 256. Elsevier, Amsterdam, 1962.
24. Kiehne, H., *Gummi, Asbest, Kunstoffe* **15**, 969 (1962); *Chem. Abstr.* **58**, 8041 (1963).
25. Korshak, V. V., *Usp. v. Obl. Sinteza Elementoorgan. Polimierov, Akad. Nauk SSSR, Inst. Elementoorgan. Soedin.* p. 5 (1966); *Chem. Abstr.* **65**, 12285 (1966).
26. Korshak, V. V., and Krongauz, E. S., *Russ. Chem. Rev. (English Transl.)* **33**, 609 (1964).
27. Mark, H., and Whitby, C. S., "Collected Papers of Wallace H. Carothers on Polymerization." Wiley (Interscience), New York, 1940.
28. Mark, H. F., *Pure Appl. Chem.* **12**, 9 (1966); *Chem. Abstr.* **66**, 4431, 46608v (1967).
29. Morgan, G. T., and Smith, M., *J. Chem. Soc.* p. 912 (1926).
30. Nielsen, L. E., "Mechanical Properties of Polymers." Reinhold, New York, 1962.
31. Rode, V. V., Rukhadze, E. G., and Terent'ev, A. P., *Usp. Khim.* **32**, 1488 (1963); *Russ. Chem. Rev. (English Transl.)* p. 666 (1963).
32. Sowerby, D. B., and Audrieth, L. F., *J. Chem. Educ.* **37**, 2, 86, and 134 (1960).
33. Takeshita, T., *Nippon Secchaku Kyokai Shi* **2**, 425 (1966); *Chem. Abstr.* **67**, 2127, 22165t (1967).
34. Tobolsky, A. V., "Properties and Structure of Polymers." Wiley, New York, 1960.
35. Vinogradova, S. V., *Usp. v. Obl. Sinteza Elementoorgan. Polimierov, Akad. Nauk SSSR, Inst. Elementoorgan. Soedin.* p. 59 (1966); *Chem. Abstr.* **65**, 12285 (1966).
36. Weil, A., *Double Liaison* **111**, 91 (1964); *Chem. Abstr.* **66**, 4431, 46597r (1967).

CHAPTER I

Carbon–Carbon Double Bond-Forming Polymerizations

Polymers containing carbon-to-carbon double bonds can be regarded as possessing the smallest possible homocyclic carbon ring, a two-membered carbon cycle. Depending on their method of preparation, polymers of this type fall into two categories: (a) polymers in which the double bond formed during the polymerization connects two carbon atoms that were not attached to each other before polymerization (or, in one case, by more than a single bond prior to polymerization), and (b) polymers obtained by the linear polymerization of an acetylenic linkage. Polymers of this type (I-1) have been extensively investigated (*1, 3, 5–10, 14, 16, 29, 37, 40*). They are not covered in this book because they are actually formed by a "ring-opening" rather than a ring-forming polymerization.

$$n \ -C\equiv C- \quad \xrightarrow{\text{Catalyst}} \quad \left[C=C \right]_n \qquad \text{(I-1)}$$

This chapter covers the synthetic methods for polymers that fall within category (a). The properties of these polymers are also discussed.

METHOD 1. CONDENSATION OF CARBONYL COMPOUNDS WITH COMPOUNDS CONTAINING ACTIVE METHYLENE GROUPS

Linear polymers can be obtained by the base-catalyzed condensation of compounds possessing active methylene groups with compounds possessing carbonyl groups. An example is shown in Eq. (I-2) (*20–23*). Anhydrous ethanol, dioxane, dimethylformamide, and dimethyl sulfoxide were suitable solvents. Low molecular weight polymers were obtained that had predominately aldehydic termination. The insolubility and infusibility of the polymer shown in Eq. (I-2) led to the belief that it was not linear (*33*). Cross-linking was ascribed to several secondary reactions like nitrile trimerizations, Michael additions, Thorpe condensations, and Cannizzaro and Tishshenko reactions. A later investigation demonstrated conclusively that no such secondary reactions take place and that the polymer is linear (23). Its insolubility and infusibility are apparently characteristic of its structure.

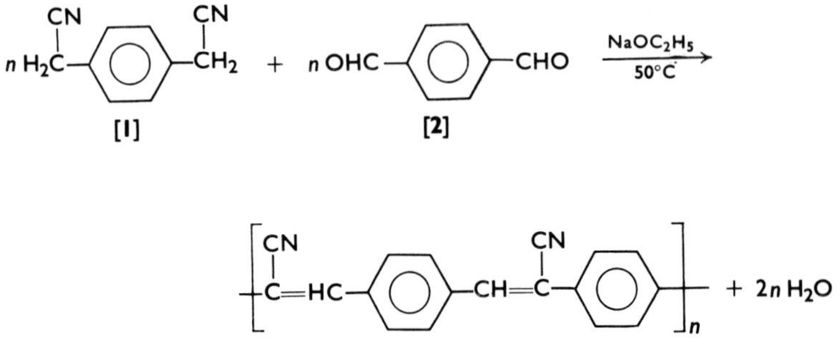

A dark-brown, insoluble, and infusible polymer was obtained by a similar polycondensation (I-3) (32). Solvents useful for this type of reaction included benzyl alcohol (44), absolute ethanol (50), mixtures of alcohol and Cellosolve (50), and even water (32). The use of piperidine as a basic catalyst was also reported (44). Temperatures ranging from room temperature (32) to 90°C (44) were employed. Reaction times of a few hours are required.

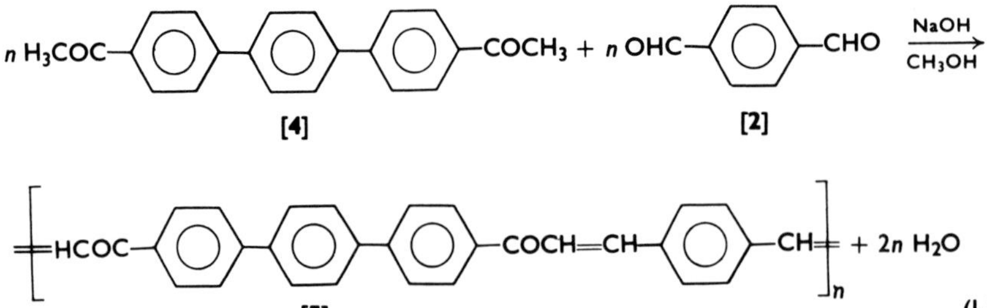

The polycondensation of an aromatic dialdehyde with a nitro-substituted p-xylene gave a high molecular weight polymer [Eq. (I-4)] (53). Preferred reaction conditions utilized a stoichiometric amount of sodium ethoxide in absolute alcohol at 60°C. The optimum reaction time was 8 hours. Sodium methoxide was too weak a base in this polymerization, whereas the use of potassium *tert*-butoxide led to secondary reactions. Interestingly, catalytic amounts of sodium ethoxide gave the parent polyols. These were easily dehydrated by 20% sulfuric acid to the unsaturated polymer shown in Eq. (I-4). This particular modification yielded polymers with molecular weights up to 10,000.

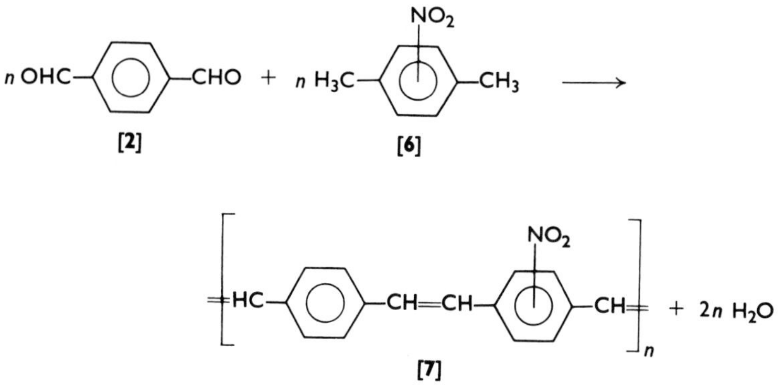

$$n\ \text{OHC} - \bigcirc - \text{CHO} \ + \ n\ \text{H}_3\text{C} - \overset{\text{NO}_2}{\bigcirc} - \text{CH}_3 \ \longrightarrow$$

[2] [6]

$$\left[\text{HC} - \bigcirc - \text{CH}{=}\text{CH} - \overset{\text{NO}_2}{\bigcirc} - \text{CH} \right]_n + 2n\ \text{H}_2\text{O} \qquad \text{(I-4)}$$

[7]

This method was also useful in the self-condensation shown in Eq. (I-5) (*53*).

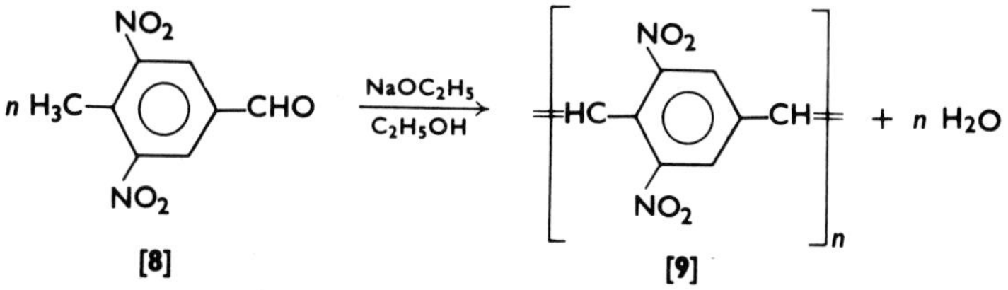

$$n\ \text{H}_3\text{C} - \overset{\text{NO}_2}{\underset{\text{NO}_2}{\bigcirc}} - \text{CHO} \ \xrightarrow[\text{C}_2\text{H}_5\text{OH}]{\text{NaOC}_2\text{H}_5} \ \left[\text{HC} - \overset{\text{NO}_2}{\underset{\text{NO}_2}{\bigcirc}} - \text{CH} \right]_n + n\ \text{H}_2\text{O} \qquad \text{(I-5)}$$

[8] [9]

In the case of the 2-picolinic aldehyde shown in Eq. (I-6), the only catalytic system that gave polymer was potassium *tert*-butoxide in dimethyl sulfoxide (*53*).

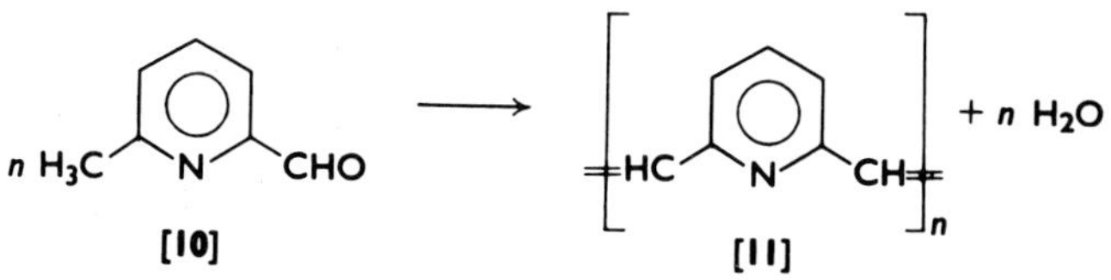

$$n\ \text{H}_3\text{C} - \overset{\bigcirc}{\underset{\text{N}}{}} - \text{CHO} \ \longrightarrow \ \left[\text{HC} - \overset{\bigcirc}{\underset{\text{N}}{}} - \text{CH} \right]_n + n\ \text{H}_2\text{O} \qquad \text{(I-6)}$$

[10] [11]

The reaction of 2,5-dimethylpyridine with terephthalaldehyde [Eq. (I-7)] yielded a crystalline polymer that softened at 210°C and possessed a specific viscosity of 0.21 (H_2SO_4). The structure [13] of this polymer was in agreement with chemical and spectroscopic evidence (44). It had aldehydic termination; its molecular weight determined by elemental analysis of its thiosemicarbazone was 5000. This polymer is soluble in several solvents: sulfuric and hydrochloric acids, benzyl alcohol, pyridine, quinoline, and m-cresol. When the polycondensation was performed at higher temperature (210°–220°C), an insoluble polymer was obtained. Whether the insolubility was due to a higher molecular weight polymer was not determined.

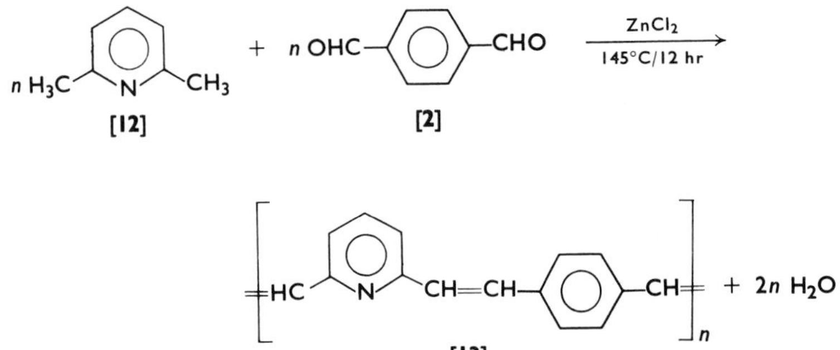

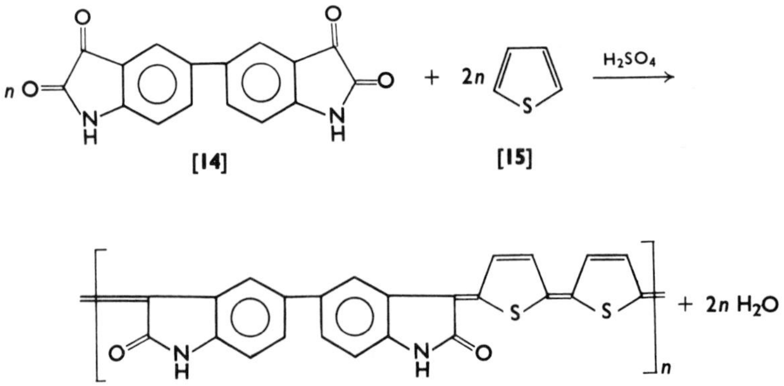

Recently, 5,5'-biisatyl has been condensed with thiophene in strong acid to yield the poly(indophenine) [16] in quantitative yield (34, 48). The reaction (I-8) is over in 5 minutes at room temperature. Viscosity data indicate that the product is of low molecular weight ([η] 0.06). It did not melt up to 500°C and carbonized when heated to 900°C. The product is, of course, related to known, monomeric vat dyes and is reducible and reoxidizable with sodium dithionite and air, respectively (48).

METHOD 2. OXIDATION OF COMPOUNDS CONTAINING TWO ACTIVE METHYLENE GROUPS

The preparation of polymers by oxidation of monomers containing two active methylene groups has been reported by two different groups (4, 11). Polyindigo [20] was prepared as shown in Eq. (I-9) (11).

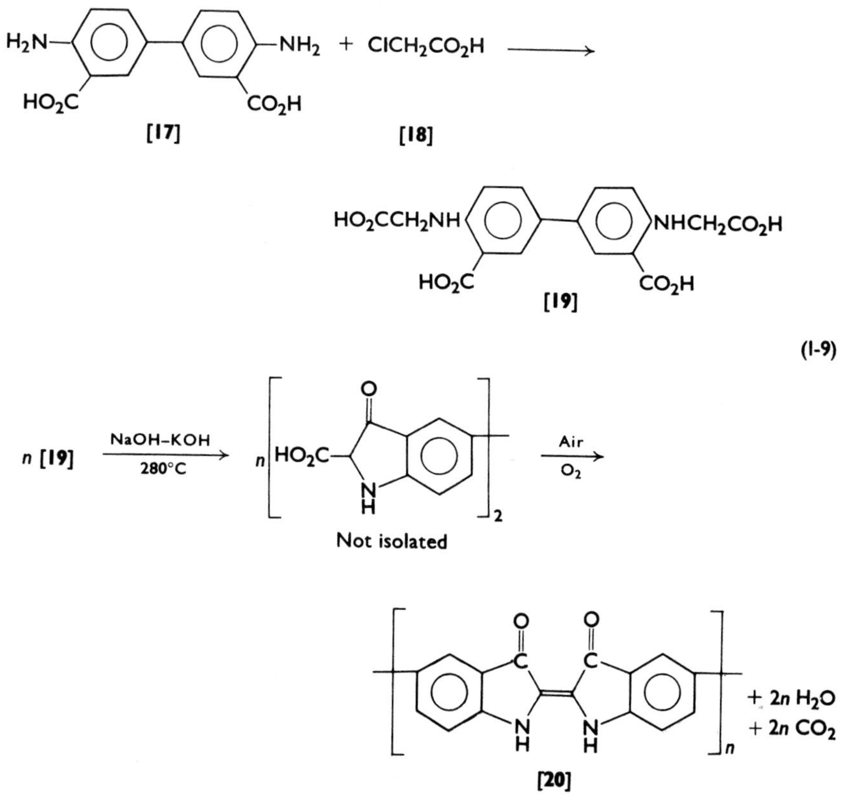

(I-9)

Not isolated

[20]

A specific viscosity of 0.13 was reported for the polymer. Other properties are listed in Table I.3 (pp. 26–28). Actual isolation and oxidation of the compound [26], Eq. (I-10), containing two active methylenes was also reported (4).

Although the conditions used for the oxidative polymerization of [26] are not yet available, the analogous monomer derived from [19] was polymerized by air at 80°C (*11*).

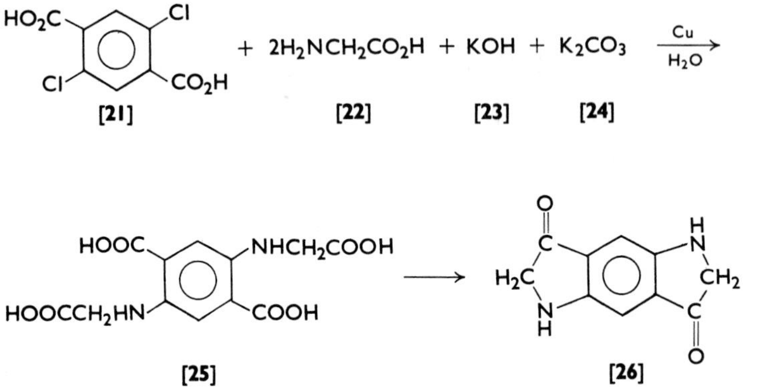

METHOD 3. BASE TREATMENT OF BIS(HALOMETHYL) COMPOUNDS

The ammonolysis of bis(halomethyl) compounds yields polymers containing double bonds (*18, 27, 49, 57*). An example is shown in Eq. (I-11).

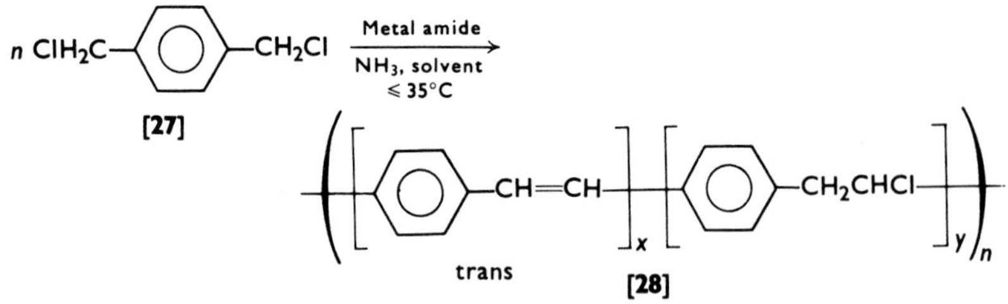

Low molecular weight polymers were obtained (*27, 28*). Tetrahydrofuran and benzene were preferred solvents. Depending on the specific metal amide (potassium, sodium, lithium), reaction temperature, order of addition of reagents, and the mole ratio of metal/monomer used, polymers of different *x/y* ratios were obtained (*18*). Elemental analyses showed that the polymers contained carbon, hydrogen, chlorine, nitrogen, and oxygen. The nitrogen and oxygen are due to terminal aminomethyl, carboxy, and carbamide groups (*18*). The following mechanism was proposed (*27, 31*):

(I-12)

Poly(*p*-xylylidene) obtained by this method was reduced by sodium/liquid ammonia to a polymer practically identical with poly(*p*-xylylene). However, contrary to linear poly(*p*-xylylene), the reduction product was insoluble in benzyl benzoate. This difference was rationalized by assuming that slightly cross-linked polymers result from this polycondensation. Dimerizations leading to cyclobutane structures were believed responsible for the cross-linking, although no direct evidence to substantiate this was presented (*27*).

A product similar to [28] was obtained by Gilch (*26*). Potassium *tert*-butoxide in *tert*-butanol polymerizes α,α'-dichloro-*p*-xylene to an insoluble, yellow, low molecular weight polymer [31] [Eq. (I-13)]. Chlorine analysis of the polymer corresponded to a degree of polymerization of 3.85. Many other dihalogenated and higher halogenated *p*-xylenes also yielded polymers under these conditions (*25, 26*). Gilch found that methoxide in *tert*-butanol was not a strong enough base to polymerize [27]. However, Wade reports success using methoxide in dimethyl sulfoxide (*56*).

(I-13)

2,5-Bis(bromomethyl)pyridine polymerizes when treated with sodium amide in liquid ammonia–tetrahydrofuran at low temperatures (*15*). Elemental analyses and bromination studies support structure [34] for the yellow product. Infrared analysis indicated the presence of trans double bonds in the product. Linear and cross-linked resins useful as fluorescent pigments were obtained from several bis and tris(bromomethyl) arenes by this reaction (*49*).

[33] **[34]** (I-14)

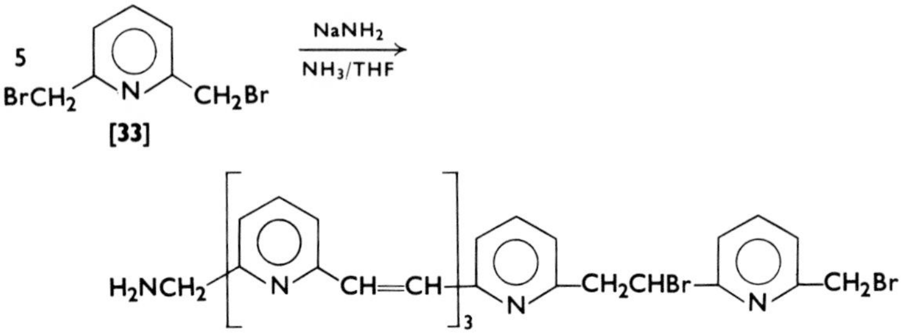

METHOD 4. POLYCONDENSATION OF METHYL KETONES

Acid-catalyzed polycondensation of methyl ketones yields linear polymers (*30*). The chlorides of beryllium, zinc, and titanium were suitable catalysts. Monomer/catalyst ratios varying from 0.1 to 1.0 were employed (*30*, *38*, *41*, *42*).

[35] **[36]** (I-15)

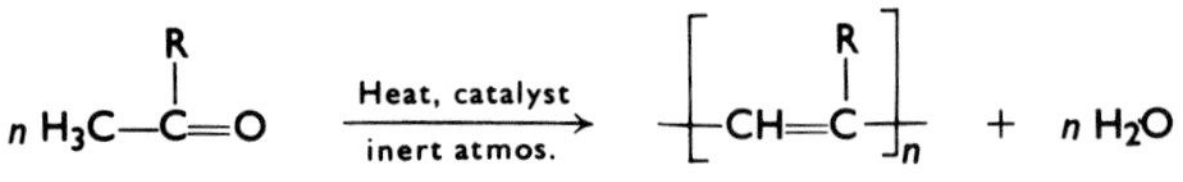

The reactions required up to 20 hours at high temperatures (200°–250°C). Solvents were not used.

[36] ; R=H, CH_3, C_6H_5 (I-16)

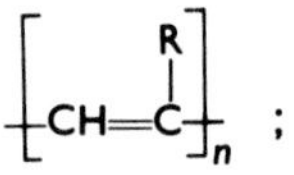

The polymers represented by formula [**36**] were dark brown to black powders. At low degrees of polymerization, they were soluble in common organic solvents like benzene and acetone. At higher molecular weight, they were completely insoluble. The polymer yields varied from 3% to 70% (*30*), increasing with an increase in catalyst concentration, temperature, and duration of the reaction.

The polycondensation of monoacetylferrocene yielded benzene-soluble, and insoluble polymers (38, 41, 42). The structure of the insoluble polymer was not determined. The difference between the two fractions could be due to their different molecular weights.

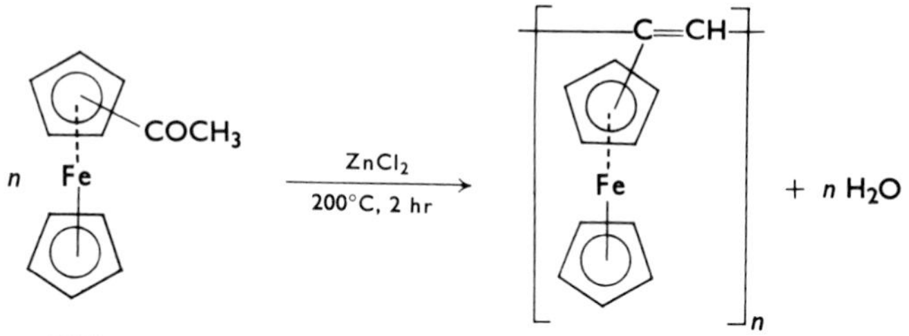

$$[37] \xrightarrow[200°C, 2\ hr]{ZnCl_2} [38] + n\ H_2O \qquad (I\text{-}17)$$

19.8% soluble
74.5% insoluble

An insoluble and infusible polymer that possessed semiconducting properties was obtained by a similar polycondensation of diacetylferrocene (38).

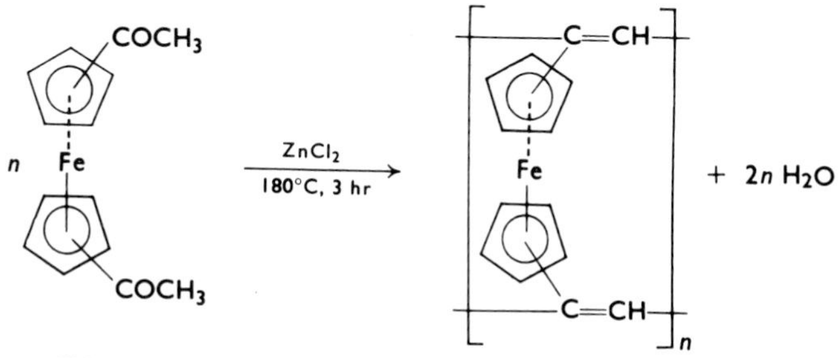

$$[39] \xrightarrow[180°C, 3\ hr]{ZnCl_2} [40] + 2n\ H_2O \qquad (I\text{-}18)$$

METHOD 5. POLYMERIZATION VIA THE WITTIG REACTION

The Wittig reaction has been applied to difunctional reactants and linear polymers were obtained (35). Poly(p-xylylidene) [42] possessing a number average molecular weight of 1200 was obtained. It was yellow due to conjugation, insoluble, added bromine to give a colorless, brominated polymer, and had a melting point greater than 400°C.

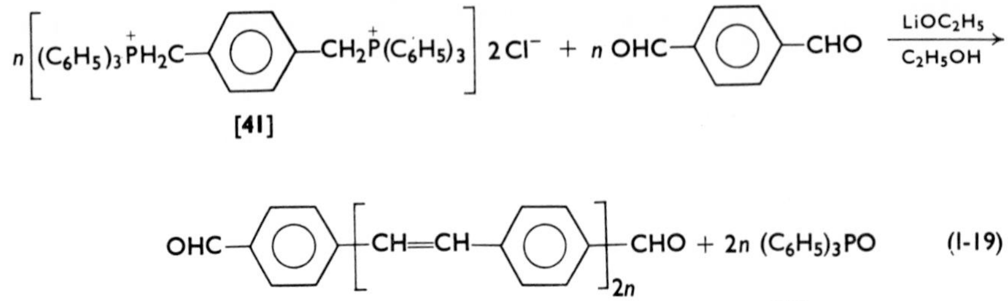

$$n\left[(C_6H_5)_3\overset{+}{P}H_2C-\text{⬡}-CH_2\overset{+}{P}(C_6H_5)_3\right]2Cl^- + n\ OHC-\text{⬡}-CHO \xrightarrow[C_2H_5OH]{LiOC_2H_5}$$

[41]

$$OHC-\text{⬡}-\left[CH=CH-\text{⬡}\right]_{2n}-CHO + 2n\ (C_6H_5)_3PO \qquad (I\text{-}19)$$

[42]   [43]

A modification in which both the ylide and the carbonyl groups are part of the same molecule was also used successfully (35). The polymer [45] was soluble, colorless, and had an inherent viscosity of 0.31 (m-cresol).

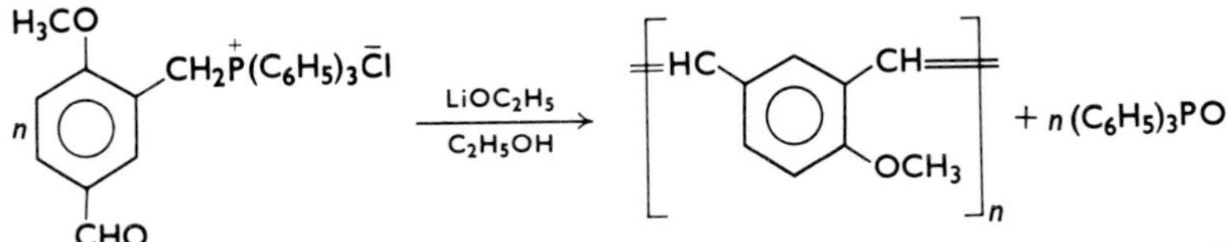

[44]   [45]   (I-20)

The following synthesis was also attempted (35):

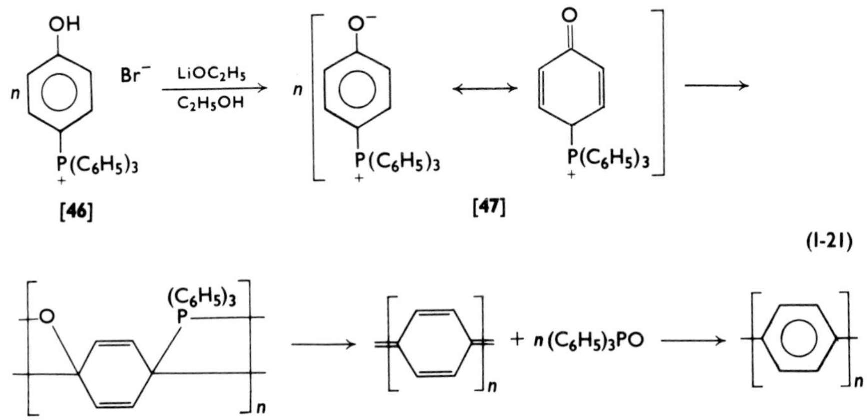

[46]   [47]

(I-21)

[48]   [49]   [50]

However, there was no evidence of reaction when the hydroxyphosphonium bromide was treated with lithium ethoxide in ethanol.

When carried out in a stepwise manner, the preparation of oligomers of the following formulae was achieved by the Wittig reaction (*17*):

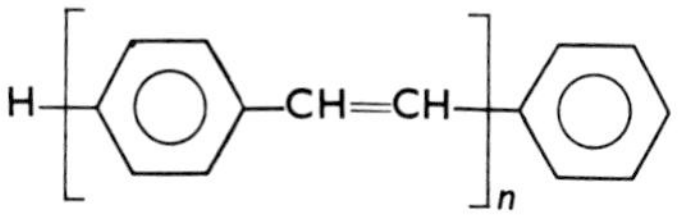

[51]
n = 2–7

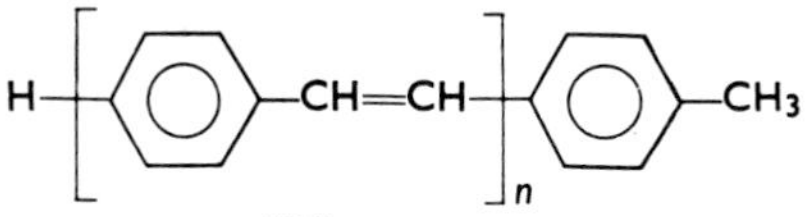

[52]
n = 4

(I-22)

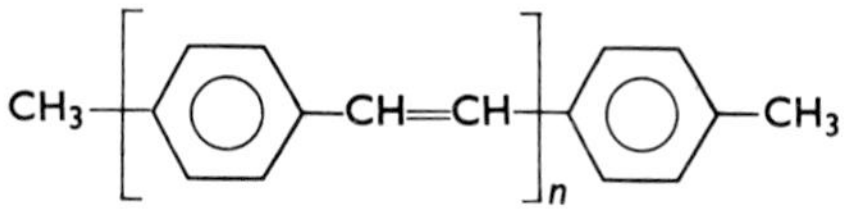

[53]
n = 4 and 5

METHOD 6. POLYMERIZATION OF TRICHLOROMETHYL COMPOUNDS

The reactions shown in Eq. (I-23) yield polymers of excellent thermal and chemical stability (*2*). Stannous or ferrous chlorides are catalysts in this reaction. Mixtures of dioxane and chloroform or dioxane and water are suitable solvents. The reactions are carried out under reflux (~100°C) for several hours. The use of an inert atmosphere is beneficial. High polymers with molecular weights up to 27,000 are obtained.

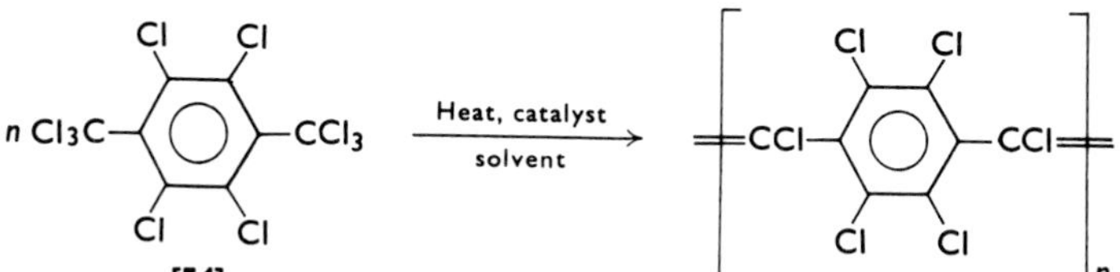

[54]

[55]

(I-23)

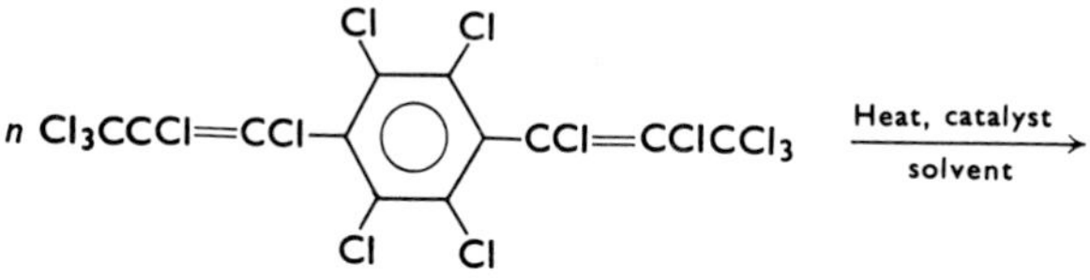

[56]

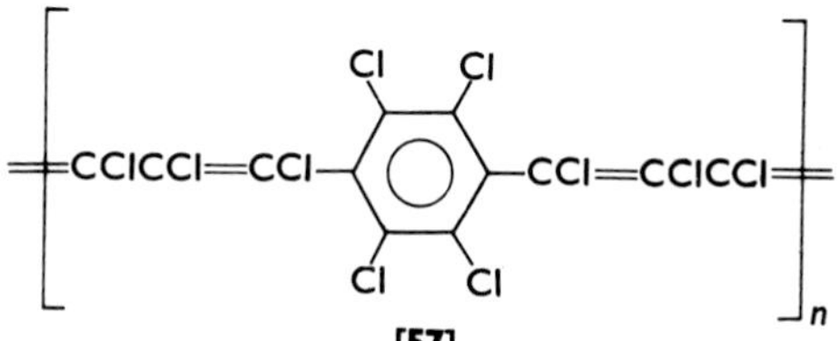

[57]

The following reaction mechanism was postulated. Due to its remarkable inertness, perchloro-*p*-xylylene [59] was considered to be an unlikely intermediate in this polymerization.

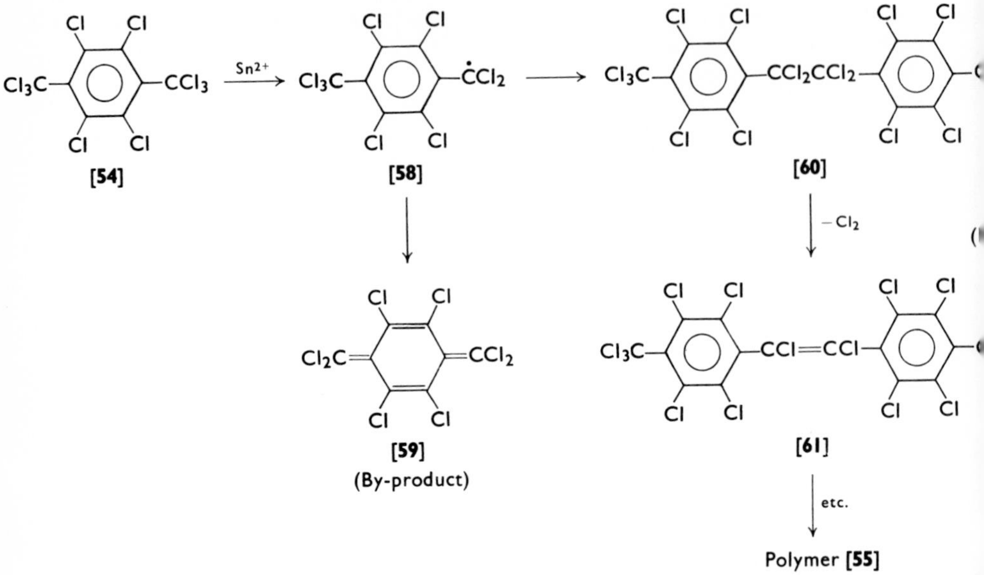

METHOD 7. WURTZ-FITTIG REACTIONS OF BIS(DIBROMOMETHYL) AROMATIC COMPOUNDS

The Wurtz-Fittig reaction of bis(dibromomethyl)arenes yields high polymer (*36*). The formulas are idealized since double-bond contents and bromine analysis indicated that the polymers were not fully conjugated. Both polymers [63] and [65] had ordered structures (X-ray diffraction) and showed good thermal stability.

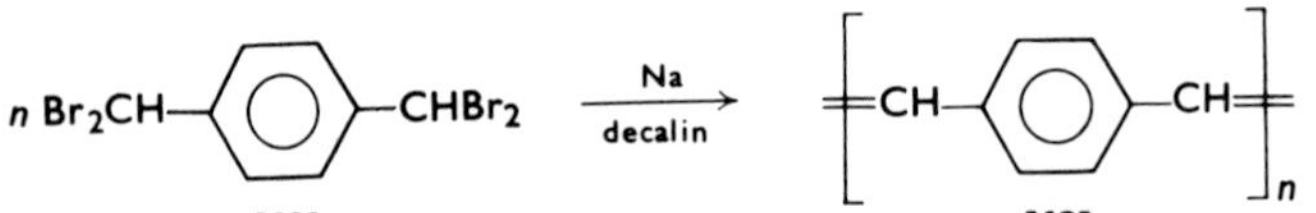

[62] [63]

$n = 70$; yellow powder

(I-25)

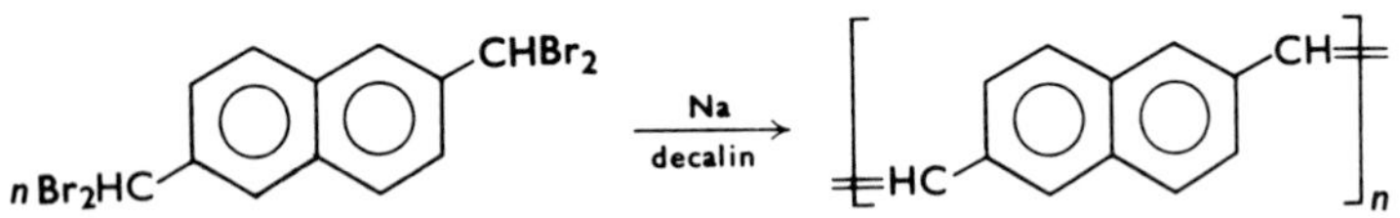

[64] [65]

$n = 90$; brown powder

(I-26)

METHOD 8. POLYMERIZATION OF VINYLCYCLOPROPANES AND VINYLCYCLO-
BUTANES

The polymerization of vinylcyclopropane shown in Eq. (I-27) is considered to be a ring-forming reaction (*19, 51*). A double bond is formed between carbon atoms 2 and 3. Prior to polymerization, these atoms were attached only by a single bond.

$$n\ \overset{1}{CH_2}{=}\overset{2}{CH}\overset{3}{CH}{-}CH_2 \quad \underset{}{\overset{R\cdot}{\longrightarrow}} \quad \left[\overset{1}{CH_2}\overset{2}{CH}{=}\overset{3}{CH}CH_2CH_2\right]_n \qquad (I\text{-}27)$$

[66]   [67]

The reaction is essentially an intra–intermolecular polymerization and can proceed via the following mechanism:

$$R\cdot + C{=}C{-}C{\overset{C}{\underset{C}{\big\langle}}} \longrightarrow R{\sim}C{-}\overset{\cdot}{C}{-}C{\overset{C}{\underset{C}{\big\langle}}} \longrightarrow$$

[66]   [68]

$${\sim}C{-}C{=}C{-}C{-}\overset{\cdot}{C} \longrightarrow \left[C{-}C{=}C{-}C{-}C\right]_n \qquad (I\text{-}28)$$

[69]   [70]

Benzoyl peroxide and α,α'-azobis(isobutyronitrile) are the preferred catalysts. The reaction is performed in bulk at 70°C. Polymers with molecular weights in the range of 5000 are obtained. The polymerizations of 1,1-dichloro-2-vinylcyclopropane (*52*) and *trans*-1,2-divinylcyclobutane (*54*) proceed by the same mechanism.

A related polymerization is the Lewis-acid-initiated polymerization of 1,1-dichloro-2,2-dimethylcyclopropane (I-29) (*13*). Infrared analysis of the product indicated that cis and trans double bonds and acetylene linkages were present. The aluminum chloride-catalyzed polymer was soluble in cold benzene, had a number average molecular weight of 2370, and softened above 360°C.

$$n\,H_3C{\overset{H_2}{\triangle}}CCl_2 \longrightarrow \left[\overset{CH_3}{\underset{CH_3}{C}}{-}CH{=}CCl\right]_n \text{ and } \left[\overset{CH_3}{\underset{CH_3}{C}}{-}C{\equiv}C\right]_n + HCl \qquad (I\text{-}29)$$

[71]   [72]   [73]

It should be noted that the well-known 1,4-polymerization of conjugated dienes could fall within the scope of this method. It results in a polymer containing a double bond between two carbon atoms that were connected by a single bond in the monomer. However, the polymerization of dienes of this type has not been covered in this book. Complete treatments are available (*24, 46, 47*).

$$n \quad \overset{}{\underset{}{>}}C{=}C{-}C{=}C\overset{}{\underset{}{<}} \quad \longrightarrow \quad \left[\overset{|}{\underset{|}{C}}{-}C{=}C{-}\overset{|}{\underset{|}{C}} \right]_n \qquad (I\text{-}30)$$

[74]   [75]

METHOD 9. POLYMERIZATION OF HALOPYRIDINES

4-Chloropyridine polymerizes to yellow-brown products by heating in bulk or solution. This general class has been termed "onium polymerization" (*12*). Solution polymerization occurs at 100°C, whereas bulk polymerization has employed temperatures up to 210°C *in vacuo*, Eq. (I-31). Potassium iodide is a catalyst for this polymerization. Structure [77] shown for the polymer was postulated to explain its specific magnetic properties. The polymer is soluble in water and hydrochloric acid and is a fairly good electrical conductor. Number average molecular weights ranged up to 1920.

$$n\,Cl{-}\!\!\!\left\langle\!\!\!\bigcirc\!\!\!\right\rangle\!\!\!{-}N \quad \overset{\text{Heat}}{\longrightarrow} \quad \left[=\!\!\!\left\langle\!\!\!\bigcirc\!\!\!\right\rangle\!\!\!=N^{+}\!\!=\quad Cl^{-} \right]_n \qquad (I\text{-}31)$$

[76]   [77]

4-Bromopyridine polymerizes at room temperature, but the 2- or 3-substituted halopyridines do not polymerize at all. A related polymerization is that of 4,4'-dipyridyl with 1,4-dibromobutane to yield water-soluble, yellow powders (*12*).

Properties of Double Bond-Containing Polymers

The majority of the double bond-containing polymers are colored because of the presence of highly conjugated systems. Their colors have encompassed the visible spectrum, having ranged from black, to brown, to yellow, to orange, to red, to colorless. The effect of conjugation on color is illustrated by polymers [78] (highly conjugated) and [79] (unconjugated) (*35*).

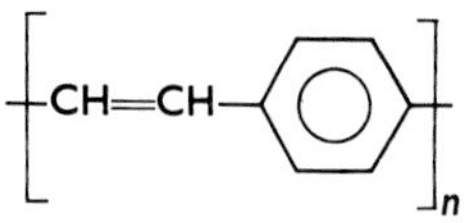

$$\left[CH=CH-\left\langle\bigcirc\right\rangle \right]_n \qquad\qquad \left[CH=CH{\underset{CH_3O}{\left\langle\bigcirc\right\rangle}} \right]_n \qquad (I\text{-}32)$$

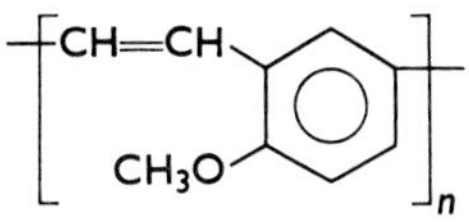

[78]   **[79]**

Yellow   Colorless

Several polymers have shown fluorescent properties in the ultraviolet region. They were patented and claimed to be useful fluorescent pigments (*49*).

Solubility properties of these polymers have varied, being dependent to a high degree upon their structure. Some were insoluble, but many have been quite soluble in the more common organic solvents (aromatics, chlorinated aliphatics and aromatics, ethers, etc.). In many instances, dimethylacetamide, dimethylformamide, dimethyl sulfoxide, *m*-cresol, pyridine, quinoline, and α-bromonaphthalene were useful solvents.

Most of the polymers that have been synthesized to date were of relatively low molecular weight (up to 5000). However, in a few instances materials with molecular weights in the 10,000–20,000 range were obtained (*2, 53*). Relatively few viscosity data are reported. Molecular weight data were obtained by elemental analysis, bromination studies, end-group analysis and by solution methods including cryoscopy, ebullioscopy, and osmometry.

The thermal stability of this type of polymer was studied in several instances (*45*). Excellent thermal stability up to 400°C is reported for the polymer possessing the following structure (*18, 36*):

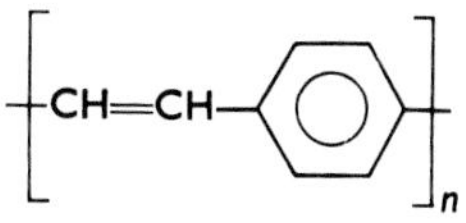

$$\left[CH=CH-\left\langle\bigcirc\right\rangle \right]_n \qquad\qquad (I\text{-}33)$$

The polymer represented by structure [80] did not degrade when heated *in vacuo* at 500°C for 1 hour (*2*). Its stability is probably enhanced by the absence of hydrogen atoms in its structure and the high resonance energy of this system. Heat treatment of this polymer (cis + trans) causes isomerization of the double bond to an all-trans configuration.

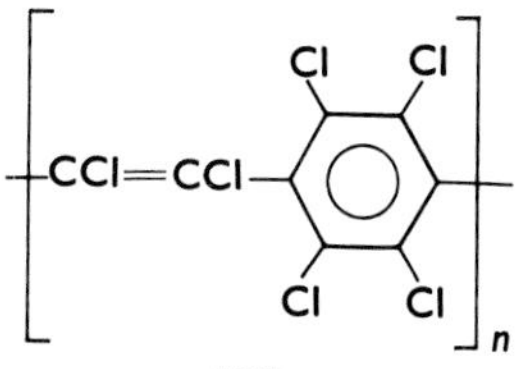

$$\left[CCl=CCl{\underset{\overset{Cl\quad Cl}{Cl\quad Cl}}{\left\langle\bigcirc\right\rangle}} \right]_n \qquad\qquad (I\text{-}34)$$

[80]

Excellent thermal stability was shown by the ferrocenyl-containing polymer represented by [38]. No change was observed on heating this material to 500°C (*42*).

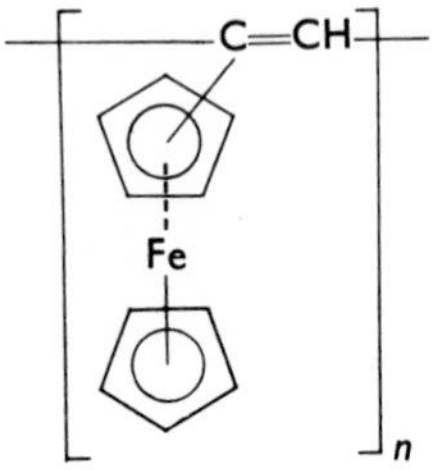

(I-35)

[38]

Good-to-excellent thermal stabilities were claimed in several other instances (*33, 44, 53*).

Very little information is available about the effect of ultraviolet radiation on polymers containing double bonds. However, the double bonds of polymer [80] isomerize to the all-trans configuration on irradiation (*2*). Dimethylformamide solutions of polymer [81] and of polymers with similar structures gelled upon irradiation with a low-pressure mercury lamp (*50*). The cross-linking was postulated to be due to cycloaddition of the double bonds forming cyclobutane rings.

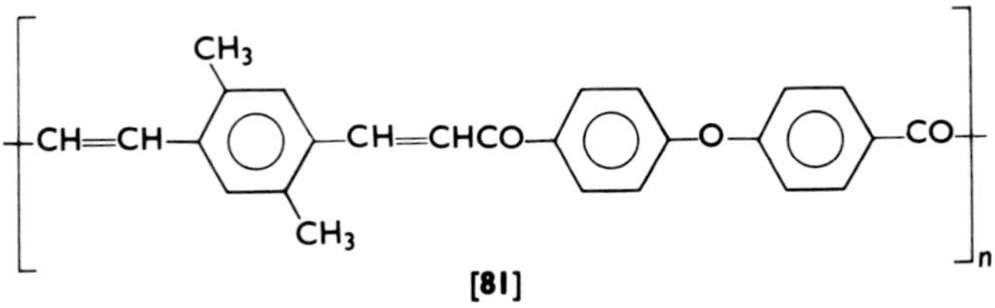

(I-36)

[81]

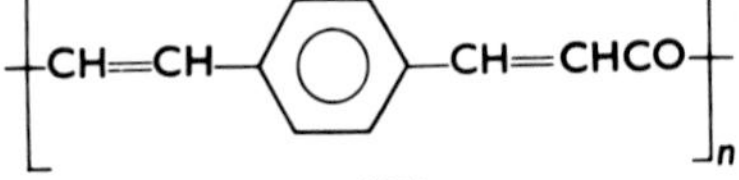

[84]

(I-37)

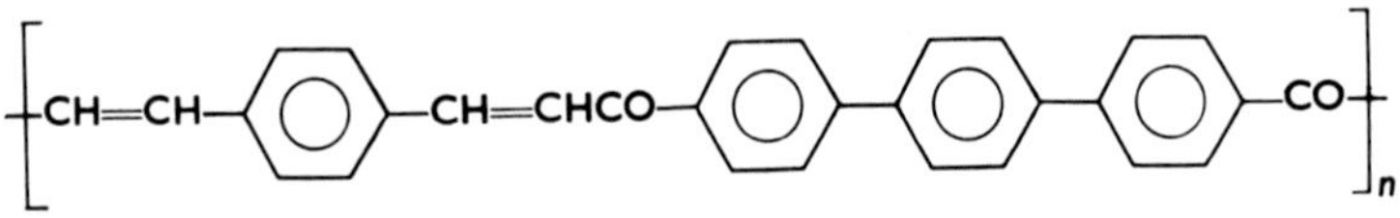

[85]

The melting point data that have been reported are not complete enough to allow a meaningful correlation of polymer melting points with structure. Discrepancies in "melting points" are observed for the same polymer, prepared by the same method but by different authors (polymer 13, Table 1.1). The situation is undoubtedly due to the differences in the methods used to obtain these values. No glass transition temperatures for any of these polymers have been reported.

Several polymers have shown semiconducting properties. Some examples are given in the accompanying table. The specific conductivity of polymers [84] and [85] increased severalfold after ultraviolet irradiation or heat treatment (32).

Practically no data on mechanical properties are available. Brittle discs were obtained by compression molding polymers 10, 11, and 14 (Table 1.1) (53).

Electrical Conductivity Data

Polymer	Specific conductivity (ohm^{-1} cm^{-1})	Temp. (°C)	References
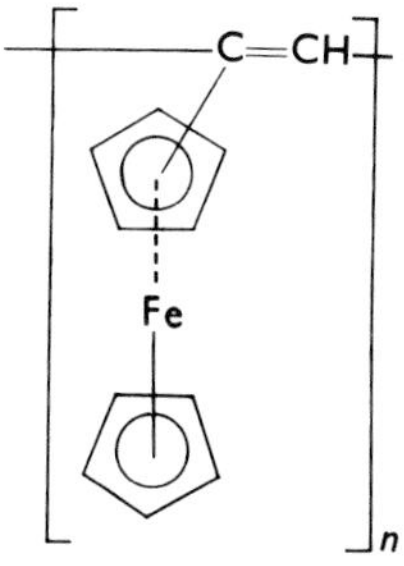 [38]	2.8×10^{-10}	50	38
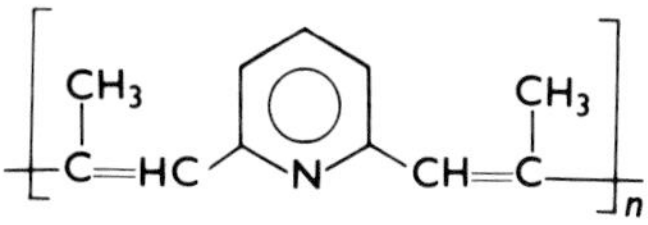 [82]	1×10^{-13}	20	43
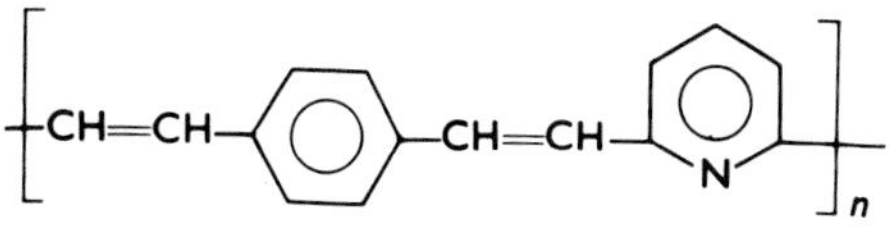 [83]	0.8×10^{-10}	100	44

TABLE 1.1
Polymers Containing Disubstituted Double Bonds

No.	Structure	Method	Solubility	Molecular weight	T_m (°C) and other properties	References
1	$-(CH=CH)_n$	4	C_6H_6, acetone	—	—	30
2	$BrCH_2-(CH=CH)_n-CH_2Br$	3	—	—	>350	31
3	$-(CH_2CH=CH-CH_2-CH_2)_n$ [67]	8	Toluene	—	—	51
4	$-(CH_2CH=CH-CH_2-CCl_2)_n$ or $-(CH_2CH=CH-CCl_2-CH_2)_n$	8	—	—	—	52
5	$-(CH_2-CH=CH-(CH_2)_2-CH=CH-CH_2)_n$ trans	8	—	—	—	54

No.	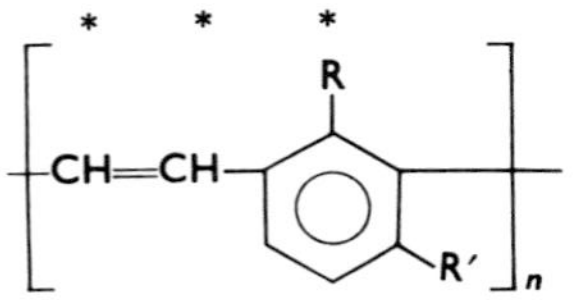 Structure	Method	Solubility	Molecular weight	T_m (°C) and other properties	References
6	R = R' = H	3	—	—	—	27
7	R = H; R' = CH_3	3	—	—	—	27
8	R = H; R' = OCH_3 [79]	3 / 5	m-Cresol	η_{inh} 0.31	180 (PMT)	27 / 35

No.	Structure / Substituents	n	Solubility	Property	Physical state	Ref.
9	R = H; R' = C_2H_5	3	—	—	—	27
10	R = R' = NO_2	1	DMAC, DMF, DMSO, dioxane	η_{Inh} 3.31	Amorphous	53
11	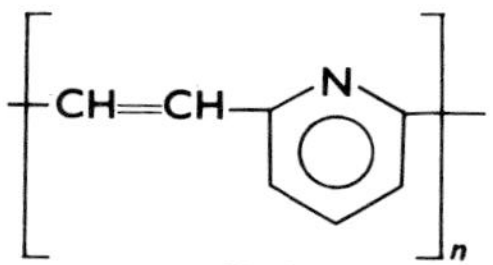 (CH=CH–pyridine) [34]	1	DMAC, DMF, DMSO, dioxane	η_{Inh} 0.60	Amorphous	53
		3	Acids	DP = 3	Infusible. Yellow. Fluorescent	15
12	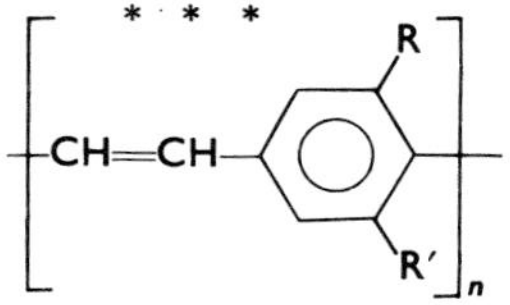 R = R' = H; trans [78]	3	Insoluble	—	>330. Amorphous	26–28, 49, 56, 57
13	R = R' = H; cis and trans [78]	5	Insoluble	—	>400	35
	R = R' = H cis and trans [78]	5	Partly in C_6H_6, xylene, and α-bromonaphthalene	—	280–300. Amorphous	55
14	R = R' = —NO_2 [9]	1	DMAC, DMF, DMSO, dioxane	η_{Inh} 2.80	Amorphous	53
15	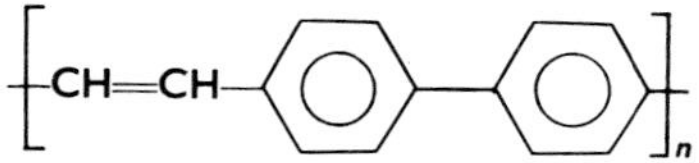 (CH=CH–biphenyl)	3	—	—	—	27

TABLE 1.1—continued

Polymers Containing Disubstituted Double Bonds

No.	Structure	Method	Solubility	Molecular weight	T_m (°C) and other properties	References
16	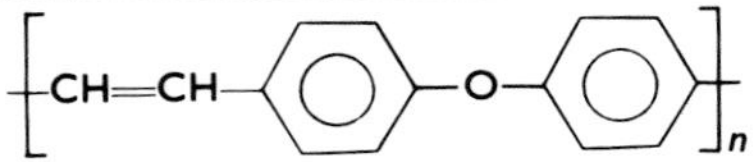 —CH=CH—⟨benzene⟩—O—⟨benzene⟩—ₙ	3	—	—	—	27
17	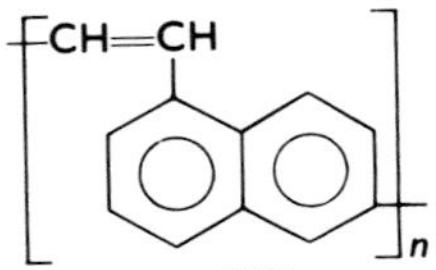 —CH=CH—⟨naphthalene⟩—ₙ **[65]**	3	—	—	—	49
18	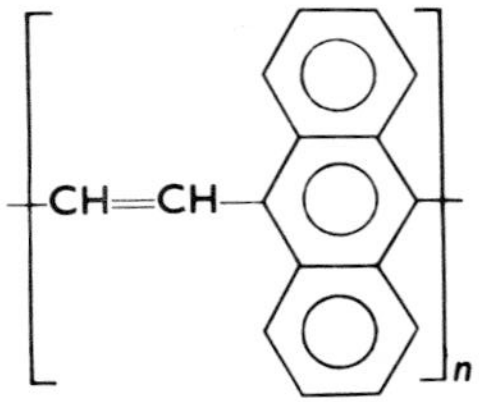 —CH=CH—⟨anthracene⟩—ₙ	3	—	—	—	27
19	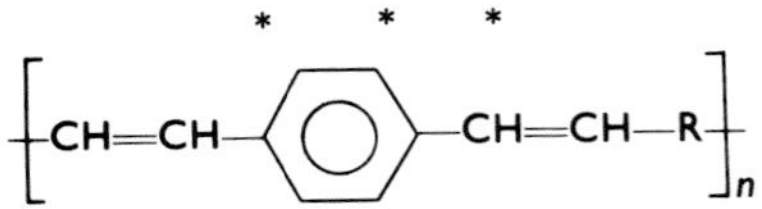 —CH=CH—⟨benzene⟩—CH=CH—R—ₙ R = —CO— **[84]**	1	Insoluble	—	Infusible	32

No.	R		Solvent	η	Properties	Yield
20	R = 1,3-C_6H_4	5	CHCl₃, xylene, α-bromonaphthalene	—	90–110	55
21	R 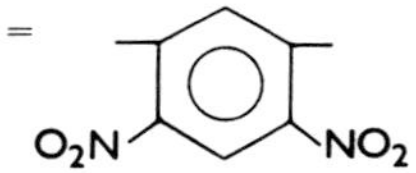 = (structure with NO_2, O_2N)	1	DMAC, DMF, DMSO, dioxane	η_{inh} 0.93	Amorphous	53
22	R 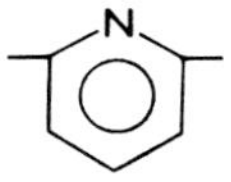 = (pyridine structure) [83]	1	H₂SO₄, benzyl alcohol, quinoline, pyridine, cresol	η_{inh} 0.21	210. Crystalline	44
23	R 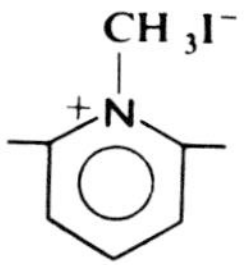 = (pyridinium, CH_3I^-)	1	Insoluble	—	Infusible	44
24	R = 1,2-C_6H_4	5	CHCl₃, xylene, α-bromonaphthalene	—	160–185	55
25	R = 4,4'-C_6H_4—CH_2—C_6H_4—	5	α-Bromonaphthalene	—	170–190	55
26	R  = —CO—(biphenyl/terphenyl structure)—CO— [85]	1	Insoluble	—	Infusible	32

* * *
*

TABLE 1.1—*continued*

Polymers Containing Disubstituted Double Bonds

No.	Structure	Method	Solubility	Molecular weight	T_m (°C) and other properties	References
	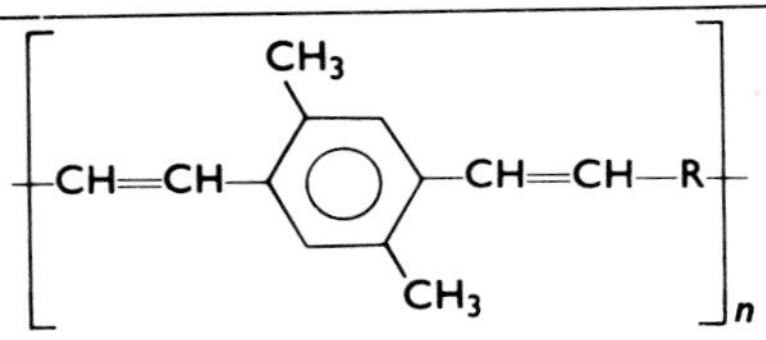					
27	R = —CO—⟨◯⟩—O—⟨◯⟩—CO— [81] 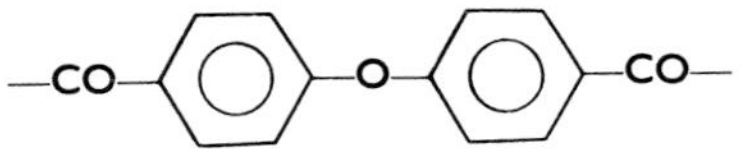	1	DMF, m-cresol	η_{inh} 0.17	182–187	*50*
28	R 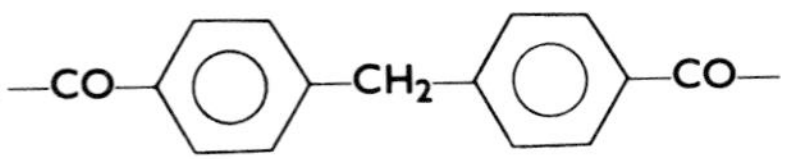 = —CO—⟨◯⟩—CH₂—⟨◯⟩—CO—	1	DMF, m-cresol	—	300 d	*50*
29	R 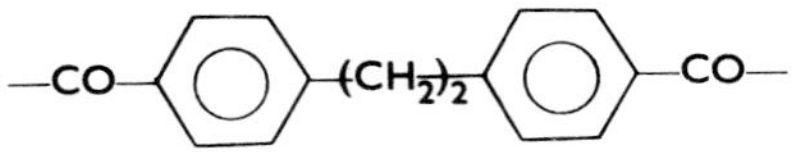 = —CO—⟨◯⟩—(CH₂)₂—⟨◯⟩—CO—	1	DMF, m-cresol	[η] 0.06	253–255	*50*
30	R 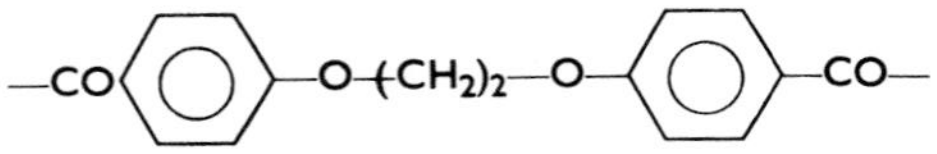 = —CO—⟨◯⟩—O—(CH₂)₂—O—⟨◯⟩—CO—	1	DMF, m-cresol	—	250 d	*50*

* * * *

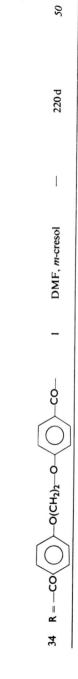

31 R = —CO—		1	DMF, m-cresol	[η] 0.15	197–202	50
32 R = —CO—		1	DMF, m-cresol	—	205 d	50
33 R = —CO—		1	DMF, m-cresol	[η] 0.17	220 d	50
34 R = —CO—		1	DMF, m-cresol	—	220 d	50

TABLE I.2

Polymers Containing Trisubstituted Double Bonds

No.	Structure	Method	Solubility	T_m(°C) and other properties	References
	$\left[\text{CH}=\overset{\text{R}}{\underset{}{\text{C}}}\right]_n$ [36]				
1	R = —CH₃ [36]	4	Acetone, C_6H_6	—	30
2	R = —C₆H₅ [36]	4	Acetone, C_6H_6	100	30
3	R = Ferrocenyl [38]	4	C_6H_6	210–270. Amorphous	38, 39, 41, 42
4		1	DMF, CHCl₃, C₆H₅NO₂	>110	23
5		1	H_2SO_4	—	23

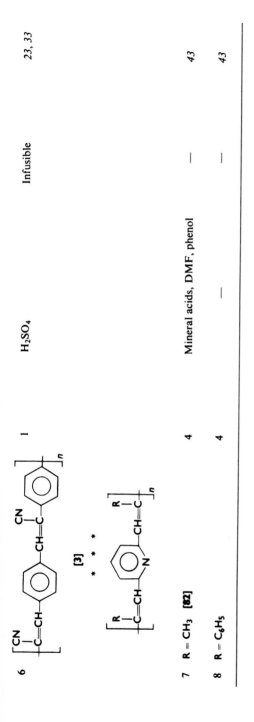

6		1	H₂SO₄	Infusible	23, 33
7	R = CH₃ [82]	4	Mineral acids, DMF, phenol	—	43
8	R = C₆H₅	4	—	—	43

TABLE 1.3

Polymers Containing Tetrasubstituted Double Bonds

No.	Structure	Method	Solubility	Molecular weight	T_m (°C)	Remarks and property data	References
1	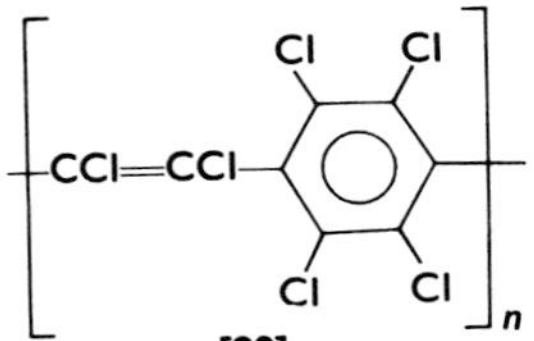 [80]	6	Partially in CHCl₃, (C₂H₅)₂O	—	—	Insoluble fraction was infusible	2
2	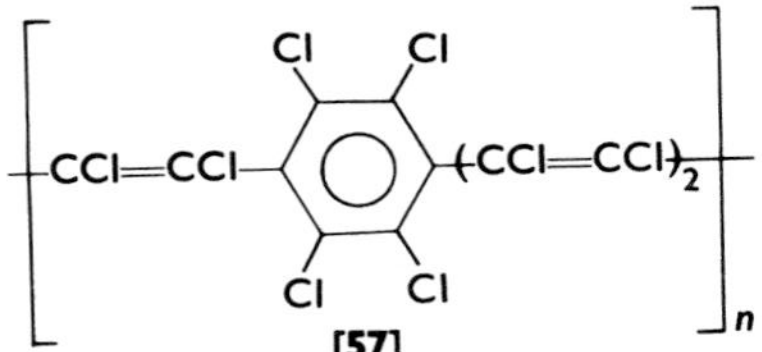 [57]	6	CCl₄	—	Infusible	—	2
3	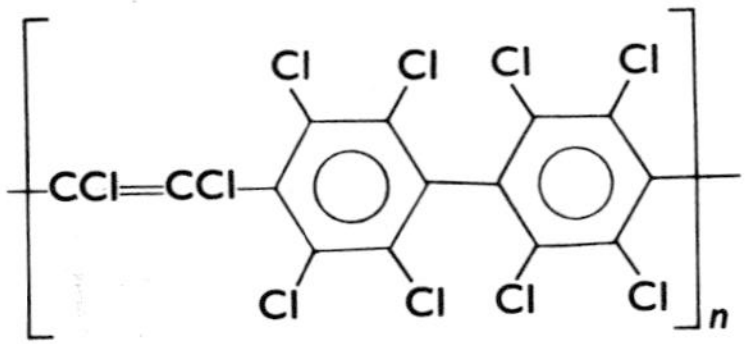	6	CCl₄	—	Infusible	—	2

27

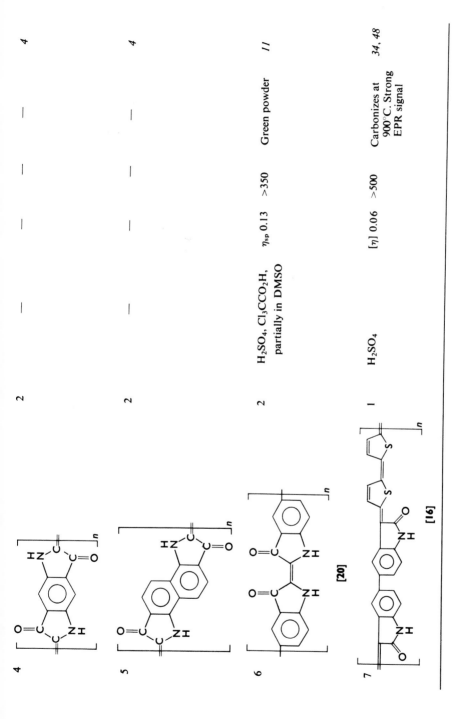

	Structure		Reagent				Ref.
4	[structure]	2	—	—	—	—	4
5	[structure]	2	—	—	—	—	4
6	[20]	2	H₂SO₄, Cl₃CCO₂H, partially in DMSO	η_{sp} 0.13	>350	Green powder	11
7	[16]	1	H₂SO₄	[η] 0.06	>500	Carbonizes at 900°C. Strong EPR signal	34, 48

TABLE 1.3—*continued*

Polymers Containing Tetrasubstituted Double Bonds

No.	Structure	Method	Solubility	Molecular weight	T_m (°C)	Remarks and property data	References
8	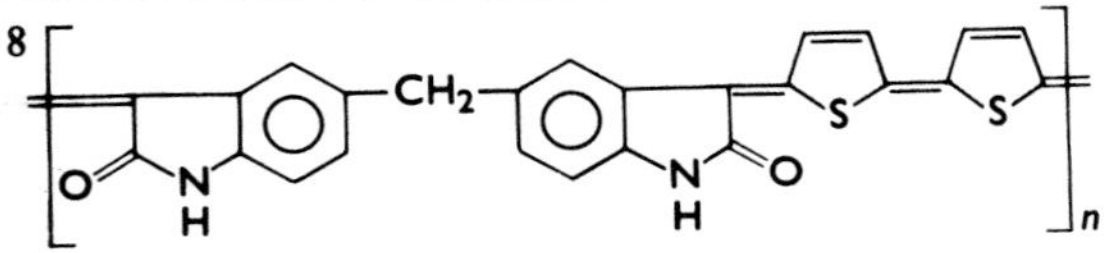	1	H_2SO_4	—	>500	—	34
9	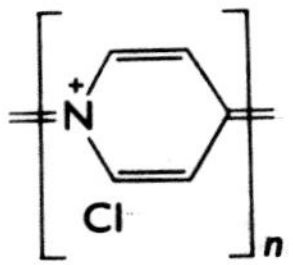	9	H_2O, HCl	1920	—	—	12

REFERENCES

1. Baker, W. O., *J. Polymer Sci.* **C4**, 1633 (1964).
2. Ballester, M., Castaner, J., and Riera, J., *J. Am. Chem. Soc.* **88**, 957 (1966).
3. Barkalov, I. M., Berlin, A. A., Goldanskii, V. I., and Dzantiev, B. G., *Vysokomolekul. Soedin.* **2**, 1103 (1960).
4. Belgian Patent 669,175 (issued to Monsanto Co.) (1965).
5. Beneš, M., Peška, J., and Wichterle, O., *Chem. & Ind. (London)* p. 562 (1962).
6. Beneš, M., Peška, J., and Wichterle, O., *J. Polymer Sci.* **C4**, 1377 (1964).
7. Berlin, A. A., *Khim. Tekhnol. Polymer.* **4**, 139 (1960).
8. Berlin, A. A., *J. Polymer Sci.* **55**, 621 (1961).
9. Berlin, A. A., Blumenfeld, L. A., Cherkashin, M. I., Kalmanson, A. E., and Selskaya, O. G., *Vysokomolekul. Soedin.* **1**, 1361 (1959).
10. Berlin, A. A., Cherkashin, M. I., Selskaya, O. G., and Limanov, V. E., *Vysokomolekul. Soedin.* **1**, 1817 (1959).
11. Berlin, A. A., Liogon'kii, B. I., and Zelenetskii, A. N., *Izv. Akad. Nauk SSSR, Ser. Khim.* No. 1, p. 225 (1967); *Chem. Abstr.* **66**, 9035, 96197f (1967).
12. Berlin, A. A., Zherebtsova, L. V., and Razvodovskii, Ye. F., *Vysokomolekul. Soedin.* **6**, 58 (1964); *Polymer Sci. (USSR) (English Transl.)* **6**, 67 (1964).
13. British Patent 1,043,485 (issued to W. R. Grace & Co.) (1966).
14. Daniels, W. E., *J. Org. Chem.* **29**, 2936 (1964).
15. Debord, D., and Gole, J., *Compt. Rend.* **C263**, 918 (1966); *Chem. Abstr.* **66**, 1113, 11224q (1967).
16. Donda, A. F., and Guerrieri, A., *Ric. Sci., Rend.* [2] **A6**, 287 (1964); *Chem. Abstr.* **63**, 1874 (1965).
17. Drefahl, G., and Plötner, G., *Chem. Ber.* **94**, 907 (1961); see also **91**, 1274 (1958).
18. Dunnavant, W. R., and Markle, R. A., *J. Polymer Sci.* **A3**, 3649 (1965); *Chem. Abstr.* **64**, 820 (1966).
19. French Patent 1,469,121 (issued to Soc. Aux. de l'Instit. Français du Caoutchouc) (1967).
20. Funke, W., *Angew. Chem.* **72**, 457 (1960).
21. Funke, W., *Angew. Chem.* **76**, 385 (1964).
22. Funke, W., and Hamann, K., German Patent 1,088,637 (1960) (Forschungsinstitut für Pigmente und Lacke) *Chem. Abstr.* **55**, 27914 (1961).
23. Funke, W., and Schütze, E. C., *Makromol. Chem.* **74**, 71 (1964).
24. Gaylord, N. G., and Mark, H. F., "Linear and Stereoregular Addition Polymers." Wiley (Interscience), New York, 1959.
25. Gilch, H. G., *J. Polymer Sci.* **A-1,4**, 1351 (1966).
26. Gilch, H. G., and Wheelwright, W. L., *J. Polymer Sci.* **A-1,4**, 1337 (1966).
27. Hoeg, D. F., Lusk, D. I., and Goldberg, E. P., *J. Polymer Sci.* **B2**, 697 (1964).
28. Hoeg, D. F., Lusk, D. I., and Goldberg, E. P., *Macromol. Syn.* **2**, 114 (1966); *Chem. Abstr.* **65**, 18687 (1966).
29. Japanese Patent 7886/63 (issued to Japanese Association for Radiation Research on Polymers) (1963).
30. Kargin, V. A., Kabanov, V. A., Zubov, V. P., Papisov, I. M., and Kurochkina, G. I., *Dokl. Akad. Nauk SSSR* **140**, 122 (1961), *Resins, Rubbers, Plastics* p. 665 (1962).
31. Kharasch, M. S., Nudenberg, W., and Fields, E. K., *J. Am. Chem. Soc.* **66**, 1276 (1944).
32. Lebsadze, T. N., Nakashidze, G. A., Eligulashvili, I. A., Talakvadze, M. V., and Zeragiya, E. M., *Soobshch. Akad. Nauk Gruz. SSR* **39**, 75 (1965); *Chem. Abstr.* **63**, 14990 (1965).
33. Lenz, R. W., and Handlovits, C. E., *J. Org. Chem.* **25**, 813 (1960).

34. Levine, I. J., U.S. Patent 3,334,074 (Union Carbide Corp.) (1967).
35. McDonald, R. N., and Campbell, T. W., *J. Am. Chem. Soc.* **82**, 4669 (1960).
36. Ouchi, K., *Australian J. Chem.* **19**, 335 (1966); *Chem. Abstr.* **64**, 14293 (1966).
37. Paushkin, Ya. M., Bocharov, B. V., Smirnov, A. P., Vishnyakova, T. P., Machus, F. F., and Panidi, I. S., *Plasticheskie Massy* p. 3 (1964); *Chem. Abstr.* **61**, 16247 (1964).
38. Paushkin, Ya. M., Polak, L. S., Vishnyakova, T. P., Patalakh, I. I., Machus, F. F., and Sokolinskaya, T. A., *J. Polymer Sci.* **C4**, 1481 (1964).
39. Paushkin, Ya. M., Polak, L. S., Vishnyakova, T. P., Patalakh, I. I., Machus, F. F., and Sokolinskaya, T. A., *Vysokomolekul. Soedin.* **6**, 545 (1964).
40. Paushkin, Ya. M., Smirnov, A. P., and Bocharov, B. V., Russian Patent 159,986 (1964); *Chem. Abstr.* **60**, 12135 (1964).
41. Paushkin, Ya. M., Vishnyakova, T. P., Patalakh, I. I., Sokolinskaya, T. A., and Machus, F. F., *Proc. Acad. Sci. USSR, Chem. Sect.* (*English Transl.*) **149**, 296 (1963).
42. Paushkin, Ya. M., Vishnyakova, T. P., Sokolinskaya, T. A., Patalakh, I. I., Machus, F. F., and Kurasheva, I. D., *Tr. Mosk. Inst. Neftekhim. i Gaz. Prom.* **44**, 15 (1963); *Chem. Abstr.* **60**, 9310 (1964).
43. Penkovsky, V. V., *Vysokomolekul. Soedin.* **6**, 1755 (1964); *Resins, Rubbers, Plastics* p. 1387 (1965).
44. Pinskaya, I. S., Vasil'eva-Sokolova, E. A., and Kudryavtsev, G. I., *Vysokomolekul. Soedin.* **7**, 2063 (1965).
45. Rabek, J. F., *Polimery* **11**, 497 (1966); *Chem. Abstr.* **67**, 4159, 44087w (1967).
46. Raff, R. A. V., and Doak, K. W., "Crystalline Olefin Polymers." Wiley (Interscience), New York, 1965.
47. Roha, M., *Fortschr. Hochpolymer.-Forsch.* **1**, 512 (1960).
48. Shopov, I., *J. Polymer Sci.* **B4**, 1023 (1966).
49. Smith, G. H., U.S. Patent 3,110,687 (Minnesota Mining and Manufacturing Co.) (1963).
50. Tabushi, I., Tanimura, N., and Oda, R., *Kogyo Kagaku Zasshi* **66**, 1717 (1963); *Chem. Abstr.* **61**, 1952 (1964).
51. Takahashi, T., and Yamashita, I., *J. Polymer Sci.* **B3**, 251 (1965); *Chem. Abstr.* **62**, 13056 (1965).
52. Takahashi, T., Yamashita, I., and Miyakawa, T., *Bull. Chem. Soc. Japan* **37**, 131 (1964).
53. Thomson, D. W., and Ehlers, G. F. L., AD 466,808 (1965). Wright Air Force Base.
54. Valvassori, A., Sartori, G., Turba, V., and Ciampelli, F., *Makromol. Chem.* **61**, 256 (1963).
55. Vansheidt, A. A., and Krakovyak, M. G., *Vysokomolekul. Soedin.* **5**, 805 (1963); *Polymer Sci.* (*USSR*) (*English Transl.*) **4**, 1522 (1963).
56. Wade, R. H., *J. Polymer Sci.* **B5**, 565 (1967); *Chem. Abstr.* **67**, 4185, 44354f (1967).
57. Zidaroff, E., and Ivanoff, D., *Naturwissenschaften* **52**, 13 (1965).

CHAPTER II

Intra–Intermolecular Polymerizations Leading to Homocyclic Carbon Rings

Intra–intermolecular polymerization or cyclopolymerization is a ring-forming polymerization method that has been widely used and studied. The principle on which it operates is shown in the following equations.

$$
n \; \text{[1]} \quad \xrightarrow{\;R\cdot\;} \quad \text{[2]} \quad \longrightarrow
$$

$$
\text{[3]} \quad \longrightarrow \quad \text{[4]} \tag{II-I}
$$

The group connecting the double bonds, X, can be composed of carbon atoms, carbon and heteroatoms, and heteroatoms. Diolefins can also be copolymerized with monoolefins via the same scheme. Cyclopolymerization is a powerful tool in synthetic polymer chemistry. It allows the preparation of carbocyclic ring-containing polymers as well as several classes of heterocyclic ring-containing polymers. The scope of this reaction has been reviewed several times (4, 19, 20, 23, 77, 91, 100, 123, 143, 168).

Historically, the development of the intra–intermolecular polymerization can be traced back to early studies on free-radical polymerizations and copolymerizations of diolefinic monomers. According to Staudinger (150), the polymerization of nonconjugated dienes should yield cross-linked polymers. However, studies of the free radical-initiated copolymerizations of methyl methacrylate with ethylene dimethacrylate, and of vinyl acetate with divinyl adipate (165) have shown the existence of a "delay" in reaching the gel point. In other words, for some unexplained reason the gel point was reached at conversions that were significantly higher than those predicted by theory. Similar results were observed in other studies (*15, 63–65, 146, 147*) and led to the postulate that the reactions were accompanied by "intramolecular cross-linking." This is shown for the case of diallyl phthalate in Eq. (II-2).

[5]   [6]   (II-2)

In a search for new ion-exchange resins, Butler tried to prepare polymeric quaternary salts from various diallylamine derivatives. He reported (*18*) that a water-soluble polymer was obtained from the free radical-initiated polymerization of diallyldiethylammonium bromide [Eq. (II-3)]. Staudinger's hypothesis (*150*) predicts that an insoluble cross-linked polymer should have been obtained. This observation led Butler (*18*) to postulate an intra–intermolecular polymerization path. The correctness of this structure was confirmed experimentally (*26*).

[7]   [8]   (II-3)

Butler's successful demonstration of the existence of the intra–intermolecular polymerization mechanism triggered widespread research in this area. As a result, excellent procedures for this type of ring-forming polymerization evolved. Cyclopolymerizations can take place by free-radical, cationic, anionic, Ziegler, and other types of initiations. These various types of intra–intermolecular polymerizations are discussed below. Only all-carbon ring-containing polymers are covered. The formation of heterocyclic polymers by this reaction will be discussed in a forthcoming volume (Part B).

METHOD 1. FREE-RADICAL INITIATION

Intra–intermolecular polymerizations can be initiated by free radicals in several ways. Typical free-radical initiators like peroxides, peracids, azobis-(isobutyronitrile), oxygen, ferrous ion/hydrogen peroxide, and persulfate can be used. The reactions can be performed in bulk, solution, or emulsion. Several types of solvents are useful. Heat and radiation (UV, ^{60}Co) were also successfully employed. Rings that ranged in size from three to six members were formed. Depending on the monomer, mono- and polycyclic polymeric systems were prepared. Typical examples are described in the following sections.

a. Three-Membered Rings

The transannular polymerization of bicyclo[2.2.1]heptadiene yields a polymer containing nortricyclene units [Eq. (II-4)] (*62, 166, 169*).

(II-4)

[9]   [10]

Dibutylperoxide (*62*) and azobis(isobutyronitrile) in bulk or benzene solution were initiators. The same polymer was obtained (*166*) by initiation with γ-irradiation (^{60}Co source). The molecular weight of this latter polymer as determined by cryoscopy was approximately 1500. The ratio of $x(x + y)$ is a measure of the extent of cyclization that occurred during the reaction. This ratio depends on the experimental conditions used. It was claimed in one instance that the free-radical polymerization of bicyclo[2.2.1]heptadiene yields polymer resulting from "1,2"-polymerization only [Eq. (II-5)] (*72*).

(II-5)

[9]   [11]

An extensive study of the copolymerization of bicyclo[2.2.1]heptadiene with vinyl monomers has been described (*170*). Radical initiators such as trialkylboranes with oxygen were employed and products well into the useful molecular weight range were obtained. On the basis of infrared evidence, all of the bicyclo[2.2.1]heptadiene was stated to be present in the polymers as nortricyclene units. Vinyl chloride copolymers were studied most extensively, but most of the other commercial vinyl monomers were also examined (*170*).

Polymerization of the ester derivative [12] gave polymer that had a molecular weight of up to 100,000 (*62*).

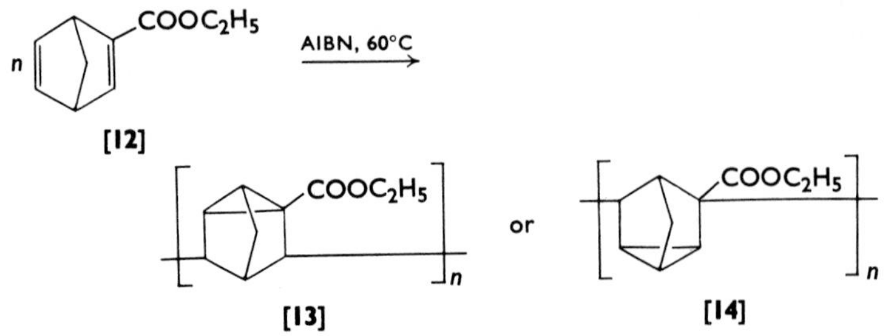

(II-6)

Unsaturated units [15] were also present in the polymer. This was substantiated by infrared examination. Furthermore, at monomer-to-polymer conversions greater than 60%, gelation occurred.

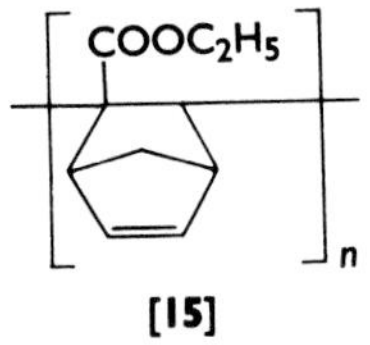

(II-7)

Three-membered rings are also formed in the copolymerization of sulfur dioxide with bicyclo[2.2.1]heptadiene (II-8) (*1*, *162*). Thermal initiation of this copolymerization is reported to give only 1,5-homoconjugative addition polymerization (*134*). The white, powdery polymer produced at 150°C is more thermally stable and alkali-resistant than the low-temperature radical-initiated polymer. Elemental analyses were consistent with a 1:1 alternating copolymer structure.

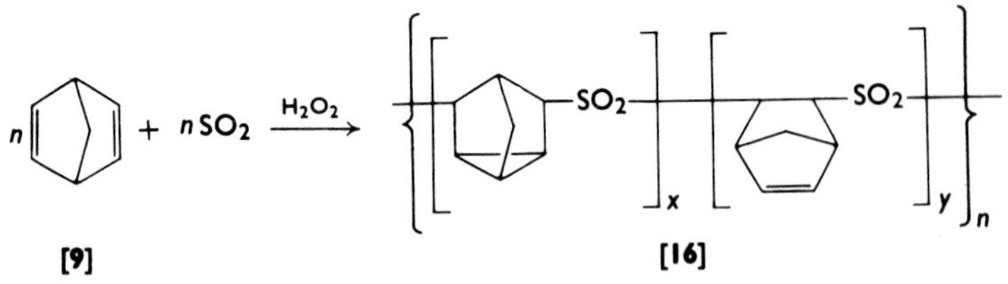

(II-8)

b. Four-Membered Rings

Perfluoro-1,4-pentadiene has been polymerized via an intra–intermolecular mechanism. Simultaneous isomerization to the 1,3-diene occurred. The latter copolymerized via the usual 1,4-addition, leading to a final polymer of structure [18] (*50*, *163*).

$$nCF_2{=}CFCF_2CF{=}CF_2 \quad \xrightarrow[\substack{11,000 \text{ atm} \\ 110°C}]{\gamma\text{-rays}}$$

[17]

$$\left\{ \left[-CF_2-\underset{\underset{CF_2}{\overset{CF_2}{\diagdown}}}{CF}\diagup CF- \right]_x \left[-CF_2CF{=}CF\underset{\overset{|}{CF}}{\overset{CF_3}{|}}- \right]_y \right\}_n \quad \text{(II-9)}$$

[18]

A recent patent describes the copolymerization of 1,4-pentadienes of various types with other monomers. Radical initiators were used and soluble polymers obtained (24). Although the structures of the products were not explicitly described, they could have possessed four-membered rings analogous to those in [18]. In addition to perfluoro-1,4-pentadiene, the other dienes mentioned were 1,4-pentadiene, 2,4-dichloro-1,4-pentadiene, 1,1-dichloro-1,4-pentadiene, and 3,3-dimethyl-1,4-pentadiene. Co-monomers included maleic anhydride and haloethylenes such as trichloroethylene. However, these copolymerizations could also have taken the path shown in Eq. (II-22).

c. Five-Membered Rings

The structure of polymer [20] was confirmed by infrared spectral analysis (99). Spectral evidence indicated that more than 90% of the monomer units were consumed via cyclopolymerization. However, polymerization in bulk or emulsion yielded cross-linked insoluble product only.

$$n CH_2{=}\underset{\underset{COOCH_3}{|}}{\overset{\overset{COOCH_3}{|}}{C}}(CH_2)_2 C{=}CH_2 \quad \xrightarrow[\text{peroxide}]{\text{Benzoyl}} \quad \left[-CH_2 \overset{\overset{CO_2CH_3}{\diagup}\;\overset{CO_2CH_3}{}}{\diagup\!\!\diagdown} - \right]_n \quad \text{(II-10)}$$

[19]   [20]

η_{inh} 0.21

Some additional examples are shown in Eqs. (II-11) and (II-12) (2).

$$n \quad \underset{\underset{HC\diagdown_{\;\;\underset{O}{C}}\diagup CH}{\overset{CH}{||}}}{\overset{\overset{C_6H_5}{|}\;\;\overset{C_6H_5}{|}}{}} \quad \xrightarrow[130°C]{\text{Peroxide}} \quad \left[\underset{HC\diagdown_{\;\;\underset{O}{C}}\diagup CH}{\overset{C_6H_5\;\;C_6H_5}{CH-CH}} \right]_n \quad \text{(II-11)}$$

[21]   [22]

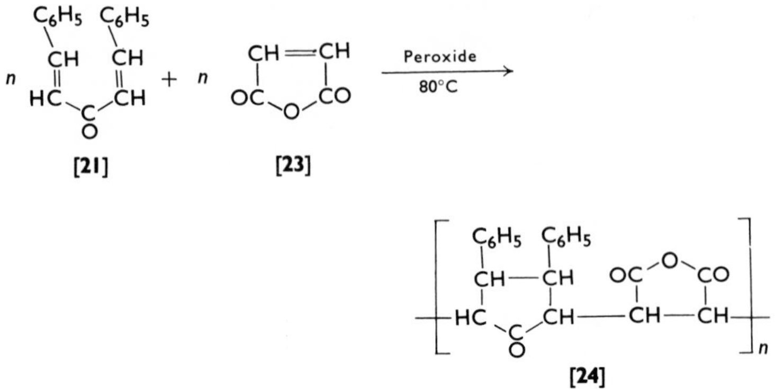

[21]   [23]

(II-12)

[24]

The polymerization of various substituted divinyl ketones was studied by Matsoyan and his students (8, 9, 102). It was shown that five- or six-membered rings can form depending on the nature and the degree of substitution of the divinyl ketones. A comparative rate study for the series of divinyl ketones, $ArCH=CHCOCH=CH_2$, showed the following relative order: $Ar = p$-$CH_3C_6H_4-> o$-$CH_3OC_6H_4-> C_6H_5-> p$-$CH_3OC_6H_4-> \beta$-methyl-β-phenyl-divinyl ketone (39). Cyclization during all of these polymerizations was postulated because of infrared evidence for the presence of conjugated unsaturation in the products.

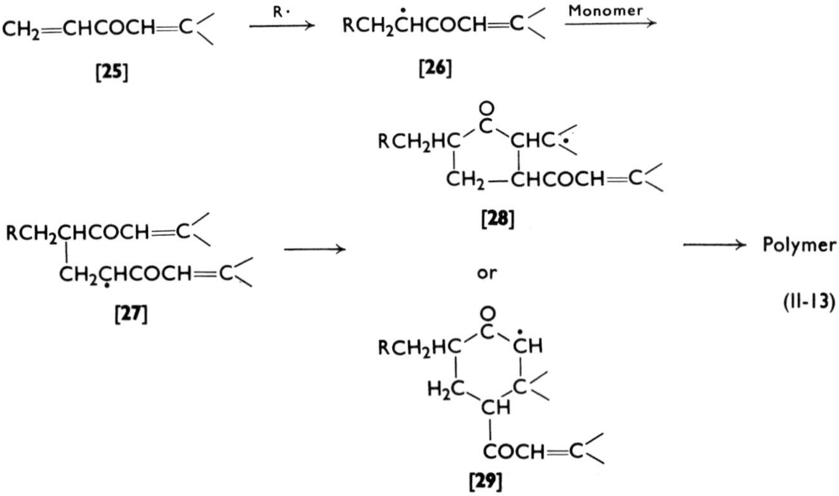

(II-13)

Polymers containing five-membered rings are formed by polymerization of vinylethynyl carbinols (82).

$$2n \ CH_2{=}CHC{\equiv}C\overset{\displaystyle R}{\underset{\displaystyle R}{C}}OH \xrightarrow[60°C]{Fe^{2+}/H_2O_2} \left[\begin{array}{c} \text{—CH}_2\text{CH—CH—} \\ \text{structure [31]} \end{array} \right]_n \qquad \text{(II-14)}$$

[30]   [31]

The following mechanism was proposed (*103, 105*).

$$CH_2{=}CHC{\equiv}C\overset{\displaystyle R}{\underset{\displaystyle R}{C}}OH \xrightarrow{R'\cdot} R'CH_2CH{=}C{=}\overset{R}{\dot{C}}{-}\overset{R}{\underset{R}{C}}{-}OH \xrightarrow{\text{Monomer}}$$

[30]   [32]

[33]   [34]

$$\xrightarrow{\quad} \text{Polymer [31]} \qquad \text{(II-15)}$$

[35]

The cyclic structure of the polymers [31] was substantiated by infrared and chemical evidence. The fact that they were soluble (acetone, methyl ethyl ketone, acetic acid, dioxane) confirms their linear character. The polymerizations were also initiated by other radical initiators [peroxides, azobis(isobutyronitrile)]. Carbinols with aliphatic, cycloaliphatic, and aromatic substituents were polymerized (*104, 106, 109, 111, 113, 119–121*). Cyclic polymers are also obtained from their acetates and ethers (*107, 113*). Nuclear magnetic resonance has been employed to study transitions in these polymers (*75, 76*). Polymers possessing molecular weights of over 1,000,000 resulted in some cases. The kinetics of polymerization (II-14) were studied (*111, 112*). Copolymerization with vinyl monomers (*108, 145*) yielded linear, soluble polymers that contained cyclic structures derived from the vinylethynyl carbinol.

A copolymer with a repeat unit containing two fused five-membered rings was obtained from 1,5-cyclooctadiene and maleic anhydride (II-16) (*47, 49*). An unidentified nitrogen-containing polymer resulted when the reaction was performed in dimethylformamide.

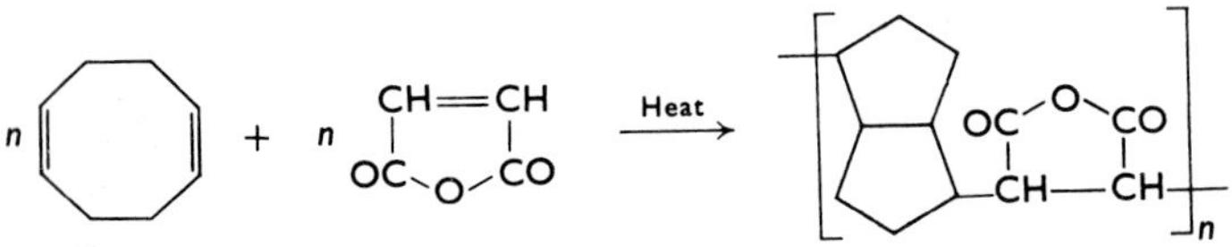

Analogous copolymers are obtained from 1,5-cyclooctadiene and other α,β-unsaturated diacids, diesters, or half-acid esters (*17*). Sulfuryl chloride co-polymerizes with 1,5-cyclooctadiene to yield polymers of moderately high molecular weight (*48*). Radical or ultraviolet initiation is effective. The polymers [38], being sulfonyl chloride-terminated, polymerize with diamines to higher molecular weight polymers (*48*).

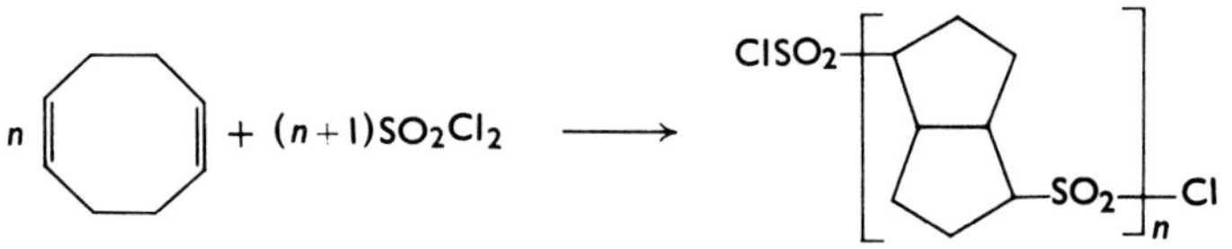

Cyclization occurred in the free-radical polymerization and copolymerization of *o*-divinylbenzene. Indane units were found in the polymer chains (*3, 6, 7*).

d. Six-Membered Rings

1,6-Heptadienes treated with free-radical initiators yield linear polymers that contain six-membered rings. An example is shown in Eq. (II-18). The polymer [40] possessed an intrinsic viscosity of 0.73 (CHCl$_3$) (*98*). Additional examples are shown in Eq. (II-19) (*127*). Polymers with intrinsic viscosities greater than 1 were obtained. Copolymerization of these diolefins with monoolefins (acrylonitrile, acrylamide, styrene, vinylidene chloride) yielded linear copolymers possessing cyclic structures derived from the diolefins (*127*).

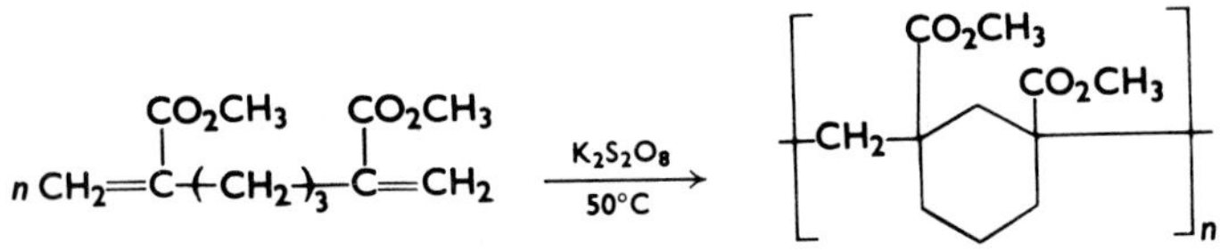

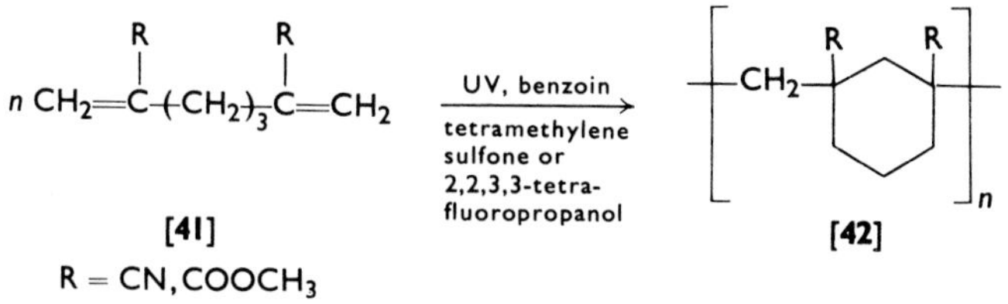

$$n \ CH_2{=}\underset{\underset{[41]}{R=CN,COOCH_3}}{\overset{R}{\underset{|}{C}}}{-}(CH_2)_3{-}\overset{R}{\underset{|}{C}}{=}CH_2 \xrightarrow[\substack{tetramethylene \\ sulfone \ or \\ 2,2,3,3\text{-}tetra\text{-} \\ fluoropropanol}]{UV, \ benzoin} \quad [42] \qquad (II\text{-}19)$$

The thermal polymerization of 2,6-diphenyl-1,6-heptadiene gave a six-membered ring-containing polymer (55).

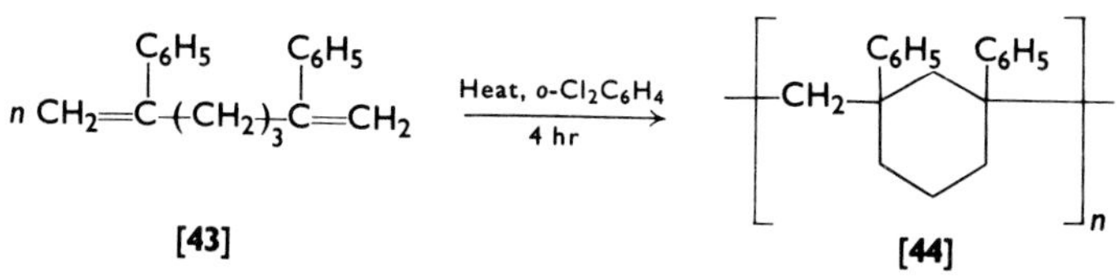

$$n \ CH_2{=}\overset{C_6H_5}{\underset{|}{C}}{-}(CH_2)_3{-}\overset{C_6H_5}{\underset{|}{C}}{=}CH_2 \xrightarrow[4 \ hr]{Heat, \ o\text{-}Cl_2C_6H_4} \quad [44] \qquad (II\text{-}20)$$

[43]

Other examples follow:

(i) Polymerization of diallyl ketones (21).

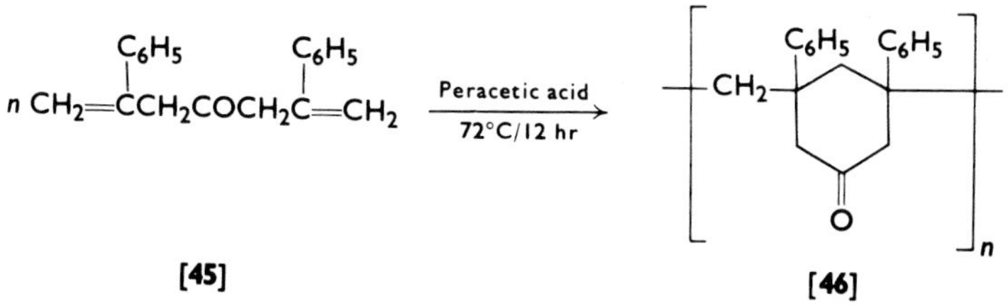

$$n \ CH_2{=}\overset{C_6H_5}{\underset{|}{C}}CH_2COCH_2\overset{C_6H_5}{\underset{|}{C}}{=}CH_2 \xrightarrow[72°C/12 \ hr]{Peracetic \ acid} \quad [46] \qquad (II\text{-}21)$$

[45]

(ii) Copolymerization of 1,4-dienes with maleic anhydride or other olefins (12, 24).

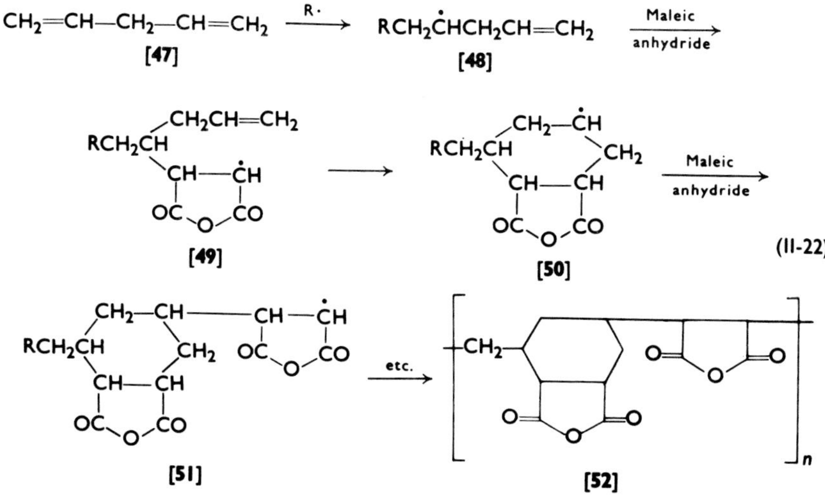

$$CH_2{=}CH{-}CH_2{-}CH{=}CH_2 \xrightarrow{R\cdot} RCH_2\overset{\cdot}{C}HCH_2CH{=}CH_2 \xrightarrow[anhydride]{Maleic}$$

[47]   [48]

[49]   [50]   (II-22)

[51]   [52]

(*iii*) Copolymerization of cyclodienes with sulfur dioxide (*133*). The transannular cyclopolymerization of *cis,trans*-1,5-cyclodecadiene with sulfur dioxide has been reported to yield a polymer of structure [54] (*129, 133*). Ammonium nitrate was the best initiator, giving nearly quantitative yields of polymer. A wide variety of solvents and nonsolvents for the polymer were useful with this catalyst system. The polymer possessed very high molecular weights (60,000) and good stability toward alkali, and was amorphous. Thermogravimetric analysis indicated that oxidative attack started at about 235°C.

$$n \quad + \quad n\,SO_2 \quad \longrightarrow \quad \qquad \qquad \text{(II-23)}$$

[53]   [55]   [54]

1,5-Cyclooctadiene is reported to yield a different type of product in a similar copolymerization. The polymer [56] was produced at room temperature in acetone with lithium nitrate (*149*). Its inherent viscosity was 0.80. Oxygen as the initiator in sulfolane gives polymer with an inherent viscosity of 1.94. High polymer was also obtained from dicyclopentadiene in this polymerization (*149*). A transannular sulfonyl bridge was postulated to exist in its structure.

$$n \quad + \quad 2n\,SO_2 \quad \longrightarrow \quad \qquad \qquad \text{(II-24)}$$

[36]   [55]   [56]

(*iv*) Copolymerization of 1,5-hexadiene with carbon monoxide (*22*). The reaction is performed in water with potassium persulfate as the initiator.

$$CH_2{=}CH{-}(CH_2)_2CH{=}CH_2 \xrightarrow{\;R\cdot\;} RCH_2\dot{C}H{-}(CH_2)_2CH{=}CH_2 \xrightarrow{\;CO\;}$$

[57]   [58]

$$RCH_2CH{-}(CH_2)_2CH{=}CH_2 \longrightarrow$$
$$\underset{\dot{C}O}{|}$$

[59]   [60]

$$\xrightarrow{\;etc.\;} \qquad \qquad \text{(II-25)}$$

[61]   [62]

(*v*) Polymerization of diacrylylmethanes (*40*). Only 50% of the polymer [64] was soluble, indicating that cross-linking accompanied the polymerization. The inherent viscosity of the soluble portion was 0.33 (dimethyl sulfoxide).

$$n\ CH_2{=}CHCOCCOCH{=}CH_2 \xrightarrow[C_6H_6]{AIBN}$$

[63]

[64]

(II-26)

(*vi*) Polymerization of perhalo-1,6-heptadienes (*51–54, 163*). A tough elastomeric polymer, [η] 0.60 (C_6F_6), was obtained that had good thermal stability.

$$n\ CF_2{=}CFCF_2CFClCF_2CF{=}CF_2 \xrightarrow[\substack{147°C;\ 13,600\ atm \\ 113\ hr}]{^{60}Co\ radiation}$$

[65]

[66]

(II-27)

(*vii*) Polymerization of 1,3-dienes (*42, 81*). The formation of six-membered rings was postulated in the free-radical polymerization of conjugated dienes. It was due to the fact that the polymers possessed a lower than theoretical (97%) double-bond content. However, more direct proof of the presence of cyclic structures in these polymers is needed.

(*viii*) Polymerization of triallylmethanes (*115*). The solubility of the polymers (chloroform, benzene, alcohol) and their residual unsaturation (22%) are in agreement with the proposed structure [68]. However, a rigorous structure proof was not offered.

$$3n\ RC(CH_2CH{=}CH_2)_3 \xrightarrow{Peroxide}$$

[67]

[68]

R = OH, CO_2CH_3, CN, $CONH_2$

(II-28)

The foregoing examples amply illustrate the scope of free radical-initiated intra–intermolecular polymerizations. Several theoretical treatments of this type of polymerization have appeared (*12, 29, 60, 61, 159, 160*). The kinetics have been described recently (*11*). A statistical study of the probability of cyclopolymerization showed that a more energetically favorable pathway must exist. Much higher extents of cyclization are observed than would be predicted on a purely statistical basis (*35*). The high "cyclopolymerization tendency" of nonconjugated dienes was explained by assuming an interaction between the electrons of the olefinic linkages (*19*). A schematic representation of this interaction is shown in (II-29). Examination of the UV spectra of several nonconjugated dienes showed the existence of a bathochromic shift of the absorption maxima relative to the values that were calculated from Woodward's rule (*25, 28, 34*). This was taken as evidence of the postulated interaction.

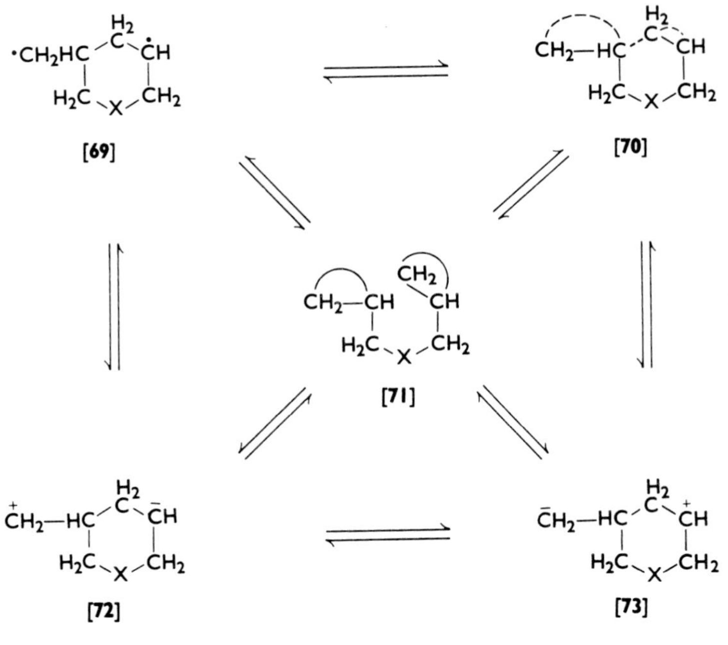

(II-29)

[69] [70] [71] [72] [73]

METHOD 2. ZIEGLER-TYPE INITIATION

a. Five-Membered Rings

The polymerization of 1,5-hexadiene yields a polymer containing cyclopentane rings (*87, 88, 97*).

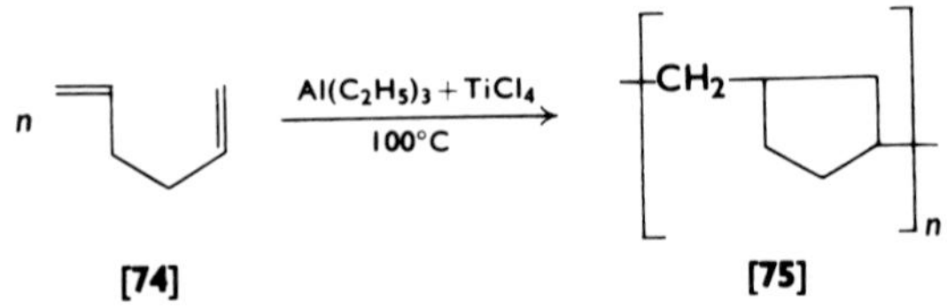

(II-30)

[74] [75]

In agreement with a cyclic polymerization mechanism, only slight residual unsaturation was found in the polymer by infrared studies. Copolymers of

1,5-hexadiene with monoolefins were prepared (89). Structural studies showed that the diene cyclized during the copolymerization. The effect of temperature and physical state of the catalyst upon the degree of cyclization was determined. 1,5-Hexadiene can polymerize by two modes:

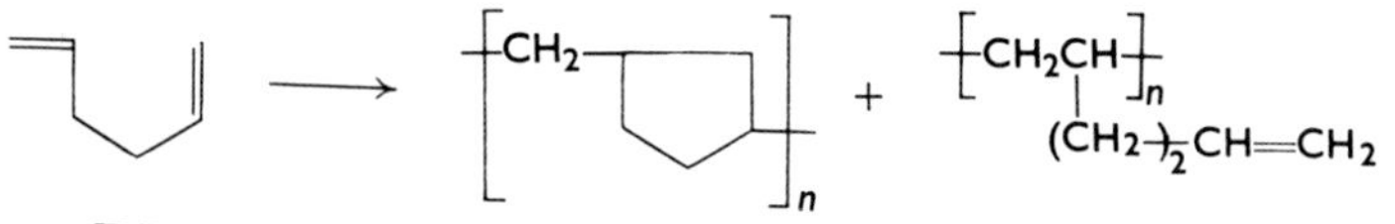

$$\text{(II-31)}$$

[74] [75] [76]
Cyclic Acyclic

Lower temperatures and homogeneous systems favor 1,2-polymerization (161). Some results are shown in the accompanying table.

Polymerization of 1,5-Hexadiene [74]

Catalyst	Temperature (°C)	% 1,2-Polymerization[a]
Al(C$_2$H$_5$)$_2$Cl + TiCl$_4$ (heterogeneous)	25	<10
Al(C$_2$H$_5$)$_2$Cl + V(acetylacetonate)$_3$ (homogeneous)	25	30–35
Al(C$_2$H$_5$)$_2$Cl + V(acetylacetonate)$_3$ (homogeneous)	−20	75–80

[a] By infrared spectroscopy.

Polymers with fused ring systems can also be prepared.

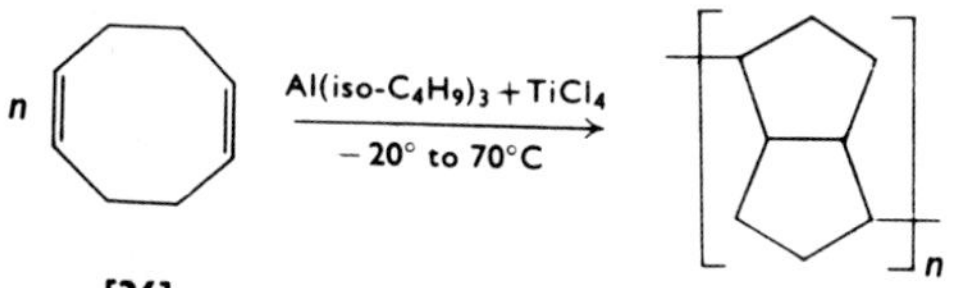

(135) (II-32)

[36] [77]
η_{inh} 0.04(C$_6$H$_6$)

(31) (II-33)

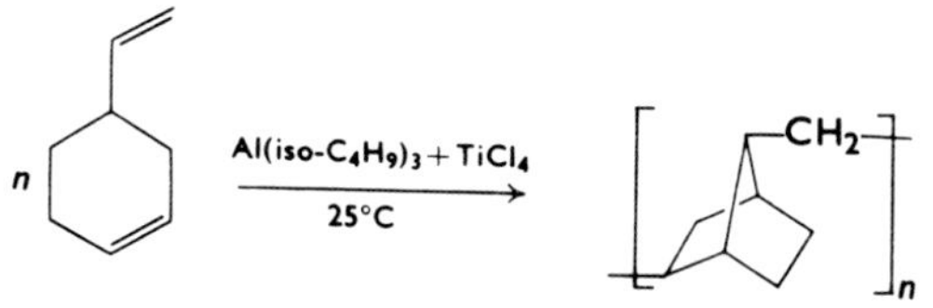

[78] [79]
[η] 0.04 (C$_6$H$_6$)

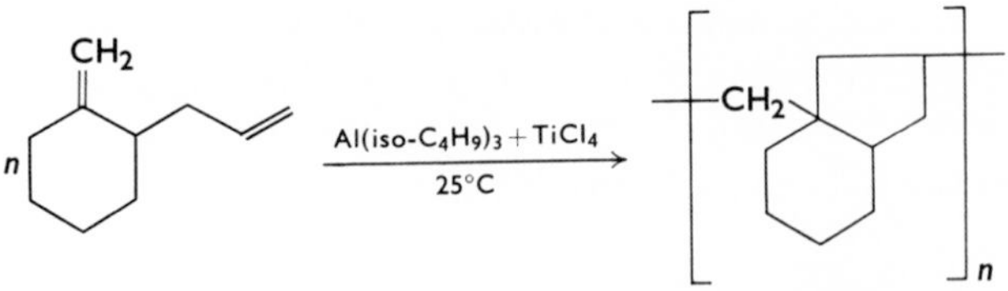

$$[80] \xrightarrow[\text{25°C}]{\text{Al(iso-C}_4\text{H}_9)_3 + \text{TiCl}_4} [81] \quad (32) \quad \text{(II-34)}$$

$[\eta]$ 0.13 (C_6H_6)

The percent cyclization in polymer [81] was 92–95% as determined by nuclear magnetic resonance spectroscopy. The residual unsaturation was due to the presence of structures [82] and [83]. The formation of structure [83] is favored since Ziegler catalysts polymerize monosubstituted olefins preferentially. A copolymer possessing a higher proportion of [82] was favored on cationic polymerization (BF_3/CH_2Cl_2, $-70°C$). The formation of structure [82] in this instance is due to the similarity of the methylene double bond in the monomer with that in isobutylene. The latter polymerizes readily on cationic initiation.

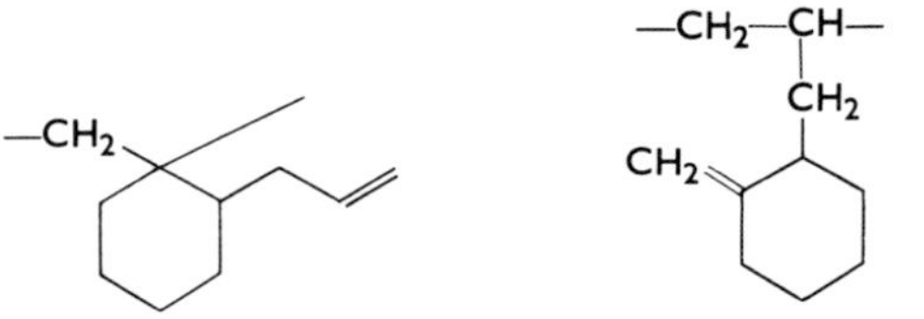

[82]   [83]   (II-35)

b. Six-Membered and Larger Rings

Polymers containing six-membered rings are formed by polymerization of 1,6-heptadienes (II-36) (21). A cumulative 1,2- and 1,4-cyclopolymerization has been observed (II-37) (28). Infrared evidence supports the repeat unit structure [87].

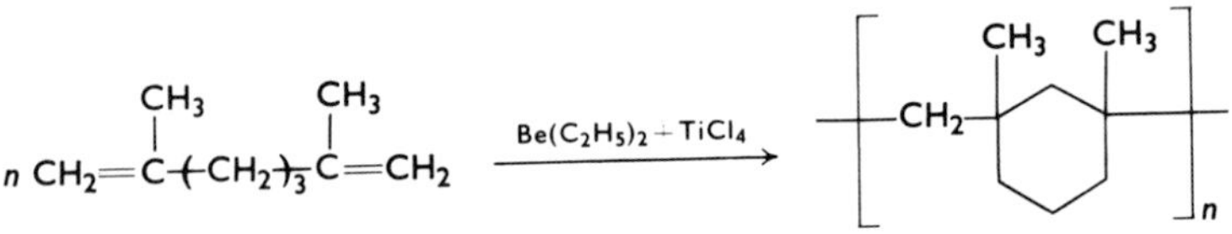

$$n \, CH_2{=}C(CH_3)(CH_2)_3C(CH_3){=}CH_2 \xrightarrow{\text{Be(C}_2\text{H}_5)_2 + \text{TiCl}_4} [85] \quad \text{(II-36)}$$

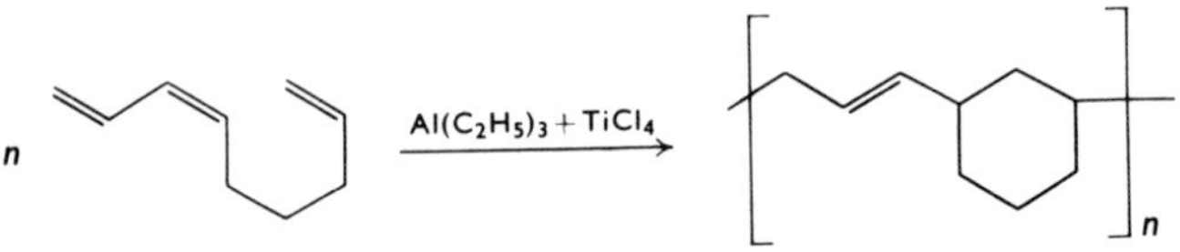

[84]

$$[86] \xrightarrow{\text{Al(C}_2\text{H}_5)_3 + \text{TiCl}_4} [87] \quad \text{(II-37)}$$

Additional examples of the remarkable specificity exhibited by this type of polymerization are shown in Eqs. (II-38), (II-39), and (II-40). Low yields of soluble, polymeric product of unspecified molecular weights were obtained when polymerization was initiated by a triisobutylaluminum–titanium tetrachloride catalyst (36). Insoluble product was also obtained. The polymer structures [89], [91], and [93] were consistent with infrared spectral data.

(II-38)

[88]   [89]

(II-39)

[90]   [91]

(II-40)

[92]   [93]

1,6-Heptadiyne leads to a polymer that possesses a system of conjugated double bonds (II-41) (153, 154). The structural assignment was based on chemical and spectroscopic evidence. However, its correctness was questioned by Hubert and Dale (68). These workers interpreted the polymerization of unconjugated diynes, $HC\equiv C(CH_2)_nC\equiv CH$, as a poly(cyclotrimerization) rather than a cyclopolymerization. The trimerization of monoacetylenes in the presence of Ziegler catalysts is well known (148).

$n\ HC\equiv C\text{-}(CH_2)_3\text{-}C\equiv CH$ $\xrightarrow{Al(iso\text{-}C_4H_9)_3 + TiCl_4}$

(II-41)

[94]   [95]

[η] 0.06 (C_6H_6)

$\overline{M}_n$ 13,500 (osmometry)

The intra–intermolecular polymerization of cis-1,3-divinylcyclopentane and cyclohexane has been effected by a Ziegler catalyst prepared from titanium tetrachloride and triisobutylaluminum (38). A 38% conversion to the bicyclo-octane polymer was obtained in 72 hours (II-42). Under similar conditions, a 20% conversion to the bicyclononane polymer [99] was obtained from *cis*-1,3-divinylcyclohexane (II-43). The polymerization of 4-vinylmethylenecyclohexane yields polymeric chains that contain bicyclo[2.2.2]octane rings (II-44) (*30, 33*).

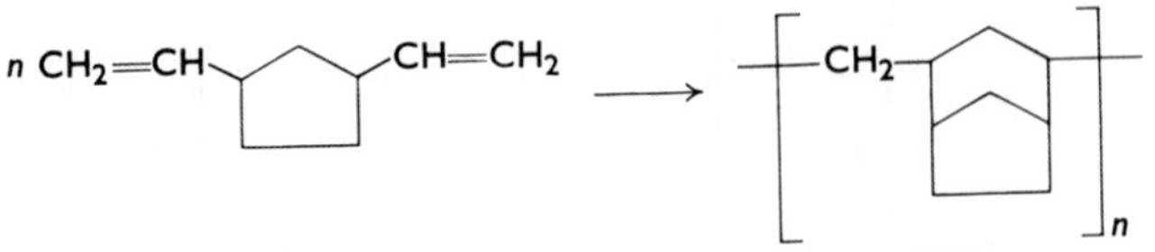

(II-42)

[96]   [97]

(II-43)

[98]   [99]

$Al(C_2H_5)_3 + TiCl_4$

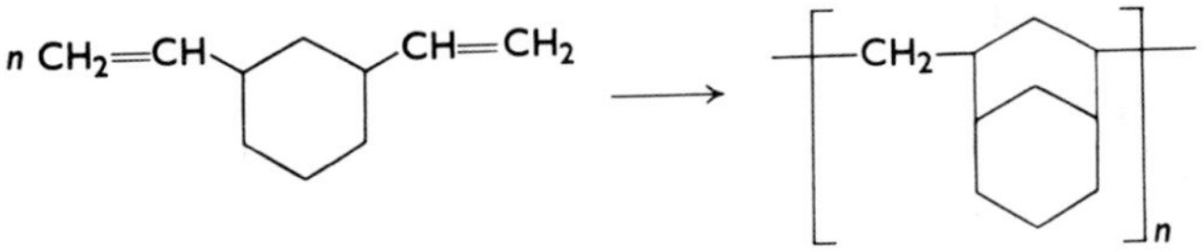

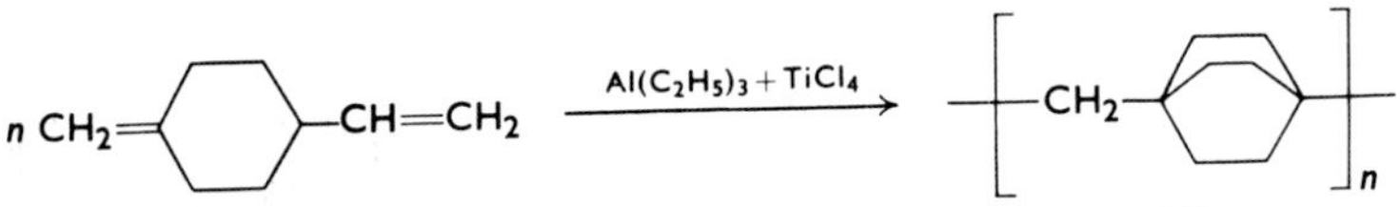

[100]   [101]   (II-44)

Bicyclic structures were also obtained from 1,4-pentadiene and triallylmethane (*144*).

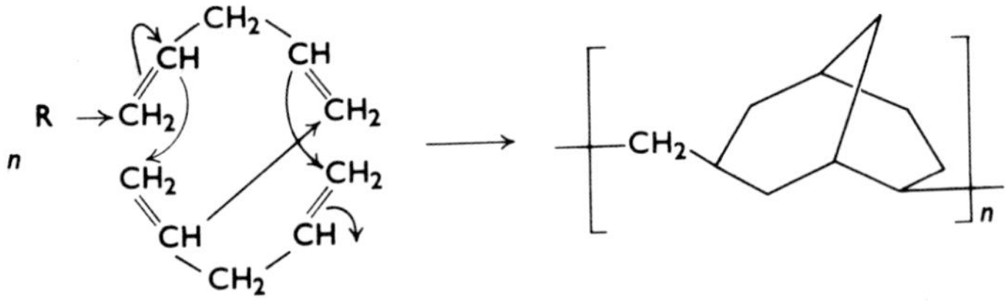

(II-45)

[102]   [103]
                        M.W. ~1200

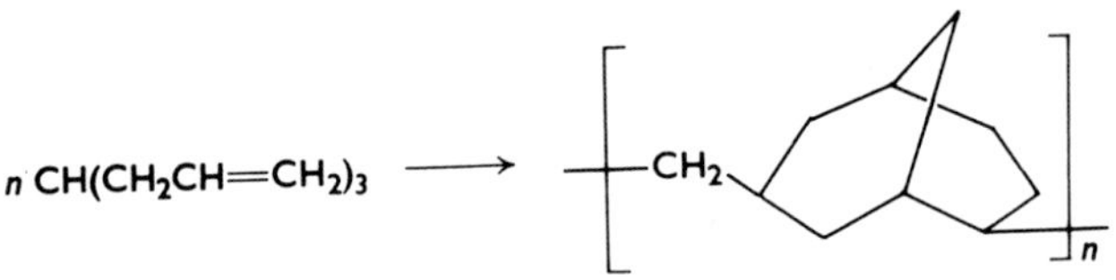

(II-46)

$n\ CH(CH_2CH{=}CH_2)_3$

[104]   [105]

Polymerization of a series of dienes of formula [106] has been studied (*13, 16, 93*). The polymers that were obtained consisted of both soluble and cross-linked, insoluble fractions. Quantitative infrared and bromination experiments indicated that the soluble polymers possessed cyclic as well as open-chain structures. The percent of cyclization depended on the size of the incipient cycle and corresponded roughly to what is obtained in other cyclization reactions. The results are summarized in the accompanying table. A similar effect of ring size versus tendency toward cyclopolymerization was observed for monomers of structures [107] (*92*).

Percent Cyclization vs. Size of the Incipient Cycle for Polymerization[a] of $CH_2{=}CH{+}CH_2{)}_x CH{=}CH_2$ [106]

x	Size of incipient cycle	Soluble polymer (C_6H_6)	
		η_{inh}	% Cyclic units
4	7	0.08	25
5	8	0.14	9
6	9	0.35	6
7	10	0.23	10
8	11	0.14	11
9	12	0.10	11
10	13	0.11	—
11	14	0.06	15
12	15	0.25	15
14	17	0.10	4
18	21	0.13	8

[a] Catalyzed by triiosbutylaluminum and titanium tetrachloride.

$$CH_2{=}CH{+}CH_2{)}_x CH{=}CH_2 \qquad \text{(II-47)}$$

[106]

$$CH_2{=}\underset{|}{\overset{C_6H_5}{C}}{+}CH_2{)}_x \underset{|}{\overset{C_6H_5}{C}}{=}CH_2 \qquad \text{(II-48)}$$

[107]

$x = 2, 3, 4$

METHOD 3. CATIONIC INITIATION

a. Three-Membered Rings

Polymerization of bicyclo[2.2.1]heptadiene yields poly(nortricyclene) (*73*).

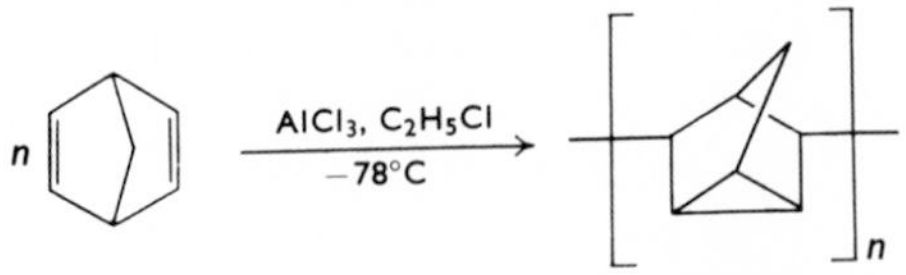

(II-49)

[9]   [108]

The molecular weight of the polymer was determined by osmometry and was 8400. Its solubility in solvents such as carbon tetrachloride, benzene, and toluene was in agreement with a linear structure. Some cross-linked, insoluble polymer that presumably possessed structure [109] was also formed. The use of higher polymerization temperatures favored cross-linking over cyclization.

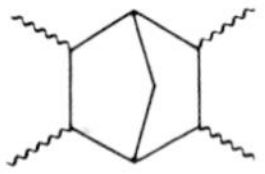

(II-50)

[109]

5-Methylenebicyclo[2.2.1]hept-2-ene has been polymerized with Lewis acid-type catalysts to yield soluble polymers (132). Aluminum chloride and boron trifluoride were used in specific examples. Apparently, the other types of initiation yield cross-linked products from this monomer (however, see Table II.1). Infrared analysis supported structure [111] for the polymer (74). The molecular weight of the polymer appeared to be low based on the viscosity data that were reported, but it could be molded and spun into fibers.

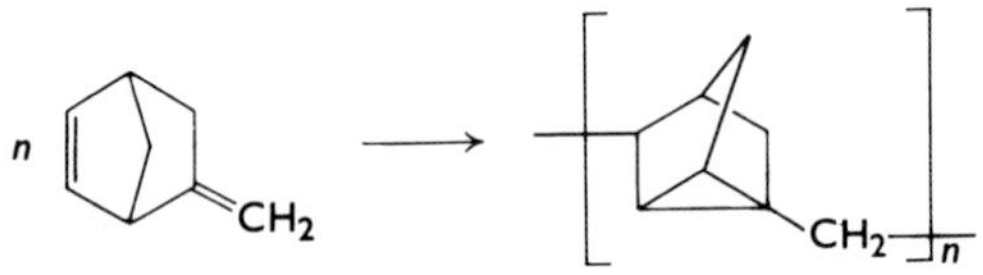

(II-51)

[110]   [111]

b. *Five-Membered Rings*

The residual unsaturation of polymer [113] (by IR techniques) was 5–10% (92).

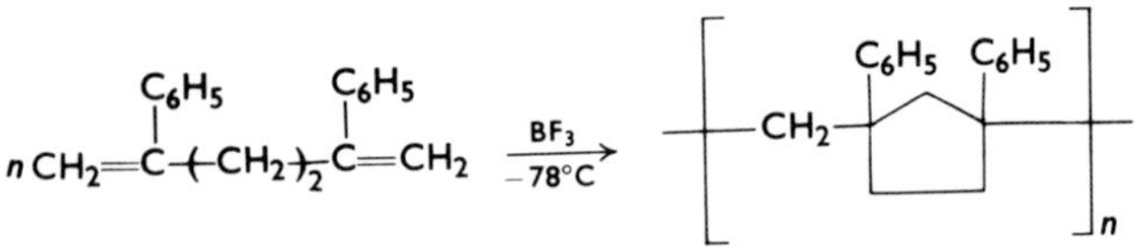

(II-52)

[112]   [113]

η_{inh} 0.083 (C_6H_6)

Appreciable cyclization accompanies the cationic polymerization of o-divinylbenzene (II-53) (5). The relative magnitudes of x and y depend on the catalyst employed. At 0°C, in toluene as solvent, there was 19% cyclization with boron trifluoride etherate. Under the same conditions as much as 47.8% cyclization occurred when stannic tetrachloride was used.

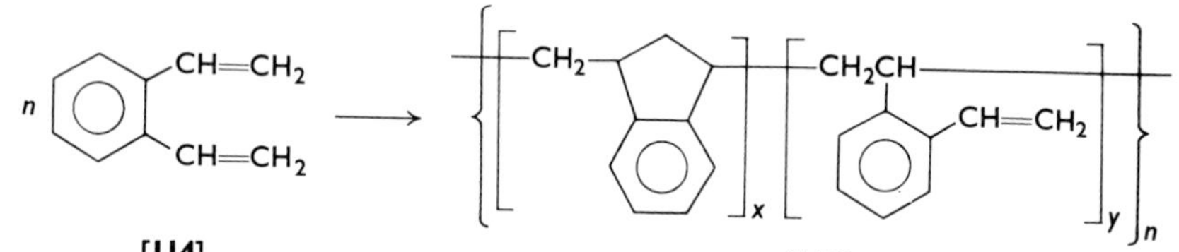

[114]   [115]   (II-53)

Treatment of appropriate monomers with cationic initiators leads to polymers containing bridged ring systems (10, 31).

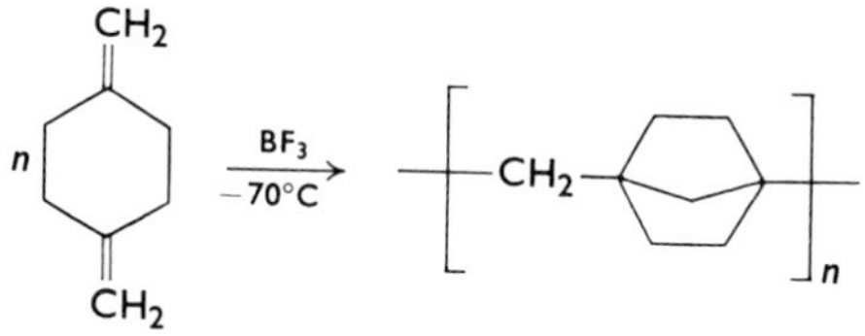

[116]   [117]   (II-54)

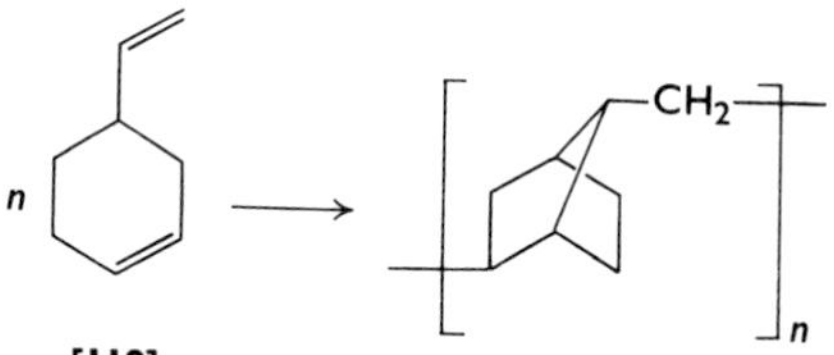

[118]   [119]   (II-55)

As was discussed earlier (Method 2, this chapter), the Ziegler-catalyzed polymerization of 2-allylmethylenecyclohexane [80] gives a soluble polymer that is essentially saturated (complete cyclization). However, cationic initiators lead to polymers that possess significant unsaturation. With boron trifluoride in methylene chloride, only 50% of the units were cyclic; boron trifluoride etherate in methylene chloride gave a higher (80%) extent of cyclization (32).

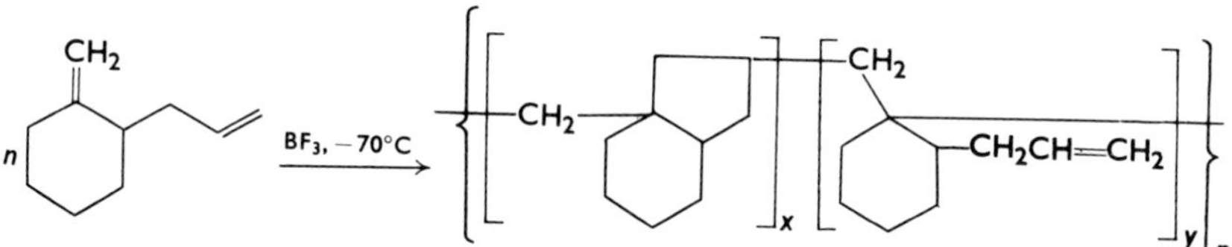

[80]   [120]

(II-56)

c. Six-Membered Rings

The polymerization of alloocimene [121] is reported in the patent literature (139–141). Silica gel, synthetic silicates, and various Lewis acids were used as the catalysts. However, no details concerning the structure of the polymeric products were given. More recently, the cationic polymerization of alloocimene was investigated by Jones (71). An intra–intermolecular polymerization mechanism was postulated (II-57). The iodine number of the polymer indicated the loss of two double bonds per monomer unit during polymerization. Interestingly, the use of Ziegler-type catalysts did not yield cyclic polymeric structures (95, 96).

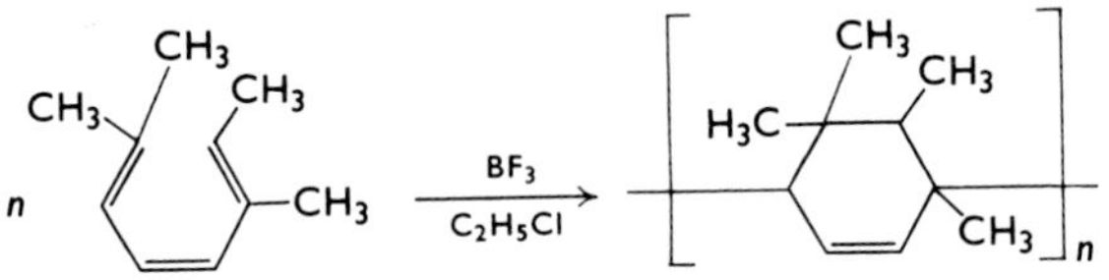

(II-57)

[121]   [122]

A polymer with a six-membered ring in the repeat unit was obtained by polymerization of myrcene (94). No cyclization took place on Ziegler catalysis.

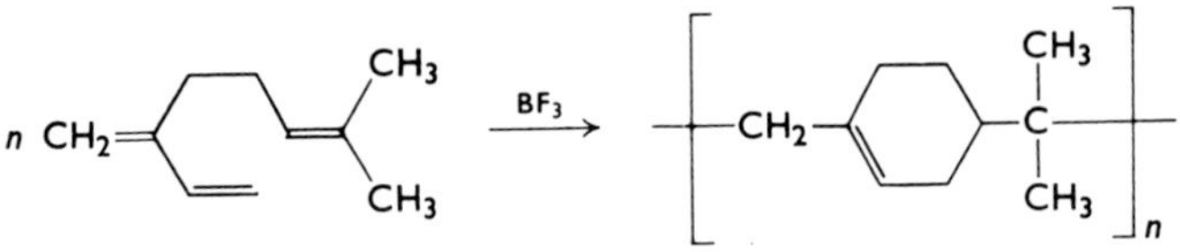

(II-58)

[123]   [124]

Polymers with bicyclic bridged structures were obtained in several instances (30, 33, 128).

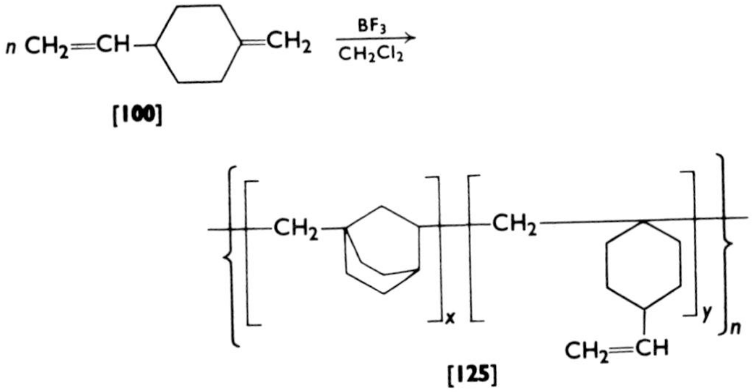

[100]

(II-59)

[125]

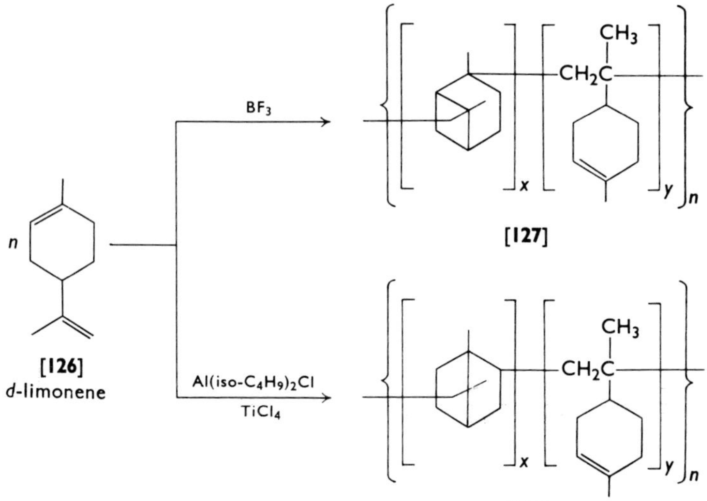

$$(II\text{-}60)$$

[126]
d-limonene

[127]

[128]

The structure of polymers [127] and [128] is not known with certainty. Nevertheless, the structures shown do contradict earlier work (*137*) in which the polymer was reported to possess structure [129].

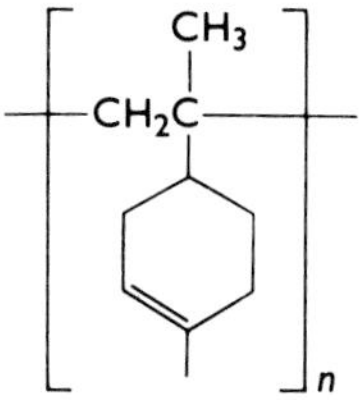

$$(II\text{-}61)$$

[129]

Ladder polymers which might be classified as arising via an intra–intermolecular polymerization were obtained from conjugated dienes under the influence of cationic initiators (*57–59*). An illustration is shown in Eq. (II-62). Intensive investigations were carried out in this field by several schools of workers (*14, 42, 43, 45, 78–80, 122, 136, 155, 157*).

$$n\,CH_2{=}C(R)CH{=}CH_2 \longrightarrow$$

[130]

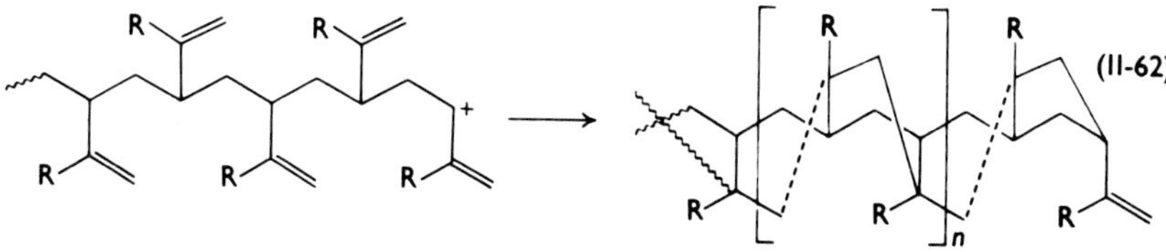

$$(II\text{-}62)$$

[131]   [132]

d. Larger Rings

Treatment of 3-methylenebicyclo[3.3.1]nonan-7-one with acids yields polymers with adamantane rings in the repeat units (151).

[133]   [134]   (II-63)

METHOD 4. ANIONIC INITIATION

The polymerization of some conjugated dienes (butadiene, isoprene, chloroprene) by an ether-free Grignard system [$(C_4H_9)_2Mg$—C_4H_9MgI] yielded polymers that possessed slightly lower than theoretical unsaturation (44, 56). Cyclization was postulated as having occurred in order to explain this result.

[135]   [136]   (II-64)

A high molecular weight product was obtained by the anionic polymerization of 2,6-diphenyl-1,6-heptadiene (55). The use of phenyllithium in 1,2-dimethoxyethane at $-40°$ to $-50°C$ yielded a polymer of lower molecular weight (92).

[137]   [138]   (II-65)
                                             η_{inh} 0.49

The condensation of methyl vinyl ketone with ethyl acrylate in the presence of sodium methoxide yields poly(diacrylylmethane) (69, 70). The polymer was isolated as its sodium salt. It is yellow-brown and soluble in water. Acidification of the aqueous solution gave the "free acid," a brilliant yellow powder that was soluble in alcohols, ketones, glacial acetic acid, and alkali. No unsaturation could be detected in it by infrared techniques. Its molecular weight was found to be about 2000 by cryoscopy. A more detailed study of this polymer revealed that it was either a copolymer of diacrylylmethane and methyl vinyl ketone or a product formed by the reaction of poly(diacrylylmethane) with methyl vinyl ketone (*130*).

$$n\ CH_2{=}CHCOCH_3 + n\ C_2H_5OCOCH{=}CH_2 \xrightarrow[0° \text{ to } -80°C]{NaOCH_3}$$

[139]   [140]

$$n \left[CH_2{=}CHCOCHCOCH{=}CH_2 \right]^- Na^+ \longrightarrow$$

[141]

Not isolated   [142]   (II-66)

The polymerization of pure diacrylylmethane with sodium methoxide in benzene was studied (*41*). The polymer was obtained as its sodium salt. It was a bright yellow powder, soluble in water, dimethyl sulfoxide and dimethylformamide. It was of relatively low molecular weight (η_{inh} 0.16). The corresponding "free acid" was insoluble.

METHOD 5. OTHER METHODS OF INITIATION

Catalysts were prepared by the interaction of molybdenum or tungsten hexacarbonyl with bicyclo[2.2.1]heptadiene or cycloheptatriene (*83*). They were described as being effective for the cyclopolymerization of [9] and [143].

[9] CO_2CH_3 (II-67)

                               [143]

The reactions were performed in bulk or inert solvents such as benzene or xylene. Temperatures ranging from 25° to 140°C were employed. Anhydrous conditions and the absence of oxygen were required. The presence of nortricyclene units in the polymers was indicated by their infrared spectra. The molecular weights of the materials were not reported.

Cyclic structures were formed when diacetylenes of the general formula

$$HC{\equiv}C{\left(CH_2\right)}_{\overline{n}}C{\equiv}CH$$ (II-68)

[144]

were treated with dicarbonyl bis(triphenylphosphine)nickel in refluxing cyclohexane (*37*). Depending on the value of *n*, the polymers were either linear, cross-linked, or possessed both aromatic and linear structures. The polymerization of a variety of mono- and disubstituted acetylenes and diacetylenes was also studied in the presence of this catalyst (*124–126*). Whether linear or aromatic structures are formed is dependent on the particular structure of the monomer.

Poly(cyclotrimerization) of diacetylenes was observed in the presence of metal carbonyls [145] and [146].

$$Co(CO)_8 \qquad\qquad \left[Co(CO)_4 \right]_2 Hg \qquad\qquad (II\text{-}69)$$

$$[145] \qquad\qquad\qquad [146]$$

Ill-defined, dark-colored polymers possessing aromatic structures were obtained (*66–68*). The same type of materials were also obtained when the reaction product of $(R_3P)_2NiX_2$ (R = alkyl or aryl; X = halogen) with sodium borohydride or lithium aluminum hydride was employed as the polymerization catalyst for a variety of acetylenic monomers (*84–86*).

55

TABLE II.1

Three-Membered Ring-Containing Polymers

No.	Structure	Method	Molecular weight	Solubility	T_m (°C)	Remarks and property data	References
1	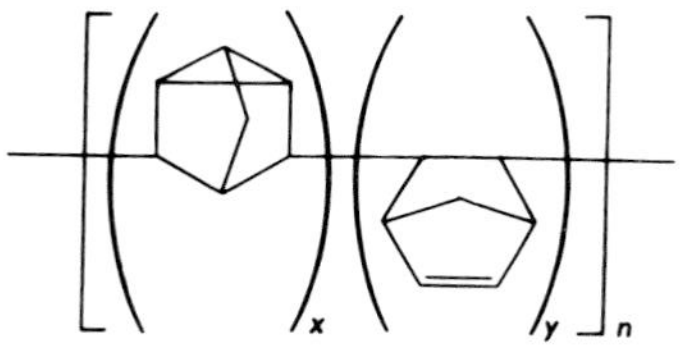 [10]	1	$[\eta]$ 0.2: 17,000 (light scattering)	$CHCl_3$, CCl_4, C_6H_6, THF	—	Ratio $y/x = 1/3.6$ (NMR) Darkens at 225°C (air) Cross-links at 238°C (air) Amorphous Properties of cast film: Heat distortion temp. = 186°C; Flexural strength = 13,300 psi; Flexural modulus = 380,000 psi; Impact strength = 3.5 ft lb/in.^{3} Structure confirmed by spectroscopic studies	131
	Copolymer of No. 1 with:	1, 3	—	—	—	—	62, 73, 83, 166, 169
2	SO_2 [16]	1	η_{inh} 1.02	DMF, DMSO	300 (Soft.)	Amorphous. $T_g = 257$°C	1, 134
		1	$[\eta]$ 0.2	—	—	—	162
3	$CH_2{=}CCl_2$	1	η_{red} 0.17	Cyclohexanone	—	34–88% Vinylidene chloride	169, 170
4	$CH_2{=}CHCl$	1	η_{red} 0.45	Cyclohexanone	—	18–87% Vinyl chloride	169, 170
5	$CH_2{=}CH{-}CN$	1	$[\eta]$ 0.19	Acetone	100	Mole ratio norbornadiene/acrylonitrile $\approx$ 0.467	131
		1	η_{red} 0.52	DMF	—	49–87% Acrylonitrile	169, 170

TABLE II.1—*continued*

Three-Membered Ring-Containing Polymers

No.	Structure	Method	Molecular weight	Solubility	T_m (C)	Remarks and property data	References
6	$CH_2=CHOCOCH_3$	1	$[\eta]$ 0.26	C_6H_6	70–100	Mole ratio norbornadiene/ vinyl acetate $\cong$ 0.72	131
		1	η_{red} 3.14	C_6H_6	—	14–94% Vinyl acetate	170
7	$CH_2=CH-COO-C_2H_5$	1	η_{red} 2.24	C_6H_6	—	57–96% Ethyl acrylate	169, 170
8	$CH_2=C(CH_3)COOCH_3$	1	$[\eta]$ 0.37	C_6H_6	80	Mole ratio norbornadiene/ methyl methacrylate = 0.12	131
		1	η_{red} 0.35	C_6H_6	—	95% Methyl methacrylate	169, 170
9	$C_6H_5CH=CH_2$	1	$[\eta]$ 0.12	C_6H_6	100–110	—	131
10	Polymer from 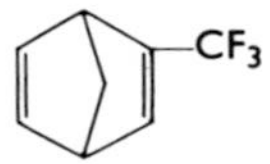 (CF₃ structure)	1	—	Acetone	250–260 d	Contains 32% fluorine	62

* * * * *

57

11 Polymer from						
	1	—	Acetone, alcohols, C_6H_6, toluene, $CHCl_3$	—	Presence of nortricyclene units shown by IR	83
12 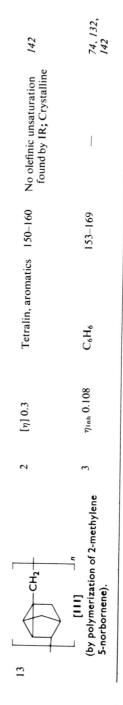 [13] [14] or a copolymer containing both types of units	1	η_{inh} 1.92; 220,000 (osmometry)	C_6H_6, acetone, CH_2Cl_2, $CHCl_3$	270	Cross-links 150°C (air) $T_g = 220$°C (from Young's modulus–temperature curve) Properties of molded film: Amorphous; Tensile strength = 4600 psi; Elongation at break = 6%; Hardness (Knoop) = 7.3	62
13 [III]	2	$[\eta]$ 0.3	Tetralin, aromatics	150–160	No olefinic unsaturation found by IR; Crystalline	142
(by polymerization of 2-methylene 5-norbornene).	3	η_{inh} 0.108	C_6H_6	153–169	—	74, 132, 142

TABLE II.2

Four-Membered Ring-Containing Polymers

No.	Structure	Method	Molecular weight	Solubility	Remarks and property data	References
1	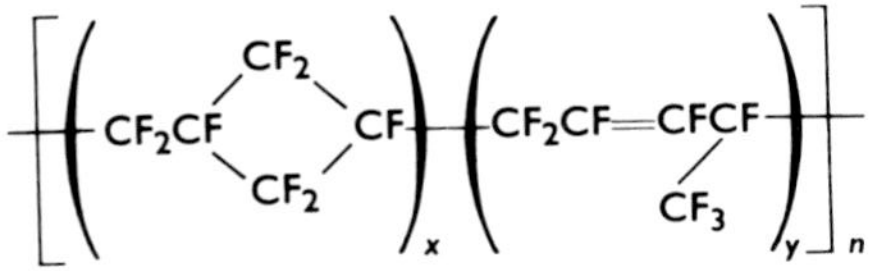 [18]	1	8000	Hexafluorobenzene	$(x + y)/y \approx 3$ to 20 (by IR) depending on experimental conditions. At low $(x + y)/y$ values polymer is rubbery. At higher values it is powdery	*24, 50, 163*
2	Copolymers from other 1,4-pentadienes	—	—	—	—	*24*

TABLE II.3

Five-Membered Ring-Containing Polymers

No.	Structure	Method	Molecular weight	Solubility	T_m (°C)	Remarks and property data	References
1	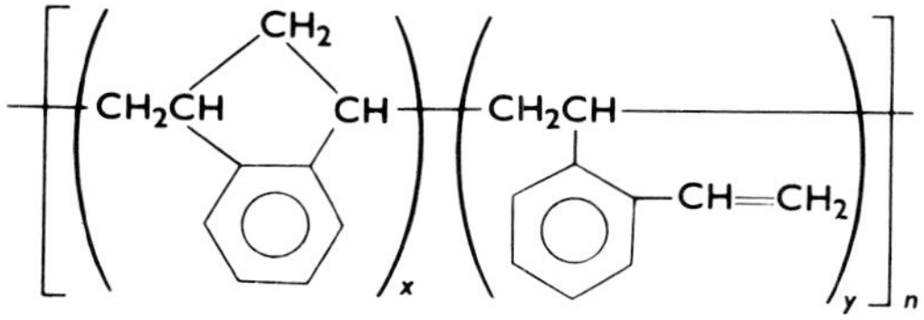 [115]	3	η_{Inh} 0.062; 2850 (osmometry)	Benzene, toluene	—	Cyclized to the extent of 77.5%	5
	(polymerization of o-divinylbenzene)	1	—	—	—	—	7
2	Copolymer of No. 1 with 2-methyl-5-vinylpyridine	1	—	Benzene	—	Double-bond content: ~70–80% of theoretical	6
	Polymers from vinylethynyl carbinols and derivatives 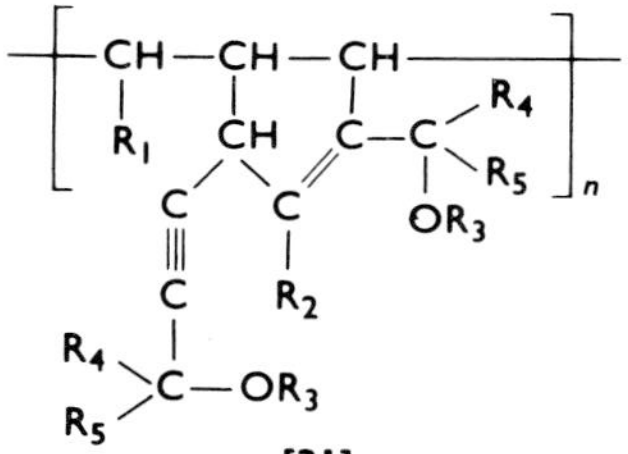 [31]						

TABLE II.3—*continued*

Five-Membered Ring-Containing Polymers

No.	Structure	Method	Molecular weight	Solubility	T_m (°C)	Remarks and property data	References
3	$R_1 = R_2 = R_3 = R_4 = R_5 = H$	1	—	Lower alcohols, acetone, methyl ethyl ketone, dioxane, acetic acid	—	—	*106*
4	$R_1 = R_2 = R_3 = R_4 = H$; $R_5 = CH_3$	1	—	Lower alcohols, acetone, methyl ethyl ketone, dioxane, acetic acid	—	—	*106*
5	$R_1 = R_2 = R_3 = R_4 = H$; $R_5 = C_2H_5$	1	—	Lower alcohols, acetone, methyl ethyl ketone, dioxane, acetic acid	—	—	*106*
6	$R_1 = R_2 = R_3 = H$; $R_4 = R_5 = CH_3$	1	η_{inh} 2.1; 1,205,000 (osmometry)	Lower alcohols, acetone, methyl ethyl ketone, dioxane, acetic acid	—	White powder. Structure substantiated by ozonization, bromination, acetylation, and IR	*75, 103, 104, 105, 109, 110, 145*

61

No.	Substituents			Solubility			Ref.
7	$R_1 = R_2 = R_3 = H; R_4 = CH_3; R_5 = C_2H_5$	1	226,000 (from viscosity data)	Lower alcohols, acetone, methyl ethyl ketone, dioxane, acetic acid	—	—	*104, 106, 111*
8	$R_1 = R_2 = R_3 = R_4 = H; R_5 = n\text{-}C_3H_7$	1	—	Lower alcohols, ketones, dioxane, acetic acid	—	—	*106*
9	$R_1 = R_2 = CH_3; R_3 = H; R_4 = R_5 = CH_3$	1	—	"Soluble"	—	—	*113*
10	$R_1 = R_2 = R_3 = H; R_4 = R_5 = C_2H_5$	1	328,000 (from viscosity data)	Lower alcohols, acetone, methyl ethyl ketone, dioxane, acetic acid	—	—	*111*
		1	—	Lower alcohols, acetone, methyl ethyl ketone, dioxane, acetic acid	—	—	*106*
11	$R_1 = R_2 = CH_3; R_3 = H; R_4 = CH_3; R_5 = C_2H_5$	1	—	"Soluble"	—	—	*113*
12	$R_1 = R_2 = R_3 = H; R_4 = CH_3; R_5 = -C(OH)(CH_3)_2$	1	—	"Soluble"	—	—	*113*
13	$R_1 = R_2 = R_3 = H; R_4 = CH_3; R_5 = C(CH_3)_3$	1	402,000 (from viscosity data)	Lower alcohols, ketones, dioxane, acetic acid	—	—	*111*
		1	—	Lower alcohols, ketones, dioxane, acetic acid	—	—	*106*

TABLE II.3—continued

Five-Membered Ring-Containing Polymers

No.	Structure	Method	Molecular weight	Solubility	T_m (°C)	Remarks and property data	References
14	$R_1 = R_2 = R_3 = H$; R_4 and $R_5 = (CH_2)_4$	1	—	CH_3OH	—	—	121
15	$R_1 = R_2 = R_3 = H$; R_4 and $R_5 = (CH_2)_5$	1	—	CH_3OH	—	—	121
16	$R_1 = R_2 = R_3 = H$; R_4 and $R_5 = -(CH_2)_2CH(CH_3)-(CH_2)_2$	1	—	CH_3OH	—	—	121
17	$R_1 = R_2 = R_3 = H$; R_4 and $R_5 = $ 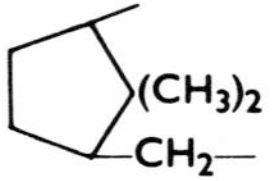 ![cyclopentane with (CH$_3$)$_2$ and CH$_2$ substituents]	1	—	CH_3OH	—	—	121
18	$R_1 = R_2 = R_3 = R_4 = H$; $R_5 = $ 2-ClC_6H_4	1	"Low"	Benzene, chloroform	—	—	119, 120
19	$R_1 = R_2 = R_3 = R_4 = H$; $R_5 = $ 4-ClC_6H_4	1	"Low"	Benzene, chloroform	—	—	119, 120
20	$R_1 = R_2 = R_3 = R_4 = H$; $R_5 = C_6H_5$	1	"Low"	Benzene, chloroform	—	—	119, 120

21	$R_1 = R_2 = R_3 = R_4 = H$; $R_5 = 2\text{-}CH_3C_6H_4$	—	"Low"	Benzene, chloroform	—	119, 120
22	$R_1 = R_2 = R_3 = R_4 = H$; $R_5 = 3\text{-}CH_3C_6H_4$	—	"Low"	Benzene, chloroform	—	119, 120
23	$R_1 = R_2 = R_3 = R_4 = H$; $R_5 = 4\text{-}CH_3C_6H_4$	—	"Low"	Benzene, chloroform	—	119, 120
24	$R_1 = R_2 = R_3 = H$; $R_4 = CH_3$; $R_5 = C_6H_5$	—	"Low"	Benzene, chloroform	—	120
25	$R_1 = R_2 = R_3 = R_4 = H$; $R_5 = 2,4\text{-}(CH_3)_2C_6H_3$	—	"Low"	Benzene, chloroform	—	119, 120
26	$R_1 = R_2 = R_3 = R_4 = H$; $R_5 = 2,5\text{-}(CH_3)_2C_6H_3$	—	"Low"	Benzene, chloroform	—	119, 120
27	$R_1 = R_2 = R_3 = R_4 = H$; $R_5 = 4\text{-}N(CH_3)_2C_6H_4$	—	"Low"	Benzene, chloroform	—	119
28	$R_1 = R_2 = R_3 = R_4 = H$; $R_5 = 2,4,6\text{-}(CH_3)_3C_6H_2$	—	"Low"	Benzene, chloroform	—	119, 120
29	$R_1 = R_2 = R_3 = R_4 = H$; $R_5 = \alpha\text{-naphthyl}$	—	"Low"	Benzene, chloroform	—	119
30	$R_1 = R_2 = R_3 = H$; $R_4 = R_5 = C_6H_5$	—	"Low"	Benzene, chloroform	—	120
31	$R_1 = R_2 = R_4 = R_5 = H$; $R_3 = COCH_3$	—	—	Benzene and "other" organic solvents	Structure shown by ozonization, hydration, and IR	107

TABLE II.3—continued

Five-Membered Ring-Containing Polymers

No.	Structure	Method	Molecular weight	Solubility	T_m (°C)	Remarks and property data	References
32	$R_1 = R_2 = R_4 = H$; $R_3 = COCH_3$; $R_5 = CH_3$	1	—	Benzene and "other" organic solvents	—	Structure shown by ozonization, hydration, and IR	107
33	$R_1 = R_2 = H$; $R_3 = COCH_3$; $R_4 = R_5 = CH_3$	1	—	Benzene and "other" organic solvents	—	Structure shown by ozonization, hydration, and IR	76, 107
34	$R_1 = R_2 = R_4 = H$; $R_3 = COCH_3$; $R_5 = n\text{-}C_3H_7$	1	—	Benzene and "other" organic solvents	—	Structure shown by ozonization, hydration, and IR	107
35	$R_1 = R_2 = R_4 = R_5 = CH_3$; $R_3 = COCH_3$	1	—	"Soluble"	—	—	113
36	$R_1 = R_2 = H$; $R_3 = COCH_3$; $R_4 = R_5 = C_2H_5$	1	—	Benzene and "other" organic solvents	—	—	107
37	$R_1 = R_2 = H$; $R_3 = COCH_3$; R_4 and $R_5 = -(CH_2)_5-$	1	—	—	—	—	121
38	$R_1 = R_2 = H$; $R_3 = COCH_3$; $R_4 = CH_3$; $R_5 = C(CH_3)_3$	1	—	Benzene and "other" organic solvents	—	—	107
39	$R_1 = R_2 = R_4 = R_5 = H$; $R_3 = CH_3$	1	—	Benzene and "other" organic solvents	—	—	107

#	Structure		Solubility	Notes	Ref
40	$R_1 = R_2 = H$; $R_3 = R_4 = R_5 = CH_3$	1	Benzene and "other" organic solvents	—	107
41	$R_1 = R_2 = H$; $R_3 = CH_2CH_2OH$; $R_4 = R_5 = CH_3$	1	Benzene and "other" organic solvents	—	107
42	$R_1 = R_2 = H$; $R_3 = CH_2CH_2SH$; $R_4 = R_5 = CH_3$	1	Benzene and "other" organic solvents	—	107
43	$R_1 = R_2 = H$; $R_3 = R_4 = CH_3$; $R_5 = C(CH_3)_3$	1	Benzene and "other" organic solvents	—	107
44	$R_1 = R_2 = H$; $R_3 = C_6H_5$; $R_4 = R_5 = CH_3$	1	Benzene and "other" organic solvents	—	107

* * *

Polymers were prepared from the monomers listed below. The structures of the polymers are probably similar to that of the poly(vinylethynyl carbinols)

#	Structure		Solubility	Notes	Ref
45	$CH_2{=}CH{-}CH{-}C{\equiv}C{-}CO_2C_2H_5$	1	Insoluble	Structure uncertain	113
46	$CH_2{=}CH{-}C{\equiv}C{-}CH_2N(CH_3)_2$	1	"Soluble"	IR indicates presence of cyclic units in the polymer	113
47	$CH_2{=}CH{-}C{\equiv}C{-}Si(CH_3)_3$	1	"Soluble"	IR indicates cyclic units	113
48	$CH_2{=}CH{-}C{\equiv}C{-}C(CH_3)CH_2CH_2$ $||$ $O{-}CH_2{-}O$	1	"Soluble"	IR indicates cyclic units	113

TABLE II.3—continued
Five-Membered Ring-Containing Polymers

No.	Structure	Method	Molecular weight	Solubility	T_m (°C)	Remarks and property data	References
49	$CH_2=CH-C\equiv C-CH_2N(C_2H_5)_2$	1	—	"Soluble"	—	IR indicates cyclic units	113
50	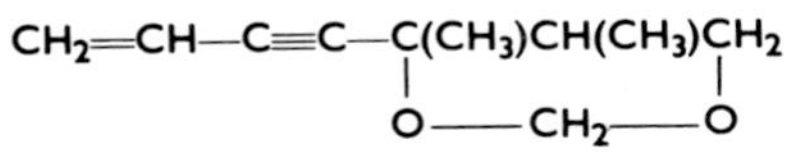 $CH_2=CH-C\equiv C-C(CH_3)CH(CH_3)CH_2-O$ $O——CH_2——O$	1	—	"Soluble"	—	IR indicates cyclic units	113
51	$CH_2=CH-C\equiv C-C(CH_3)_2-C_6H_4OH\text{-}p$	1	—	"Soluble"	—	IR indicates cyclic units	113
52	$CH_2=CH-C\equiv C-C(CH_3)_2-C_6H_4OCH_3\text{-}p$	1	—	"Soluble"	—	IR indicates cyclic units	113
53	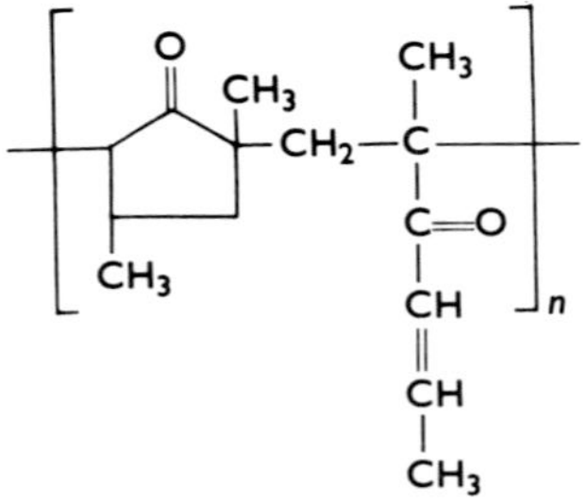 (by polymerization of 2-methyl-1,4-hexadien-3-one)	1	$[\eta]$ 0.11	Benzene	145–150	Structure confirmed by bromination and IR	101

No.	Structure					Ref.
54	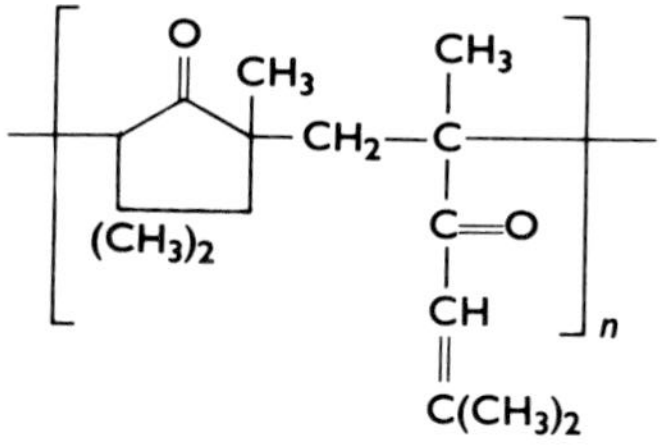 (by polymerization of 2,5-dimethyl-1,4-hexadien-3-one)	1	—	—	—	101
55	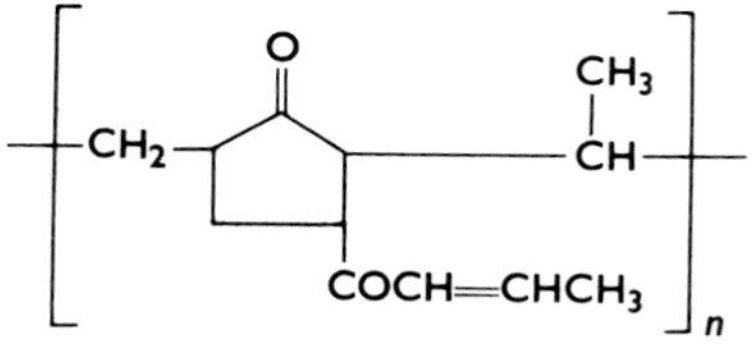 (by polymerization of vinyl propenyl ketone)	1	η_{inh} 0.18; 13,000	Aromatics, chlorinated aliphatic hydrocarbons	$T_g = 92.5°C$ (from thermomechanical curve)	9
56	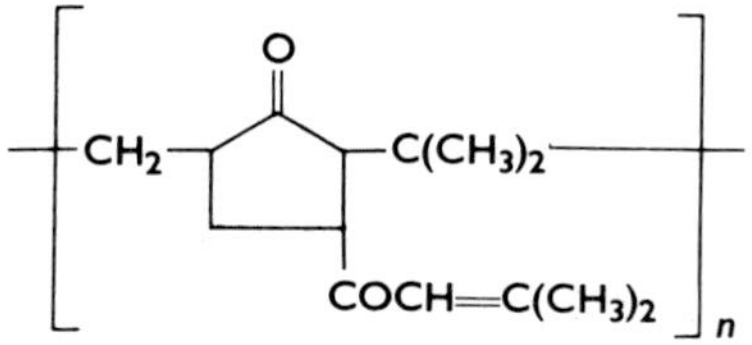 (by polymerization of vinyl isobutenyl ketone)	1	η_{inh} 0.44	Aromatics, chlorinated aliphatic hydrocarbons	$T_g = 138°C$ (from thermomechanical curve)	9

TABLE II.3—*continued*

Five-Membered Ring-Containing Polymers

No.	Structure	Method	Molecular weight	Solubility	T_m (°C)	Remarks and property data	References
57	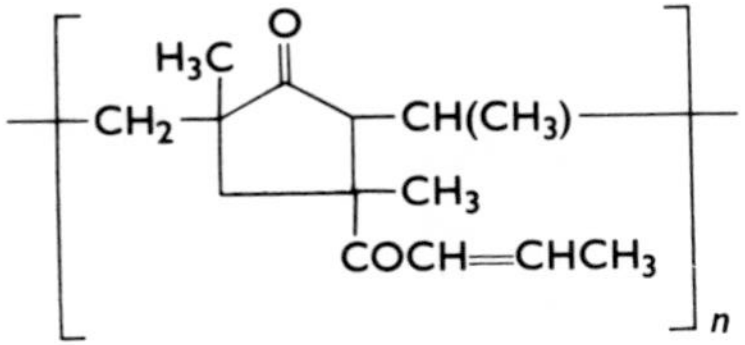 (by polymerization of propenyl isopropenyl ketone)	1	η_{inh} 0.27; >10,000	Aromatics, chlorinated aliphatic hydrocarbons	—	$T_g = 120\,°C$ (from thermomechanical curve)	9
57a	Poly(1-phenylpentadiene-1,4-one-3)	1	—	$CHCl_3$, $C_6H_5CH_3$	—	—	39
57b	Poly[1-(p-tolyl)pentadiene-1,4-one-3]	1	—	$CHCl_3$, $C_6H_5CH_3$	—	—	39
57c	Poly[1-(p-methoxyphenyl)pentadiene-1,4-one-3]	1	—	$CHCl_3$, $C_6H_5CH_3$	—	—	39
57d	Poly[(1-o-methoxyphenyl)pentadiene-1,4-one-3]	1	—	$CHCl_3$, $C_6H_5CH_3$	—	—	39

No.	Structure		Mol wt	Solubility		Remarks	Ref.
58	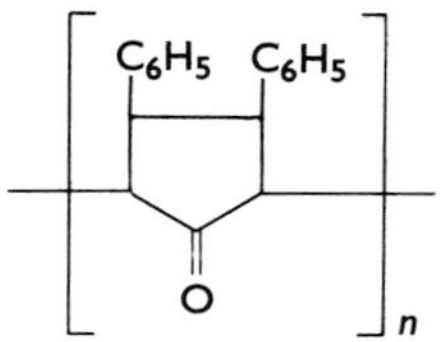 C$_6$H$_5$ C$_6$H$_5$ [22]	1	2500	Acetone, benzene, chloroform, dioxane	—	Cyclic linear structure indicated by absence of unsaturation and solubility	2
59	Copolymer of **58** with maleic anhydride [24]	1	η_{inh} 0.069; 960	Acetone, benzene, chloroform, dioxane	—	Cyclic linear structure indicated by absence of unsaturation and solubility. Polymer was stable up to 300°C	2
60	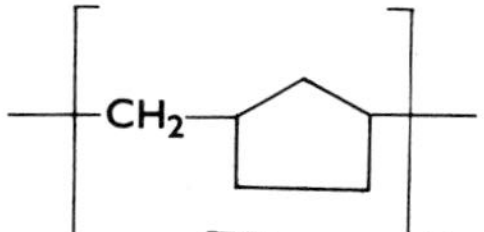 CH$_2$ [75]	2	η_{inh} 1.52	Tetralin, partially soluble in n-heptane and in benzene	146	Contains some residual unsaturation. Film had following mechanical properties: Elongation = 310%; Tensile strength = 4360 psi; d = 1.009 g/cc Apparent modulus of elasticity $\times 10^{-5}$ at 0°C, 0.93; −25°C, 1.70; −50°C, 2.40 Crystalline	87, 88, 97

TABLE II.3—*continued*

Five-Membered Ring-Containing Polymers

No.	Structure	Method	Molecular weight	Solubility	T_m (°C)	Remarks and property data	References
61	$\left[\left(\text{CH}-\text{CH}_3\right)_x-\left(\text{CH}_2\text{CH}-(\text{CH}_2)_2-\overset{\text{CH(H)}}{\underset{\text{CH}_2(\text{H})}{\underset{||}{\text{CH}}}}\right)_y\right]_n$	2	$[\eta]\,0.09$ 1250 (ebullioscopy)	Tetralin, *n*-heptane, benzene, chloroform	—	Ratio: $y/x \simeq 5.2$ (IR). Ratio: inner double bond/vinyl double bond in the noncyclic part of the polymer chain $\simeq 4$ (IR, ozonization studies)	*138*
62	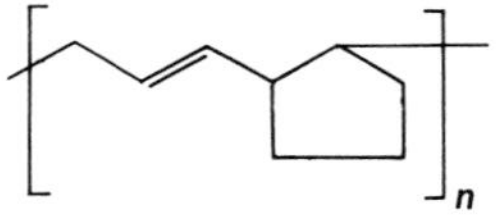 (by polymerization of 1,3,7-octatriene)	2	$[\eta]\,0.09$	Benzene	—	—	*27, 28*
63	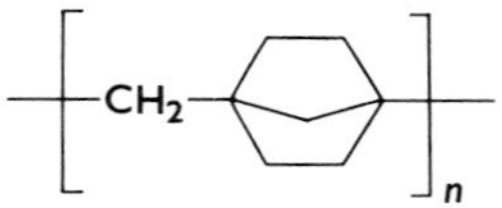 [117] (by polymerization of 1,4-dimethylene cyclohexane)	3	$[\eta]\,0.07$	Xylene, other aromatics	>250	Contains negligible residual unsaturation	*10*

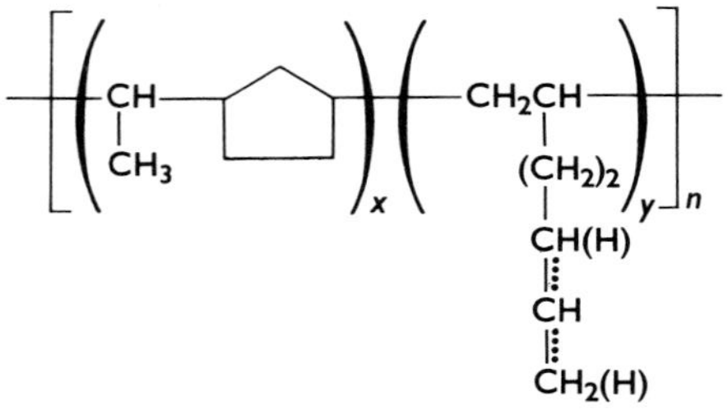

No.	Structure / Description		Mol wt / viscosity	Solubility	m.p. (°C)	Properties	Refs.
64	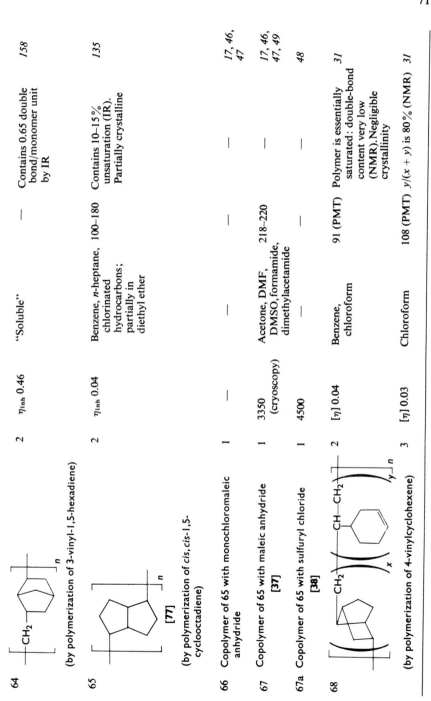 (by polymerization of 3-vinyl-1,5-hexadiene)	2	η_{inh} 0.46	"Soluble"	—	Contains 0.65 double bond/monomer unit by IR	158
65	[77] (by polymerization of cis,cis-1,5-cyclooctadiene)	2	η_{inh} 0.04	Benzene, n-heptane, chlorinated hydrocarbons; partially in diethyl ether	100–180	Contains 10–15% unsaturation (IR). Partially crystalline	135
66	Copolymer of 65 with monochloromaleic anhydride	1	—	—	—	—	17, 46, 47
67	Copolymer of 65 with maleic anhydride [37]	1	3350 (cryoscopy)	Acetone, DMF, DMSO, formamide, dimethylacetamide	218–220	—	17, 46, 47, 49
67a	Copolymer of 65 with sulfuryl chloride [38]	1	4500	—	—	—	48
68	(by polymerization of 4-vinylcyclohexene)	2	$[\eta]$ 0.04	Benzene, chloroform	91 (PMT)	Polymer is essentially saturated: double-bond content very low (NMR). Negligible crystallinity	31
		3	$[\eta]$ 0.03	Chloroform	108 (PMT)	$y/(x+y)$ is 80% (NMR)	31

TABLE II.3—*continued*

Five-Membered Ring-Containing Polymers

No.	Structure	Method	Molecular weight	Solubility	T_m (°C)	Remarks and property data	References
69	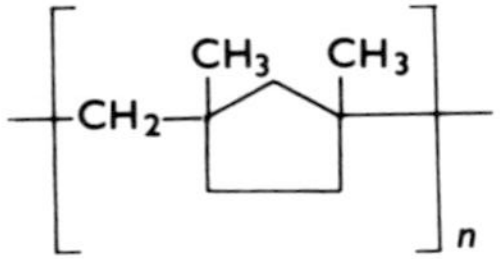 (cyclopentane ring with CH$_3$, CH$_3$; —CH$_2$—)$_n$	2	η_{inh} 0.1	Benzene, chloroform, diethyl ether	80–85	3–13% of monomer units are not cyclized (IR)	97
70	(cyclopentane ring with CO$_2$CH$_3$, CO$_2$CH$_3$; —CH$_2$—)$_n$ [20]	3	$\bar{M}_n$ 1800	Heptane, 1,2-dichloroethane	—	—	90
	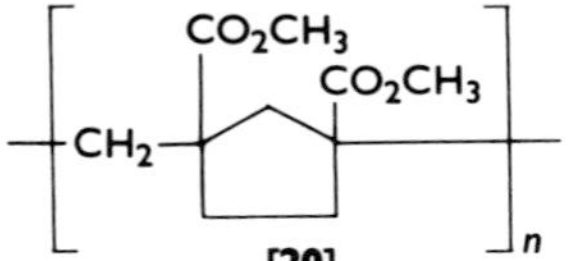	1	η_{inh} 0.21	Benzene, chloroform	110–120	Cyclized to the extent of 90% (IR)	99
71	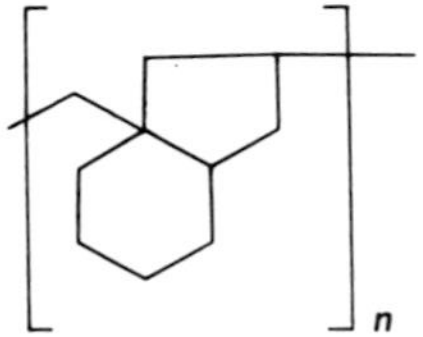 (bicyclic ring structure)$_n$ (by polymerization of 2-allylmethylene cyclohexane)	3	$[\eta]$ 0.04	Chloroform, methylene chloride	60–82 (PMT)	Cyclized to the extent of 54% (NMR). Residual unsaturation is due to units: 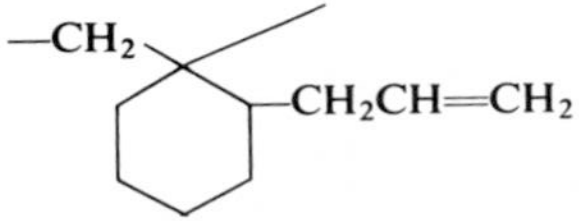 (—CH$_2$—, cyclohexane ring with CH$_2$CH=CH$_2$) Amorphous	32

73

| 71 | 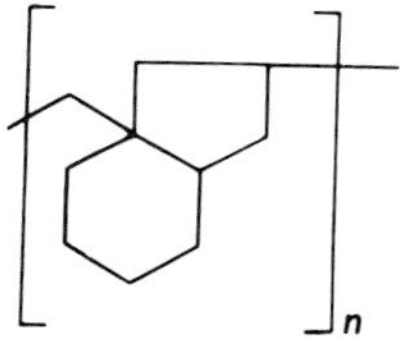 | 2 | $[\eta]$ 0.13 | Benzene, n-hexane | 98 (PMT) | Cyclized to the extent of 92–95% (NMR). Amorphous. Residual unsaturation due to units: 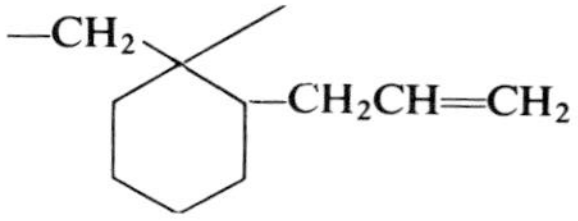 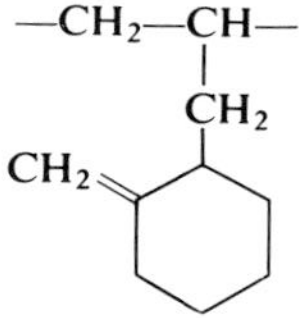 | 32 |

(by polymerization of 2-allylmethylene cyclohexane)

$-CH_2$ with $-CH_2CH=CH_2$

and

$-CH_2-CH-$, $-CH_2$, $CH_2=$

72		3	η_{inh} 0.083	Benzene	185–210	Residual unsaturation (IR) $\approx$ 5–10%	92
		1	—	—	150–170	Residual unsaturation (IR) < 5%	92
		2	η_{inh} 0.072	Benzene	157–177	Residual unsaturation (IR) = 3–5%	92

[113]

TABLE II.4

Six-Membered Ring-Containing Polymers

No.	Structure	Method	Molecular weight	Solubility	T_m (°C)	Remarks and property data	References
1	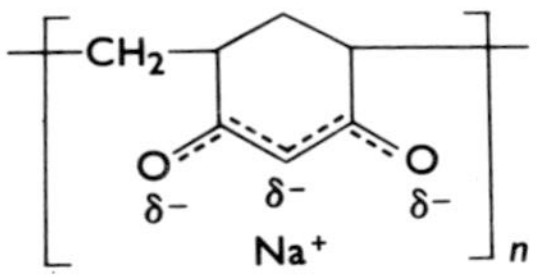 poly(diacrylylmethane)	4	—	H_2O	—	Yellow-brown powder According to (130) material is the sodium salt of a copolymer of diacrylyl-methane and methyl vinyl ketone or the sodium salt of the reaction product of poly(diacrylylmethane) with methyl vinyl ketone	69, 70
		4	η_{inh} 0.16	H_2O, DMSO, DMF, dimethylacet-amide	>350	Bright yellow powder	41
2	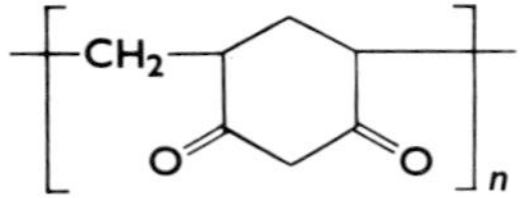 [142]	4	2000 (cryoscopy)	Alcohols, ketones, dioxane, DMF, glacial acetic acid, alkali hydroxides, Na_2CO_3, NH_4OH	—	Brilliant yellow powder Does not contain residual unsaturation (IR) According to (130) material is a copolymer of diacrylylmethane and methyl vinyl ketone or the reaction product of poly(diacrylylmethane) with methyl vinyl ketone	69, 70
		4	—	Insoluble	—	—	41

75

No.	Structure		[η] / M	Solvent		Comments	Reference
3	[64] (by polymerization of 4,4-dimethyl-1,6-heptadiene-3,5-dione)	1	[η] 0.32	DMSO, C_6H_6	>350	—	40
4	[95] (by polymerization of 1,6-heptadiyne)	2	[η] 0.058; 13,500 (osmometry)	Benzene	—	Chemical and infrared evidence in agreement with structure. However, according to (68) the polymer is a poly(cyclotrimer) of 1,6-heptadiyne	153, 154
5	[124] (by polymerization of myrcene)	3	η_{inh} 0.055	Benzene, n-heptane	86–90	Structure confirmed by chemical evidence	94
6	[122] (by polymerization of alloocimene)	3	—	C_2H_5Cl, CCl_4, dioxane, benzene	68–70	Chemical evidence supports the structure of the polymer	71

TABLE II.4—continued

Six-Membered Ring-Containing Polymers

No.	Structure	Method	Molecular weight	Solubility	T_m (°C)	Remarks and property data	References
7	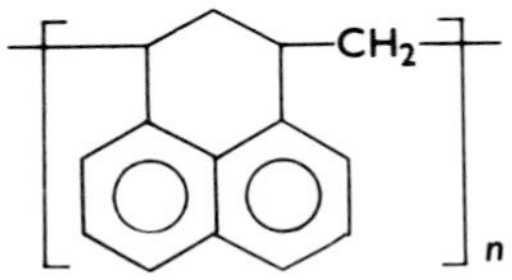 (by polymerization of 1,8-divinylnapthalene)	1	η_{inh} 0.35; 1620	Benzene	204	Cyclic linear structure supported by solubility and infrared evidence	152
8	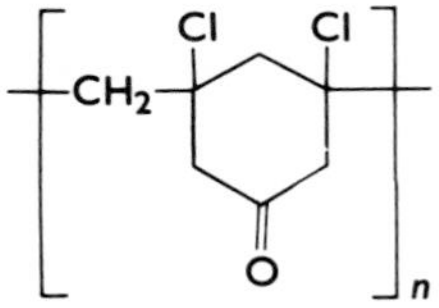	1	—	"Soluble"	—	—	21
9	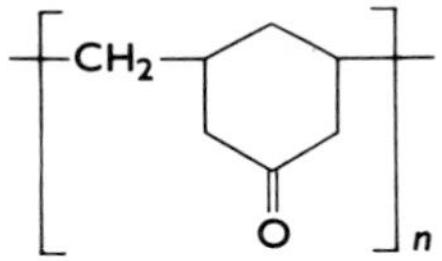	1	—	$CHCl_3$	—	—	21

10	—	—	22

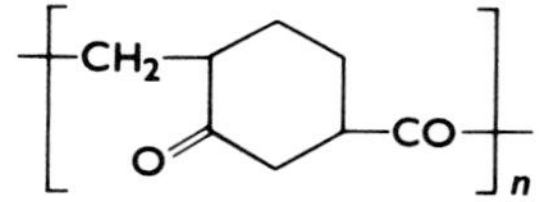

[62]

(by copolymerization of 1,5-hexadiene with carbon monoxide)

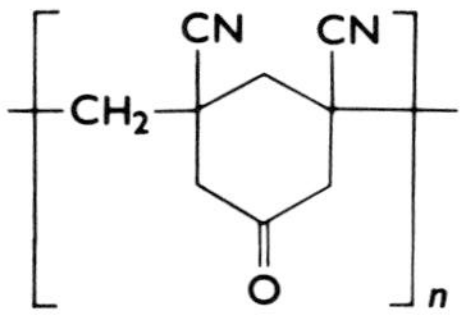 11	"Soluble"	—	21

12 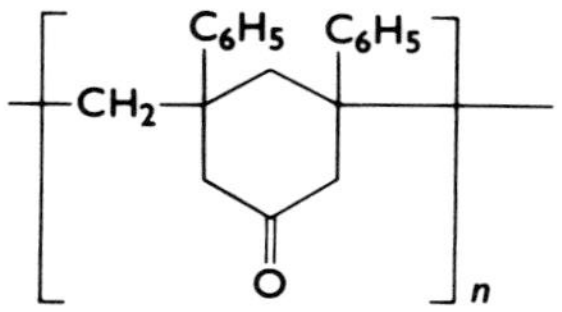	CHCl₃	—	21

[46]

13	CHCl₃, benzene, toluene	—	Structure confirmed by IR and chlorination studies	102

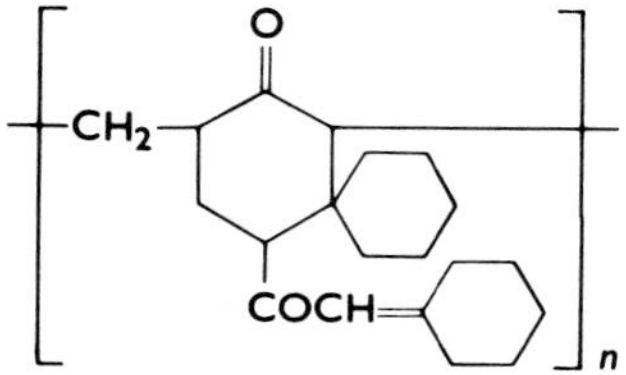

(by polymerization of β,β-pentamethylenedivinyl ketone)

TABLE II.4—continued

Six-Membered Ring-Containing Polymers

No.	Structure	Method	Molecular weight	Solubility	T_m (°C)	Remarks and property data	References
14	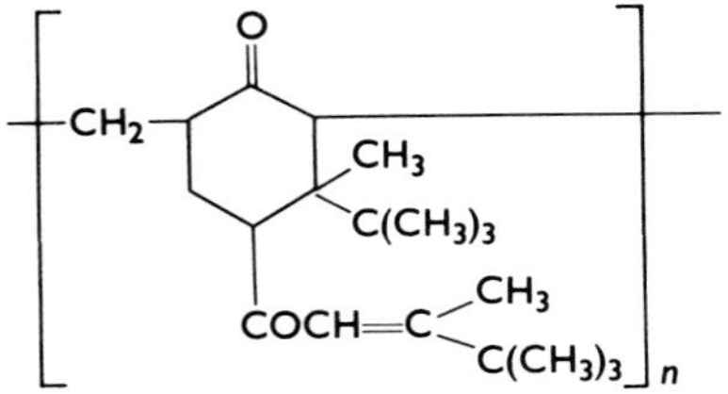 (by polymerization of β-methyl-β-tert-butyldivinyl ketone)	1	—	CHCl₃, benzene, toluene	—	Structure confirmed by IR and chlorination studies	102
15	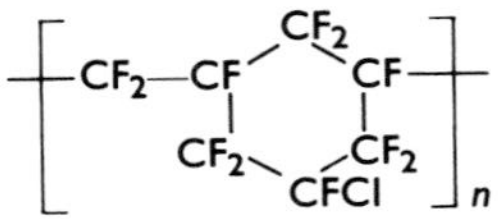 [66]	1	[η] 0.6	Hexafluoro-benzene, diene monomer	—	No unsaturation present (IR) in the polymer. Polymer forms tough, flexible films and is thermally very stable. Loss of wt. at 235°C after 0.5 hr is 6.4%	51, 52, 156, 163, 164
16	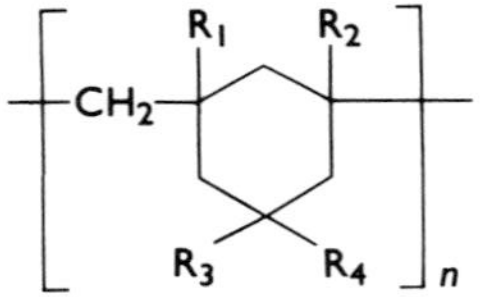 R₁ = R₂ = R₃ = H; R₄ = Cl	1	—	"Soluble"	—	Cyclic linear structure confirmed chemically and by IR	118

No.	Structure		η_{inh} / MW	Solubility	mp (°C)	Remarks	Ref.
17	$R_1 = R_2 = R_3 = R_4 = H$	2	η_{inh} 0.4	Benzene	210–230	Cyclized to the extent of 90–95% (IR). Chemical transformations support assigned cyclic structure	97
18	$R_1 = R_2 = R_3 = H; R_4 = OH$	1	—	"Soluble"	—	Cyclic linear structure confirmed chemically and by IR	118
19	$R_1 = R_2 = Cl; R_3 = H; R_4 = COOH$	1	$\eta_{inh} \sim 0.15$; ~20,000 (ebullioscopy)	"Soluble"	—	Virtual absence of residual unsaturation shown by IR and bromination studies. Polymer cross-links at 280°C; is dehydrohalogenated with $NaOH + H_2O$	117
20	$R_1 = R_2 = R_3 = H; R_4 = COCl$	1	—	"Soluble"	—	Cyclic linear structure confirmed chemically and by IR	118
21	$R_1 = R_2 = R_3 = H; R_4 = CN$	1	$\eta_{inh} \sim 0.05$; ~7000 (ebullioscopy)	"Soluble"	65–70	Virtual absence of unsaturation shown by IR and bromination studies	117
22	$R_1 = R_2 = R_3 = H; R_4 = COOH$	1	12,000 (ebullioscopy)	Acetic acid, hot alcohol, CCl_4, C_6H_6	130–142	Percent unsaturation in the polymer = 1.87% (bromination studies). On heating polymer decarboxylates to poly(hexahydrobenzyl)	116
23	$R_1 = R_2 = R_3 = H; R_4 = CONH_2$	1	—	"Soluble"	—	Cyclic linear structure confirmed by IR and chemical evidence	118

TABLE II.4—*continued*

Six-Membered Ring-Containing Polymers

No.	Structure	Method	Molecular weight	Solubility	T_m (°C)	Remarks and property data	References
24	$R_1 = R_2 = CN; R_3 = R_4 = H$ **[42]**	1	$[\eta]$ 1.94; 163,000 (osmometry)	DMF, butyrolactone, tetramethylene sulfone	—	No unsaturation present in the polymer (IR). Clear films were obtained from DMF solutions. Amorphous. Drawing did not induce crystallinity in the films	127
		1	η_{inh} 0.655	DMF	—	Cyclic linear structure supported by IR	99
	Copolymer of **24** with:						
25	Vinylidene chloride	1	$[\eta]$ 0.88	DMF	—	No unsaturation present (IR). Percent vinylidene chloride (wt.) = 79.3%	127
26	Acrylonitrile	1	$[\eta]$ 1.41	DMF	—	No unsaturation present in polymer (IR). Percent acrylonitrile (wt.) = 80.7%	127
27	Acrylamide	1	$[\eta]$ 1.91	DMF	—	—	127
28	Methyl acrylate	1	$[\eta]$ 1.30	DMF	—	Percent weight of methyl acrylate = 65.5%	127
29	Isoprene	1	$[\eta]$ 1.29	DMF	—	Percent isoprene in copolymer not disclosed	127

30 Styrene	1	$[\eta]$ 1.26	DMF	—	Percent weight styrene in copolymer = 68.8%. Practically no aliphatic unsaturation present (IR)	127
31 $R_1 = R_2 = H; R_3 = CN; R_4 = COOH$	1	—	"Soluble"	270–300	—	117
32 $R_1 = R_2 = COOH; R_3 = R_4 = H$	1	—	Aqueous bases	460 d	Cyclic structure confirmed by chemical and spectroscopic (IR) means	98
33 Copolymer of 32 with acrylonitrile	1	$[\eta]$ 1.66	DMF	—	Percent weight acrylonitrile in copolymer = 90.6%	127
34 $R_1 = R_2 = R_3 = H; R_4 = COCH_3$	1	—	CCl_4, C_6H_6, CH_3COOH, hot C_2H_5OH	—	—	116
35 $R_1 = R_2 = R_3 = H; R_4 = OCOCH_3$	1	—	"Soluble"	—	—	118
36 $R_1 = R_2 = CONH_2; R_3 = R_4 = H$	1	—	Insoluble	>250	IR data not clear: polymer's insolubility may be a consequence of cross-linked structure	99
37 Copolymer of 36 with acrylonitrile	1	$[\eta]$ 1.15	DMF	—	Percent weight acrylonitrile in copolymer = 91.3%	127
38 $R_1 = R_2 = CH_3; R_3 = R_4 = H$ [85]	2	—	$CHCl_3$	—	—	21
39 $R_1 = R_2 = CH_3; R_3 = CN; R_4 = H$	1	—	—	—	—	114
40 $R_1 = R_2 = R_3 = H; R_4 = COOC_2H_5$	1	—	"Soluble"	—	—	118
41 $R_1 = R_2 = R_3 = H; R_4 = CON(CH_3)_2$	1	—	"Soluble"	—	—	118

TABLE II.4—*continued*

Six-Membered Ring-Containing Polymers

No.	Structure	Method	Molecular weight	Solubility	T_m (°C)	Remarks and property data	References
42	$R_1 = R_2 = CH_3$; $R_3 = CN$; $R_4 = COOH$	1	—	—	—	—	114
43	$R_1 = R_2 = H$; $R_3 = CN$; $R_4 = COOC_2H_5$	1	—	"Soluble"	76–84	—	117
44	Copolymer of 43 with acrylonitrile	1	—	—	—	—	167
45	Copolymer of 43 with ethyl acrylate	1	—	—	—	Good adhesive	167
46	$R_1 = R_2 = H$; $R_3 = CN$; $R_4 = COOC_4H_9$ Copolymer with ethyl acrylate	1	—	—	—	Good adhesive	167
47	$R_1 = R_2 = H$; $R_3 = R_4 = COCH_3$	1	—	—	65–75	—	117
48	$R_1 = R_2 = COOCH_3$; $R_3 = R_4 = H$ [40]	1	$[\eta]$ 2.03	DMF, butyrolactone, C_6H_6, 2,2,3,3-tetra-fluoro-propanol tetra-methylene sulfone	—	Practically no unsaturation present (IR). Clear films can be cast from DMF solution of polymer. Amorphous. Crystallinity (in films) was not induced by drawing	127
		1	η_{inh} 0.73	$CHCl_3$, C_6H_6	300	No unsaturation found (IR). Oxidation with $KClO_4$ yields aromatic product showing aromatic m-substitution (IR, UV)	98, 99

49	Copolymer of 48 with acrylonitrile	1	$[\eta]$ 1.28	DMF	—	Percent weight acrylonitrile in copolymer = 94.8%	127
50	$R_1 = R_2 = Cl$; $R_3 = COCH_3$; $R_4 = COOC_2H_5$	1	—	"Soluble"	—	—	118
51	$R_1 = R_2 = H$; $R_3 = COCH_3$; $R_4 = COOC_2H_5$	1	14,900 (ebullioscopy)	CCl_4, C_6H_6, CH_3COOH, hot C_2H_5OH	53–64	Unsaturation in polymer (IR, bromination) = 3.22%	116
52	$R_1 = R_2 = Cl$; $R_3 = R_4 = COOC_2H_5$	1	—	Acetone	—	—	21, 117
53	$R_1 = R_2 = CH_3$; $R_3 = CN$; $R_4 = COOC_2H_5$	1	—	—	—	—	114
54	$R_1 = R_2 = COOC_2H_5$; $R_3 = R_4 = H$	1	η_{lnh} 0.14	$CHCl_3$, C_2H_5OH	125–135	Impurities in monomer thought responsible for the low molecular weight obtained	98
55	$R_1 = R_2 = H$; $R_3 = R_4 = COOC_2H_5$	1	η_{lnh} 0.11; 12,400 (ebullioscopy)	C_6H_6, CCl_4, CH_3COOH, hot alcohol	42–55	Unsaturation in polymer (bromination) = 1.28%	116

Copolymer of 55 with:

56	Vinyl bromide	1	—	—	—	—	167
57	Vinyl chloride	1	η_{lnh} 0.07	C_6H_6	—	—	167
58	Vinylene carbonate	1	—	—	—	—	167
59	Acrylonitrile	1	η_{lnh} 0.41	DMF, C_6H_6	—	Mole percent acrylonitrile in copolymer ~30%	167

TABLE II.4—*continued*

Six-Membered Ring-Containing Polymers

No.	Structure	Method	Molecular weight	Solubility	T_m (°C)	Remarks and property data	References
60	Acrylic acid	1	—	—	—	—	167
61	Maleic anhydride	1	η_{Inh} 0.10	CH_2Cl_2	—	Useful as cross-linking agent for epoxy resins	167
62	Vinyl acetate	1	η_{Inh} 0.08	C_6H_6	—	Mole percent of vinyl acetate in copolymer ~8.3%. Good adhesive at room temperature	167
63	Methyl methacrylate	1	—	—	—	—	167
64	Ethyl acrylate	1	η_{Inh} 0.42	CH_2Cl_2, C_6H_6	—	Possesses rubbery characteristics. No indication of allylic unsaturation found (IR)	167
65	CH_2=CHCOOCH$_2$(CF$_2$)$_2$CF$_3$	1	—	—	—	Polymer claimed to be a "solvent resistant rubber"	167
66	Styrene	1	η_{Inh} 0.02	C_6H_6	—	—	167
67	$R_1 = R_2 = H$; $R_3 = R_4 = COOC_4H_9$ Copolymer with acrylonitrile	1	—	—	—	—	167
68	$R_1 = R_2 = H$; $R_3 = R_4 = COOC_{18}H_{37}$ Copolymer with ethyl acrylate	1	—	—	—	—	167

No.	Structure / Substituents		Viscosity	m.p. (PMT)	Solvent	Notes	Refs.
69	$R_1 = R_2 = H; R_3 = C_6H_5; R_4 = CN$	1	—	—	"Soluble"	—	118
70	$R_1 = R_2 = R_3 = H; R_4 = COOC_6H_5$	1	—	—	"Soluble"	—	118
71	$R_1 = R_2 = R_3 = H; R_4 = OCOC_6H_5$	1	—	—	"Soluble"	—	118
72	$R_1 = R_2 = R_3 = H; R_4 = CONHC_6H_5$	1	—	—	"Soluble"	—	118
73	$R_1 = R_2 = CH_3; R_3 = COCH_3; R_4 = COOC_2H_5$	1	—	—	—	—	21
74	$R_1 = R_2 = CH_3; R_3 = R_4 = COOC_2H_5$	1	—	—	—	—	114
75	$R_1 = R_2 = C_6H_5; R_3 = R_4 = H$ [138]	4	η_{inh} 0.49	300 (PMT)	CHCl$_3$, THF, C$_6$H$_6$	Polymer is essentially saturated (IR)	55, 92
		1, 2, 3	η_{inh} 0.35	—	—	Negligible unsaturation present in lower molecular weight polymers (IR)	55, 92
76	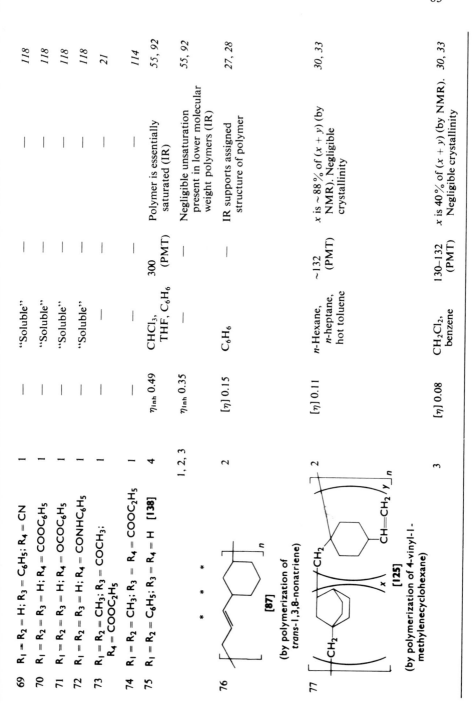 [87] (by polymerization of trans-1,3,8-nonatriene)	2	$[\eta]$ 0.15	—	C$_6$H$_6$	IR supports assigned structure of polymer	27, 28
77	[125]	2	$[\eta]$ 0.11	~132 (PMT)	n-Hexane, n-heptane, hot toluene	x is ~88% of (x + y) (by NMR). Negligible crystallinity	30, 33
	(by polymerization of 4-vinyl-1-methylenecyclohexane)	3	$[\eta]$ 0.08	130–132 (PMT)	CH$_2$Cl$_2$, benzene	x is 40% of (x + y) (by NMR). Negligible crystallinity	30, 33

86

TABLE II.4—continued

Six-Membered Ring-Containing Polymers

No.	Structure	Method	Molecular weight	Solubility	T_m (°C)	Remarks and property data	References
78	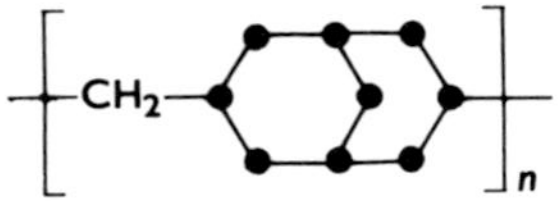 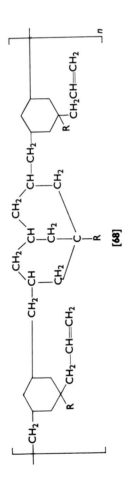 [105] (by polymerization of triallylmethane)	2	1200	"Soluble"	75	Cyclized to the extent of 90% (IR). Amorphous	144
79	Polymer from d-limonene (see structure in text) [127] [128]	3	η_{inh} 0.07	Benzene, n-heptane	73–78	—	128
80	Polymer from α-pinene (structure not determined)	3	η_{inh} 0.02	Benzene, n-heptane	114–119	—	128

* * *

[68]

(by polymerization of substituted triallylmethanes)

	R						
81	R = OH	1	—	CHCl₃, alcohol, benzene	88–92	Structure assigned on the basis of bromination and IR studies	115
82	R = CN	1	—	CHCl₃, alcohol, benzene	78–84	Structure assigned on the basis of bromination and IR studies	115
83	R = CONH₂	1	—	CHCl₃, alcohol, benzene	132–136	Structure assigned on the basis of bromination and IR studies	115
84	R = OCOCH₃	1	—	CHCl₃, alcohol, benzene	—	Structure assigned on the basis of bromination and IR studies	115
85		1	—	DMF	—	—	12, 24
86		1	—	DMF	—	—	12, 24

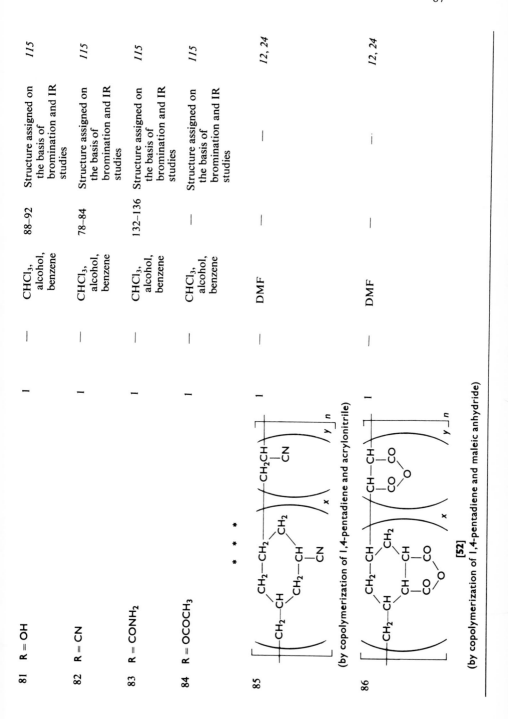

85 (by copolymerization of 1,4-pentadiene and acrylonitrile)

86 (by copolymerization of 1,4-pentadiene and maleic anhydride)

[52]

TABLE II.4—continued

Six-Membered Ring-Containing Polymers

No.	Structure	Method	Molecular weight	Solubility	T_m (°C)	Remarks and property data	References
87	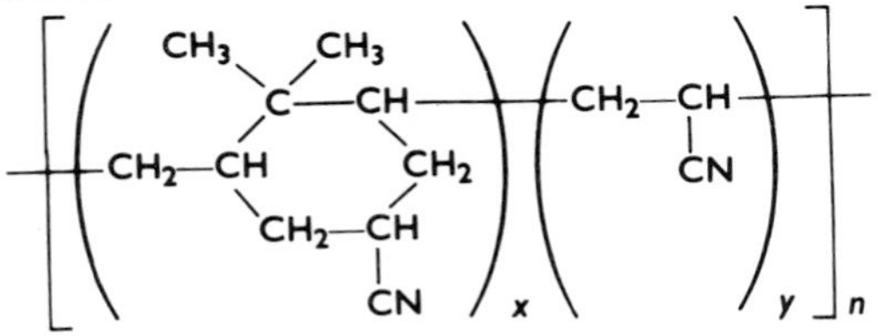 (by copolymerization of 3,3-dimethyl-1,4-pentadiene and acrylonitrile)	1	$[\eta]$ 0.48–0.71	DMF	—	Solubility and IR support the assigned cyclic, linear polymer structure. Several polymers were prepared (mole fraction of acrylonitrile was in the range of 0.972 to 0.865)	29
88	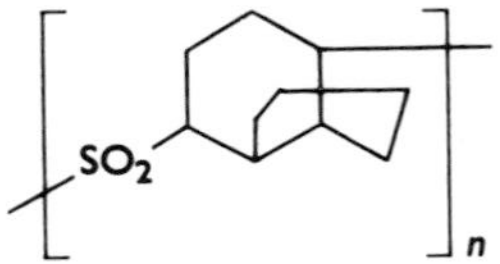 [54] (from cis,trans-1,5-cyclodecadiene and sulfur dioxide)	1	η_{inh} 1.03; 60,900 (osmometry)	CHCl₃, 1,2-dichloroethane, γ-butyrolactone, DMSO, m-cresol	235 d	Amorphous. Thermal and alkaline stability studied	129, 133
88a	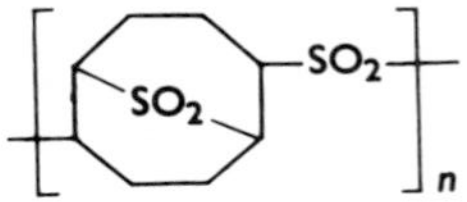 [56] (polymer from 1,5-cyclooctadiene and sulfur dioxide)	1	η_{inh} 0.80, 1.94	DMSO	—	Analyzed for 2SO₂:1COD	149

88b Polymer from dicyclopentadiene and sulfur dioxide   1 η_{inh} 0.32   —   —   Analyzed for 2SO$_2$:1DCPD —   *149*

Entry	Structure		η_{inh}	Solvent			Ref.
89	[structure]	2	—	Heptane	—	—	*36*
90	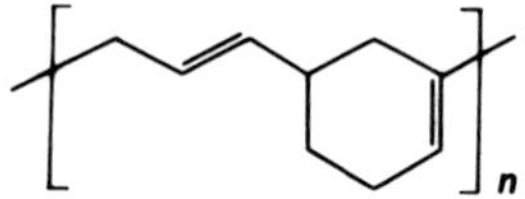 [structure] (by polymerization of 1,3,6,8-nonatetraene) [89]	2	—	Heptane	—		*36*
91	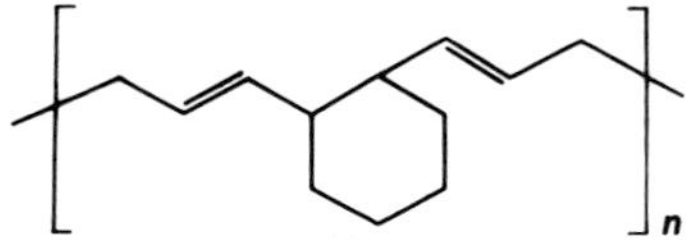 [structure] (by polymerization of 1,3,9,11-dodecatetraene) [91]	2	—	Heptane	—		*36*
92	[structure] (by polymerization of 3,6-dimethylene-1,7-octadiene) [93]	2	—	Cyclohexane 116			*38*
93	[structure] (from cis-1,3-divinylcyclopentane) [97]	2	—	Benzene 110			*38*
	[structure] (from cis-1,3-divinylcyclohexane) [99]						

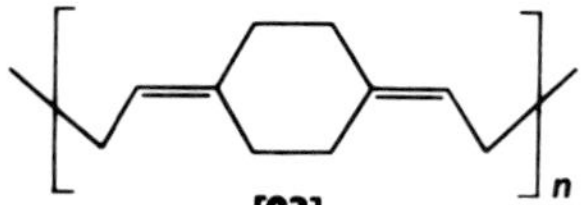

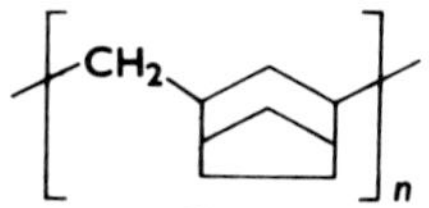

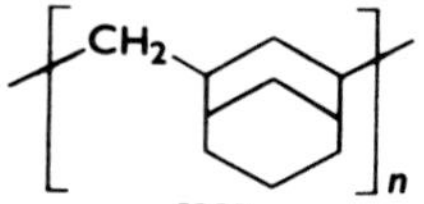

TABLE II.5

Polymers Containing Larger Rings

No.	Structure	Method	Molecular weight	Solubility	Remarks and property data	References
1	Polymer from 1,7-octadiyne	2	$[\eta]$ 0.063	Xylene	Structure uncertain. No acetylenic unsaturation found in the polymer (IR)	153, 154
2	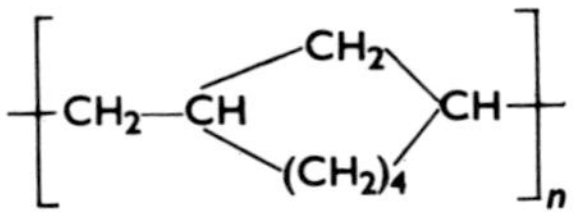	2	η_{inh} 0.067; 567 (ebullioscopy)	Benzene	Cyclized to the extent of 25% (IR, bromination studies)	93
3	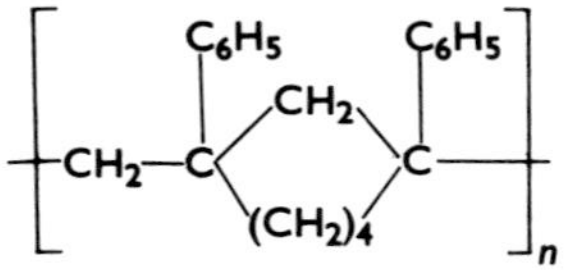	2	η_{inh} 0.04	Benzene	Residual unsaturation in polymer (IR) ~5–10%. $T_m = 185°–210°C$	92
		3	η_{inh} 0.021	Benzene	No residual unsaturation found in this polymer (IR). $T_m = 115°–150°C$	92
4	Polymer from 1,8-nonadiyne	2	$[\eta]$ 0.067	Xylene	Structure uncertain	153, 154
5	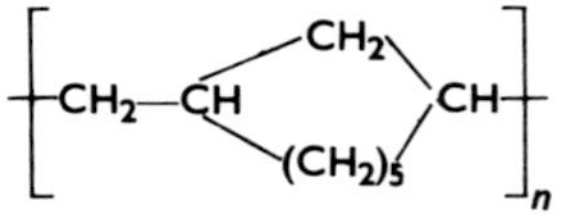	2	η_{inh} 0.14	Benzene	Cyclized to the extent of 9% (IR and bromination studies)	93

6   3 | | | 151

[134]

(by polymerization of 3-methyl-enebicyclo[3.3.1]nonan-7-one)

* * * *

7	x = 6	2	η_{Inh} 0.35	Benzene	Cyclized to the extent of 6% (IR and bromination studies)	93
8	x = 7	2	η_{Inh} 0.23	Benzene	Cyclized to the extent of 10% (IR and bromination studies)	93
9	x = 8	2	η_{Inh} 0.14	Benzene	Cyclized to the extent of 11% (IR and bromination studies)	93
10	x = 9	2	η_{Inh} 0.104	Benzene	Cyclized to the extent of 11% (IR and bromination studies)	93
11	x = 10	2	η_{Inh} 0.11	Benzene	—	93
12	x = 11	2	η_{Inh} 0.062	Benzene	Cyclized to the extent of 15% (IR and bromination studies)	93
13	x = 12	2	η_{Inh} 0.25	Benzene	Cyclized to the extent of 15% (IR and bromination studies)	93
14	x = 14	2	η_{Inh} 0.10	Benzene	Cyclized to the extent of 4% (IR and bromination studies)	93
15	x = 18	2	η_{Inh} 0.126	Benzene	Cyclized to the extent of 8% (IR and bromination studies)	93

REFERENCES

1. Alexander, R. J., and Doyle, J. R., *J. Polymer Sci.* **B1**, 625 (1963).
2. Arbuzova, I. A., and Mosevich, I. K., *Vysokomolekul. Soedin.* **6**, 13 (1964); *Resins, Rubbers, Plastics* p. 219 (1965).
3. Aso, C., *J. Polymer Sci.* **39**, 475 (1959).
4. Aso, C., *Kagaku (Kyoto)* **20**, 29 (1965); *Chem. Abstr.* **64**, 12812 (1966).
5. Aso, C., and Kita, R., *Kogyo Kagaku Zasshi* **68**, 707 (1965); *Chem. Abstr.* **63**, 8485 (1965).
6. Aso, C., and Nawata, T., *Kogyo Kagaku Zasshi* **68**, 549 (1965); *Chem. Abstr.* **63**, 8485 (1965); *Resins, Rubbers, Plastics* p. 2137 (1965).
7. Aso, C., Nawata, T., and Kamao, H., *Makromol. Chem.* **68**, 1 (1963); *Chem. Abstr.* **60**, 3104 (1964).
8. Avetyan, M. G., Darbinyan, E. G., and Matsoyan, S. G., *Izv. Akad. Nauk Arm. SSR, Khim. Nauki* **16**, 247 (1963); *Chem. Abstr.* **60**, 666 (1964).
9. Avetyan, M. G., Darbinyan, E. G., Saakayan, A. A., Kinoyan, F. S., and Matsoyan, S. G., *Vysokomolekul. Soedin.* **6**, 3 (1964); *Resins, Rubbers, Plastics* p. 2811 (1964).
10. Ball, L. E., and Harwood, H. J., *Am. Chem. Soc., Div. Polymer Chem., Preprints* **1**, 59 (1961).
11. Barton, J. M., *J. Polymer Sci.* **B4**, 513 (1966).
12. Barton, J. M., Butler, G. B., and Chapin, E. C., *J. Polymer Sci.* **A3**, 501 (1965); *Chem. Abstr.* **62**, 14830 (1965).
13. Belgian Patent 551,851 (issued to Phillips Petroleum Co.) (1957).
14. Binder, J. L., *J. Polymer Sci.* **B4**, 19 (1966).
15. Blout, E. R., and Ostberg, B. E., *J. Polymer Sci.* **1**, 230 (1946).
16. British Patent 776,326 (issued to E. I. duPont de Nemours & Co.) (1957); *Chem. Abstr.* **51**, 15178 (1957).
17. British Patent 1,015,215 (issued to Pittsburgh Plate Glass Co.) (1965).
18. Butler, G. B., mentioned in C. S. Marvel, *J. Polymer Sci.* **48**, 101 (1960), that this author described the intra–inter mechanism at the 1955 Gordon Research Conference.
19. Butler, G. B., *J. Polymer Sci.* **48**, 279 (1960).
20. Butler, G. B., *Pure Appl. Chem.* **4**, 299 (1962).
21. Butler, G. B., U.S. Patent 3,044,986 (Peninsular Chemical Research, Inc.) (1962).
22. Butler, G. B., U.S. Patent 3,239,488 (Peninsular Chemical Research, Inc.) (1966).
23. Butler, G. B., *Encycl. Polymer Sci. Technol.* **4**, 568 (1966); *Chem. Abstr.* **65**, 17052 (1966).
24. Butler, G. B., U.S. Patent 3,320,216 (Peninsular Chemical Research, Inc.) (1967); *Chem. Abstr.* **67**, 2143, 22329z (1967).
25. Butler, G. B., *Am. Chem. Soc., Div. Polymer Chem., Preprints* **8**, No. 1, 35 (1967).
26. Butler, G. B., and Angelo, R. J., *J. Am. Chem. Soc.* **79**, 3128 (1957).
27. Butler, G. B., and Brooks, T. W., *Am. Chem. Soc., Div. Polymer Chem., Preprints* **3**, 168 (1962).
28. Butler, G. B., and Brooks, T. W., *J. Org. Chem.* **28**, 2699 (1963).
29. Butler, G. B., and Kasat, R. B., *J. Polymer Sci.* **A3**, 4205 (1965).
30. Butler, G. B., and Miles, M. L., *Am. Chem. Soc., Div. Polymer Chem. Preprints* **3**, 288 (1962); *Chem. Abstr.* **61**, 5768 (1964).
31. Butler, G. B., and Miles, M. L., *J. Polymer Sci.* **A3**, 1609 (1965); *Chem. Abstr.* **62**, 16388 (1965); *Resins, Rubbers, Plastics* p. 2155 (1965).
32. Butler, G. B., and Miles, M. L., *Polymer Eng. Sci.* **6**, 71 (1966); *Chem. Abstr.* **64**, 14284 (1966).

33. Butler, G. B., Miles, M. L., and Brey, W. S., Jr., *J. Polymer Sci.* **A3**, 723 (1965); *Chem. Abstr.* **62**, 13245 (1965).
34. Butler, G. B., and Raymond, M. A., *J. Org. Chem.* **30**, 2410 (1965).
35. Butler, G. B., and Raymond, M. A., *J. Polymer Sci.* **A3**, 3413 (1965).
36. Butler, G. B., and Raymond, M. A., *J. Macromol. Chem.* **1**, 201 (1966); *Chem. Abstr.* **65**, 10677 (1966).
37. Colthup, E. C., and Meriwether, L. S., *J. Org. Chem.* **26**, 5169 (1961).
38. Corfield, G. C., Crawshaw, A., Butler, G. B., and Miles, M. L., *Chem. Commun.* p. 238 (1966); *Chem. Abstr.* **65**, 5537 (1966).
39. Darbinyan, E. G., Avetyan, M. G., and Matsoyan, S. G., *Arm. Khim. Zh.* **19**, 527 (1966); *Chem. Abstr.* **66**, 3564, 37578h (1967).
40. DeWinter, W., and Marvel, C. S., *J. Polymer Sci.* **A2**, 5123 (1964); *Chem. Abstr.* **62**, 6465 (1965).
41. DeWinter, W., Marvel, C. S., and Abdul-Karim, A., *J. Polymer Sci.* **A1**, 3261 (1963).
42. Dolgoplosk, B. A., Belonovskaya, G. P., Boldyreva, I. I., Kropacheva, E. N., Nelson, K. V., Rosinoer, Ya. M., and Chernova, J. D., *J. Polymer Sci.* **53**, 209 (1961).
43. Dolgoplosk, B. A., Erusalimskii, B. L., Milovskaya, E. B., and Belonovskaya, G. P., *Dokl. Akad. Nauk SSSR* **120**, 783 (1958).
44. Dolgoplosk, B. A., Erusalimskii, B. L., Kovunenko, A. P., and Merkureva, A. V., *Vysokomolekul. Soedin.* **4**, 1333 (1962); *Resins, Rubbers, Plastics* p. 389 (1963).
45. Dolgoplosk, B. A., and Tiniakova, E. I., *Dokl. Akad. Nauk SSSR* **146**, 362 (1962); *Resins, Rubbers, Plastics* p. 2105 (1963).
46. Dowbenko, R., British Patent 1,015,215 (Pittsburgh Plate Glass Co.) (1965); *Chem. Abstr.* **64**, 8399 (1966).
47. Dowbenko, R., U.S. Patent 3,261,815 (Pittsburgh Plate Glass Co.) (1966); *Chem. Abstr.* **65**, 15539 (1966).
48. Dowbenko, R., U.S. Patent 3,317,490 (Pittsburgh Plate Glass Co.) (1967); *Chem. Abstr.* **67**, 2028, 21509w (1967).
49. Dowbenko, R., and Chang, W-H., *J. Polymer Sci.* **B2**, 469 (1964).
50. Fearn, J. E., Brown, D. W., and Wall, L. A., *J. Polymer Sci.* **A-1, 4**, 131 (1966).
51. Fearn, J. E., and Wall, L. A., *Am. Chem. Soc., Div. Polymer Chem., Preprints* **3**, 370 (1962).
52. Fearn, J. E., and Wall, L. A., *Soc. Plastics Engrs. Trans.* **3**, 231 (1963); *Resins, Rubbers, Plastics* p. 647 (1964).
53. Fearn, J. E., and Wall, L. A., AD 435087; *Chem. Abstr.* **63**, 18272 (1965); *U.S. Govt. Res. Rept.* **39**, 19 (1964).
54. Fearn, J. E., and Wall, L. A., AD 617256; *Chem. Abstr.* **64**, 8321 (1966); *U.S. Govt. Res. Rept.* **40**, 53 (1965).
55. Field, N. D., *J. Org. Chem.* **25**, 1006 (1960).
56. Fo-Shung, W., Dolgoplosk, B. A., and Erusalimskii, B. L., *Vysokomolekul. Soedin.* **2**, 541 (1960).
57. Gaylord, N. G., Kössler, I., Matyska, B., and Mach, K., *Am. Chem. Soc., Div. Polymer Chem., Preprints* **8**, 174 (1967).
58. Gaylord, N. G., Kössler, I., Stolka, M., and Vodenhal, J., *J. Am. Chem. Soc.* **85**, 641 (1963).
59. Gaylord, N. G., Kössler, I., Stolka, M., and Vodenhal, J., *J. Polymer Sci.* **A2**, 3969 (1964); *Resins, Rubbers, Plastics* p. 1093 (1965).
60. Gibbs, W. E., *J. Polymer Sci.* **A2**, 4815 (1964); *Chem. Abstr.* **62**, 1748 (1965).
61. Gibbs, W. E., and McHenry, R. J., *J. Polymer Sci.* **A2**, 5277 (1964); *Chem. Abstr.* **62**, 10518 (1965).

62. Graham, P. J., Buhle, E. L., and Pappas, N., *J. Org. Chem.* **26**, 4658 (1961); *Resins, Rubbers, Plastics* p. 1669 (1962).
63. Haward, R. N., *J. Polymer Sci.* **14**, 535 (1954).
64. Haward, R. N., and Simpson, W., *J. Polymer Sci.* **18**, 440 (1955).
65. Holt, T., and Simpson, W., *Proc. Roy. Soc.* **A238**, 154 (1956).
66. Hubel, W., and Hoogzand, C., *Chem. Ber.* **93**, 103 (1960).
67. Hubel, W., and Merényi, R., *Chem. Ber.* **96**, 930 (1963).
68. Hubert, A. J., and Dale, J., *J. Chem. Soc.* p. 3160 (1965).
69. Jones, J. F., *Abstr. 132nd Meeting Am. Chem. Soc., New York* p. 26T (1957).
70. Jones, J. F., *J. Polymer Sci.* **33**, 7 (1958).
71. Jones, J. F., *J. Polymer Sci.* **33**, 513 (1958).
72. Kargin, V. A., Platé, N. A., and Dudnik, L. A., *Vysokomolekul. Soedin.* **1**, 420 (1959); *Polymer Sci. (USSR) (English Transl.)* **1**, 151 (1960).
73. Kennedy, J. P., and Hinlicky, J. A., *Polymer* **6**, 133 (1965); *Chem. Abstr.* **63**, 3047 (1965).
74. Kennedy, J. P., and Makowski, H. S., *J. Macromol. Sci.* **A-1**, No. 3, 345 (1967); *Chem. Abstr.* **67**, 4184, 44351c (1967).
75. Kocharyan, N. M., Pikalov, A. P., Yan, S. A., Kagramanyan, A. V., and Markosyan, E. A., *Vysokomolekul. Soedin.* **8**, 635 (1966).
76. Kocharyan, N. M., Pikalov, A. P., Kagramanyan, A. V., Markosyan, E. A., and Yan, S. A., *Vysokomolekul. Soedin.* **8**, 640 (1966).
77. Kolesnikov, G. S., and Davydova, S. L., *Russ. Chem. Rev. (English Transl.)* **29**, 679 (1960).
78. Kössler, I., Vodenhal, J., and Stolka, M., *J. Polymer Sci.* **A3**, 2081 (1965); *Chem. Abstr.* **63**, 3068 (1965).
79. Kössler, I., Štolka, M., and Mach, K., *J. Polymer Sci.* **C4**, 977 (1963).
80. Kropacheva, E. N., Dolgoplosk, B. A., Otten, V. F., and Golodova, K. G., *Zh. Obshch. Khim.* **29**, 1853 (1959).
81. Lee, T. S., Kolthoff, I. M., and Mairs, M. A., *J. Polymer Sci.* **3**, 66 (1948).
82. Lenz, R. W., and Handlovits, C. E., *J. Org. Chem.* **25**, 813 (1960).
83. Leto, J. R., and Olsen, L. M., U.S. Patent 3,192,191 (American Cyanamid Co.) (1965); *Chem. Abstr.* **63**, 11728 (1965).
84. Luttinger, L. B., *J. Org. Chem.* **27**, 1591 (1962).
85. Luttinger, L. B., *Chem. & Ind. (London)* p. 1135 (1960).
86. Luttinger, L. B., and Colthup, E. C., *J. Org. Chem.* **27**, 3752 (1962).
87. Makowski, H. S., and Shim, B. K. C., *Am. Chem. Soc., Div. Polymer Chem., Preprints* **1**, 101 (1960).
88. Makowski, H. S., Shim, B. K. C., and Wilchinsky, Z. W., *J. Polymer Sci.* **A2**, 1549 (1964); *Resins, Rubbers, Plastics* p. 523 (1965).
89. Makowski, H. S., Shim, B. K. C., and Wilchinsky, Z. W., *J. Polymer Sci.* **A2**, 4973 (1964).
90. Marek, M., Roosová, M., and Doskočilová, D., *J. Polymer Sci.* **C(16)**, 971 (1967).
91. Marvel, C. S., *J. Polymer Sci.* **48**, 101 (1960).
92. Marvel, C. S., and Gall, E. J., *J. Org. Chem.* **25**, 1784 (1960).
93. Marvel, C. S., and Garrison, W. E., Jr., *J. Am. Chem. Soc.* **81**, 4737 (1959).
94. Marvel, C. S., and Hua, C. C. L., *J. Polymer Sci.* **45**, 25 (1960).
95. Marvel, C. S., and Kiener, P. E., *J. Polymer Sci.* **61**, 311 (1962); *Resins, Rubbers, Plastics* p. 3069 (1962).
96. Marvel, C. S., Kiener, P. E., and Vessel, E. D., *J. Am. Chem. Soc.* **81**, 4694 (1959).
97. Marvel, C. S., and Stille, J. K., *J. Am. Chem. Soc.* **80**, 1740 (1958).

98. Marvel, C. S., and Vest, R. D., *J. Am. Chem. Soc.* **79**, 5771 (1957).
99. Marvel, C. S., and Vest, R. D., *J. Am. Chem. Soc.* **81**, 984 (1959).
100. Matsoyan, S. G., *Usp. Khim.* **35**, 70 (1966); *Chem. Abstr.* **64**, 12799 (1966).
101. Matsoyan, S. G., and Avetyan, M. G., *J. Gen. Chem. USSR (English Transl.)* **30**, 2412 (1960).
102. Matsoyan, S. G., Avetyan, M. G., and Darbinyan, E. G., *Izv. Akad. Nauk Arm. SSR, Khim. Nauki* **17**, 412 (1964); *Chem. Abstr.* **62**, 1747 (1965).
103. Matsoyan, S. G., and Morlyan, N. M., *Izv. Akad. Nauk Arm. SSR, Khim. Nauki* **16**, 347 (1963); *Chem. Abstr.* **60**, 10796 (1964).
104. Matsoyan, S. G., and Morlyan, N. M., *Izv. Akad. Nauk Arm. SSR, Khim. Nauki* **16**, 571 (1963); *Chem. Abstr.* **61**, 726 (1964).
105. Matsoyan, S. G., and Morlyan, N. M., *Vysokomolekul. Soedin.* **6**, 945 (1964); *Resins, Rubbers, Plastics* p. 825 (1965).
106. Matsoyan, S. G., and Morlyan, N. M., *Izv. Akad. Nauk Arm. SSR, Khim. Nauki* **17**, 319 (1964); *Chem. Abstr.* **61**, 13430 (1964).
107. Matsoyan, S. G., and Morlyan, N. M., *Izv. Akad. Nauk Arm. SSR, Khim. Nauki* **17**, 329 (1964); *Chem. Abstr.* **61**, 13430 (1964).
108. Matsoyan, S. G., and Morlyan, N. M., *Izv. Akad. Nauk Arm. SSR, Khim. Nauki* **17**, 522 (1964); *Chem. Abstr.* **62**, 14832 (1965).
109. Matsoyan, S. G., Morlyan, N. M., and Gevorkyan, E. T., Russian Patent 155,605 (1963); *Chem. Abstr.* **60**, 4275 (1964).
110. Matsoyan, S. G., Morlyan, N. M., and Gevorkyan, E. T., Russian Patent 155,606 (1963); *Chem. Abstr.* **60**, 4277 (1964).
111. Matsoyan, S. G., Morlyan, N. M., and Kinoyan, F. S., *Vysokomolekul. Soedin.* **7**, 1159 (1965); *Chem. Abstr.* **63**, 14982 (1965).
112. Matsoyan, S. G., Morlyan, N. M., and Saakyan, A. A., *Izv. Akad. Nauk Arm. SSR, Khim. Nauki* **15**, 405 (1962); *Chem. Abstr.* **58**, 6930 (1963).
113. Matsoyan, S. G., Morlyan, N. M., and Saakyan, A. A., *Izv. Akad. Nauk Arm. SSR, Khim. Nauki* **18**, 68 (1965); *Chem. Abstr.* **63**, 8494 (1965).
114. Matsoyan, S. G., Pogosyan, G. M., and Cholakyan, A. A., *Izv. Akad. Nauk Arm. SSR, Khim. Nauki* **18**, 178 (1965); *Chem. Abstr.* **63**, 14693 (1965).
115. Matsoyan, S. G., Pogosyan, G. M., and Eliazyan, M. A., *Vysokomolekul. Soedin.* **5**, 777 (1963); *Resins, Rubbers, Plastics* p. 2721 (1963).
116. Matsoyan, S. G., Pogosyan, G. M., and Skripnikova, R. K., *Vysokomolekul. Soedin.* **4**, 1142 (1962); *Resins, Rubbers, Plastics* p. 2455 (1962).
117. Matsoyan, S. G., Pogosyan, G. M., Skripnikova, R. K., and Mushegyan, A. V., *Vysokomolekul. Soedin.* **5**, 183 (1963); *Resins, Rubbers, Plastics* p. 1911 (1963).
118. Matsoyan, S. G., Pogosyan, G. M., Skripnikova, R. K., and Nikogosyan, L. L., *Izv. Akad. Nauk Arm. SSR, Khim. Nauki* **15**, 541 (1962); *Chem. Abstr.* **59**, 7655 (1963).
119. Matsoyan, S. G., and Saakyan, A. A., *Izv. Akad. Nauk Arm. SSR, Khim. Nauki* **16**, 159 (1963); *Chem. Abstr.* **59**, 8879 (1963).
120. Matsoyan, S. G., and Saakyan, A. A., *Izv. Akad. Nauk Arm. SSR, Khim. Nauki* **17**, 676 (1964); *Chem. Abstr.* **63**, 7114 (1965).
121. Matsoyan, S. G., and Saakyan, A. A., *Izv. Akad. Nauk Arm. SSR, Khim. Nauki* **18**, 60 (1965); *Chem. Abstr.* **63**, 8493 (1965).
122. Matyska, B., Mach, K., Vodenhal, J., and Kössler, I., *Collection Czech. Chem. Commun.* **30**, 2569 (1965); *Chem. Abstr.* **63**, 10069 (1965).
123. Mercier, J., *Ind. Chim. Belge* **25**, 359 (1960), *Resins, Rubbers, Plastics* p. 1437 (1961).
124. Meriwether, L. S., Colthup, E. C., and Kennerly, G. W., *J. Org. Chem.* **26**, 5163 (1961).

125. Meriwether, L. S., Colthup, E. C., Kennerly, G. W., and Reusch, R. N., *J. Org. Chem.* **26**, 5155 (1961).
126. Meriwether, L. S., Leto, M. F., Colthup, E. C., and Kennerly, G. W., *J. Org. Chem.* **27**, 3930 (1962).
127. Milford, G. N., *J. Polymer Sci.* **41**, 295 (1959).
128. Modena, M., Bates, R. B., and Marvel, C. S., *J. Polymer Sci.* **A3**, 949 (1965); *Chem. Abstr.* **62**, 11921 (1965).
129. Netherlands Patent Appl. 66, 17437 (issued to Rhone Poulenc) (1967).
130. Otsu, T., Mulvaney, J. E., and Marvel, C. S., *J. Polymer Sci.* **46**, 546 (1960).
131. Pellon, J., Kugel, R. L., Marcus, R., and Rabinowitz, R., *J. Polymer Sci.* **A2**, 4105 (1964); *Resins, Rubbers, Plastics* p. 1097 (1965).
132. Pledger, H., Jr., U.S. Patent 3,252,957 (Dow Chemical Co.) (1966); *Chem. Abstr.* **65**, 7305 (1966).
133. Ramp, F. L., *Am. Chem. Soc., Div. Polymer Chem., Preprints* **7**, 582 (1966).
134. Ramp, F. L., and Trapasso, L. E., U.S. Patent 3,290,272 (B. F. Goodrich Co.) (1966).
135. Reichel, B., Marvel, C. S., and Greenley, R. Z., *J. Polymer Sci.* **A1**, 2935 (1963); *Resins, Rubbers, Plastics* p. 1115 (1964).
136. Richardson, W. S., *J. Polymer Sci.* **13**, 325 (1954).
137. Roberts, W. J., and Day, A. R., *J. Am. Chem. Soc.* **72**, 1226 (1950).
138. Romanov, L. M., Verkhoturova, A. P., Kissin, Yu. V., and Rakova, G. V., *Vysokomolekul. Soedin.* **5**, 719 (1963); *Resins, Rubbers, Plastics* p. 2743 (1963).
139. Rummelsburg, A. L., U.S. Patent 2,341,948 (Hercules Powder Co.) (1944); *Chem. Abstr.* **38**, 4725 (1944).
140. Rummelsburg, A. L., U.S. Patent 2,351,786 (Hercules Powder Co.) (1944); *Chem. Abstr.* **38**, 5336 (1944).
141. Rummelsburg, A. L., U.S. Patent 2,373,419 (Hercules Powder Co.) (1945); *Chem. Abstr.* **39**, 4528 (1945).
142. Sartori, G., Valvassori, A., Turba, V., and Lachi, M. P., *Chim. Ind. (Milan)* **45**, 1529 (1963); *Resins, Rubbers, Plastics* p. 2283 (1964).
143. Schulz, R. C., *Kolloid-Z. Z. Polymere* **216-217**, 309 (1967).
144. Shelden, R. A., *Dissertation Abstr.* **25**, 2404 (1964); *Chem. Abstr.* **62**, 6568 (1965).
145. Sidel'kovskaya, F. P., Ragova, E. V., Ibragimov. F., and Shostakovskii, M. M., *Izv. Akad. Nauk SSSR, Ser. Khim.* p. 1228 (1966); *Bull. Acad. Sci. USSR, Div. Chem. Sci. (English Transl.)* p. 1179 (1966); *Chem. Abstr.* **65**, 16926h (1966).
146. Simpson, W., and Holt, T., *J. Polymer Sci.* **18**, 335 (1955).
147. Simpson, W., Holt, T., and Zetie, R. J., *J. Polymer Sci.* **10**, 489 (1953).
148. Smith, W. R., British Patent 802,510 (Imperial Chemical Industries, Ltd.) (1958); *Chem. Abstr.* **53**, 8070 (1959).
149. Spainhour, J. D., U.S. Patent 3,331,819 (Phillips Petroleum Co.) (1967).
150. Staudinger, H., and Heuer, W., *Chem. Ber.* **67**, 1159 (1934).
151. Stetter, H., Gaertner, J., and Tacke, P., *Angew. Chem.* **77**, 171 (1965); *Chem. Abstr.* **62**, 10349 (1965).
152. Stille, J. K., and Foster, R. T., *J. Org. Chem.* **28**, 2703 (1963).
153. Stille, J. K., and Frey, D. A., *Abstr. 135th Meeting Am. Chem. Soc. Boston* p. 17S (1959).
154. Stille, J. K., and Frey, D. A., *J. Am. Chem. Soc.* **83**, 1697 (1961).
155. Stolka, M., Vodenhal, J., and Kössler, I., *J. Polymer Sci.* **A2**, 3987 (1964).
156. Strauss, S., and Wall, L. A., *Am. Chem. Soc., Div. Polymer Chem., Preprints* **3**, 376 (1962).
157. Tinyakova, E. I., Zhuravleva, T. G., Kurengina, T. N., Kirikova, N. S., and Dolgoplosk, B. A., *Dokl. Akad. Nauk SSSR* **144**, 592 (1962); *Proc. Acad. Sci. USSR, Chem. Sect. (English Transl.)* **144**, 479 (1962).

158. Trifan, D. S., and Hoglen, J. J., *J. Am. Chem. Soc.* **83**, 2021 (1961); *Resins, Rubbers, Plastics* p. 2567 (1961).
159. Trossarelli, L., and Guaita, M., *J. Macromol. Chem.* **1**, 471 (1966); *Chem. Abstr.* **66**, 325, 2792w (1967).
160. Trossarelli, L., Guaita, M., and Priola, A., *Ric. Sci., Rend.* [2] **A8**, 379 (1965); *Chem. Abstr.* **64**, 5272 (1966).
161. Valvassori, A., Sartori, G., and Ciampelli, F., *Chim. Ind. (Milan)* **44**, 1095 (1962); *Resins, Rubbers, Plastics* p. 879 (1963).
162. Vanhaeren, G., and Butler, G. B., *Am. Chem. Soc., Div. Polymer Chem., Preprints* **6**, 709 (1965); *Chem. Abstr.* **66**, 4434, 46634a (1967).
163. Wall, L. A., *Am. Chem. Soc., Div. Polymer Chem., Preprints* **7**, 1112 (1966).
164. Wall, L. A., and Fearn, J. E., U.S. Patent 3,211,637 (1965); *Chem. Abstr.* **64**, 17800 (1966).
165. Walling, C., *J. Am. Chem. Soc.* **67**, 441 (1945).
166. Wiley, R. H., Rivera, W. H., Crawford, T. H., and Bray, N. F., *J. Polymer Sci.* **61**, S38 (1962); err. cf. *J. Polymer Sci.* **A2**, 5025 (1964).
167. Wright, C. D., U.S. Patent 3,247,170 (Minnesota Mining and Manufacturing Co.) (1966); *Chem. Abstr.* **64**, 19922 (1966).
168. Yoda, N., *Kagaku To Kogyo (Tokyo)* **18**, 656 (1965); *Chem. Abstr.* **63**, 3041 (1965).
169. Zutty, N. L., *J. Polymer Sci.* **A1**, 2231 (1963); *Resins, Rubbers, Plastics* p. 523 (1964).
170. Zutty, N. L., U.S. Patent 3,287,327 (Union Carbide Corp.) (1966); *Chem. Abstr.* **66**, 2832, 29415n (1967).

CHAPTER III

Diels-Alder Polymerizations

The reaction of a diene with a dienophile to yield ring-containing compounds is known as the Diels-Alder reaction. The use of this reaction for the preparation of polymers has been especially attractive to polymer chemists because of the wide variety of reactants that can undergo the reaction. Polymers formed from such reactions have been referred to as Diels-Alder polymers in the literature. The requisite reactants for such a polymerization are depicted schematically in Eq. (III-1).

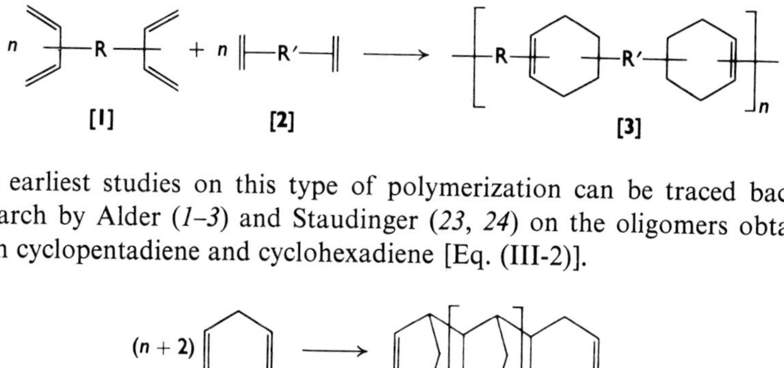

$$n \quad [1] \quad + n \quad [2] \quad \longrightarrow \quad [3] \quad (\text{III-1})$$

The earliest studies on this type of polymerization can be traced back to research by Alder (1–3) and Staudinger (23, 24) on the oligomers obtained from cyclopentadiene and cyclohexadiene [Eq. (III-2)].

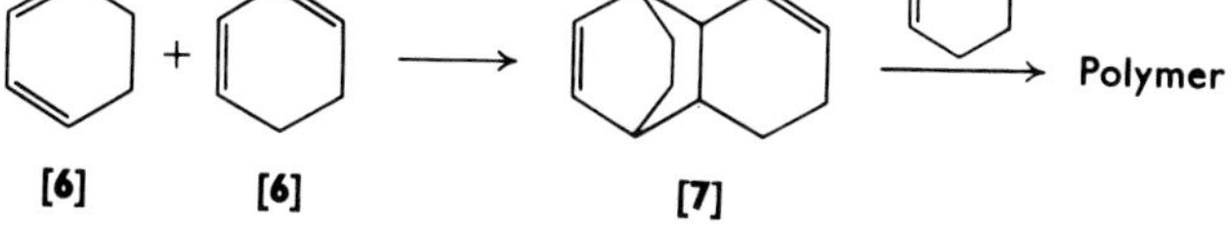

$$(n + 2) \quad [4] \quad \longrightarrow \quad [5]$$

$$[6] + [6] \longrightarrow [7] \longrightarrow \text{Polymer} \qquad (\text{III-2})$$

More recently (4, 5, 13, 14) the reaction has been developed for the preparation of high molecular weight polymers. Appropriate starting materials led to

99

products possessing high softening temperatures and good thermal stability. Reviews of this type of polymerization have been published (*16, 25*).

METHOD 1. POLYMERIZATION OF BIS(DIENOPHILES) WITH BIS(DIENES)

Polymerization of a bis(diene) with a bis(dienophile) has yielded high molecular weight polymer. The reaction can be carried out in solvents such as *s*-tetrachloroethane and dimethylformamide, or in bulk. Optimum reaction temperatures vary with the particular case. No catalysts are required. An example of such a polymerization is shown in Eq. (III-3) (*6*).

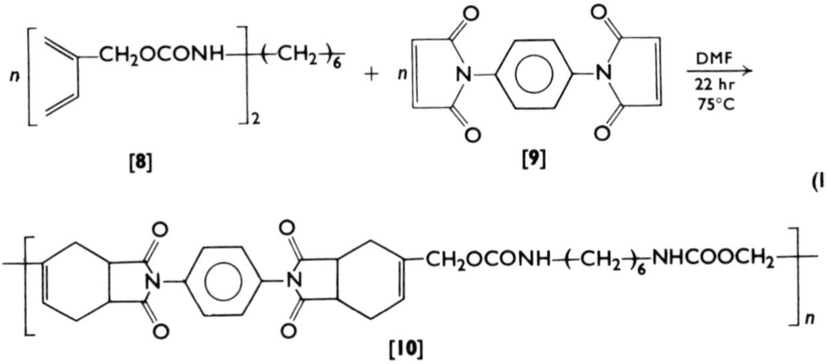

[8]   [9]

(III-3)

[10]
[η] 0.20 (DMF)

The bis(diene) was prepared by reaction of 2-(hydroxymethyl)-1,3-butadiene with hexamethylene diisocyanate (*6*).

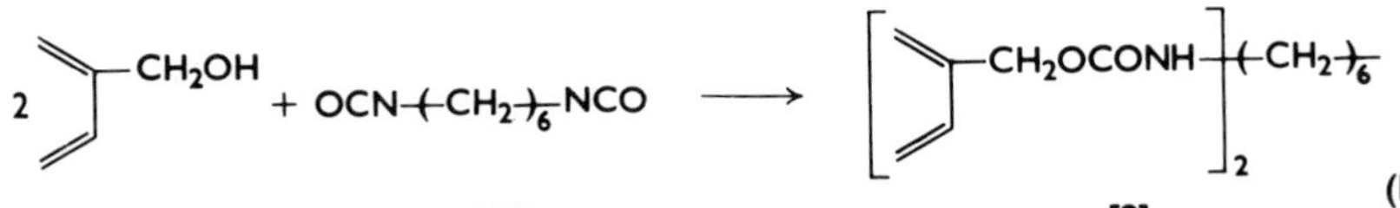

[11]   [12]   [8]

(III-4)

Bis(maleimides) prepared from aromatic diamines (benzidine, *p*-phenylene-diamine, *o*-tolidine, *o*-anisidine) were condensed with 1,8-diphenyloctatetraene and related bis(dienes). Polymers that softened above 300°C with molecular weights of approximately 3000 were obtained (*18*). A Diels-Alder polymerization has been described that yields a "ladder" polymer. The cyclic oligomeric esters [13] and [14] give low molecular weight polymer when heated in toluene (*7*). *p*-Benzoquinone has also been polymerized with [14]. A chloroform-soluble product with a molecular weight of about 2000 was obtained (*7*).

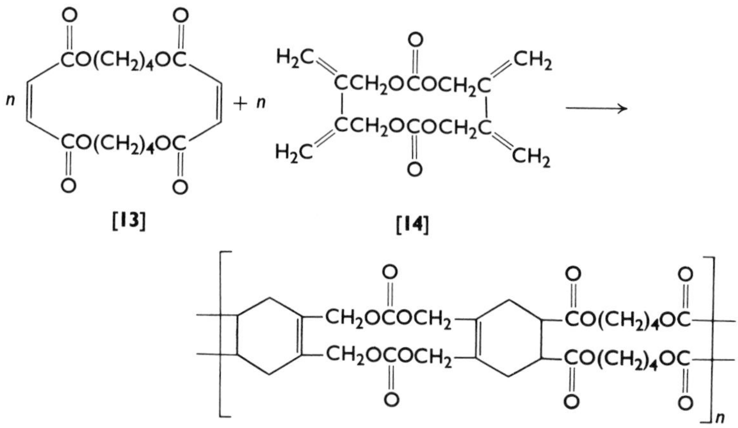

[13]   [14]

(III-5)

[15]

Bis(dienes) containing ferrocene groups have been polymerized with related bis(dienophiles). Polymer [16] was obtained from 1,1′-bis(dimethyl-4-iso-prenylsilyl)ferrocene and 1,1′-bis(dimethylvinylsilyl)ferrocene (*11*).

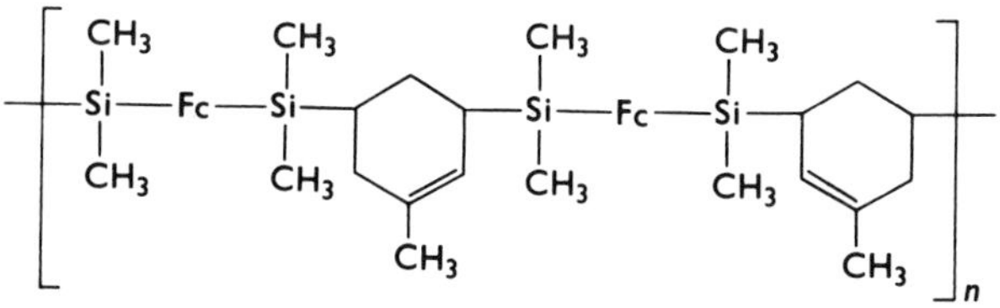

(III-6)

[16]
Fc = ferrocenylene

Several bis(dienes) were prepared by the condensation of sodium or potassium cyclopentadienyl with various dihalo compounds (*22, 29, 30*).

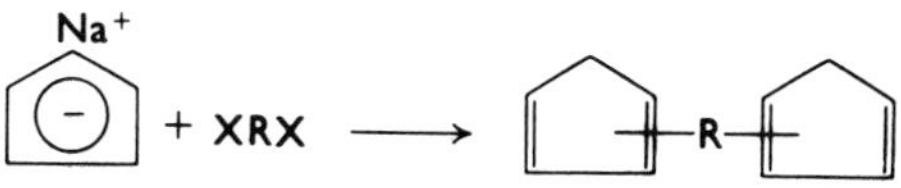

[17]   [18]   [19]
X = halogen

(III-7)

The uncatalyzed homopolymerization of the dienes [19] in benzene or toluene yielded low molecular weight (η_{inh} <0.12), soluble polymers (*29*). Polymerization in bulk, also without catalyst, gave insoluble cross-linked resins (*22, 29, 30*). Whether the cross-linking reaction involved a Diels-Alder (*22*) or a vinyl (*29*) polymerization was not determined.

The bis(dienes) [19] were also useful as cross-linking agents for linear poly(dienes) and unsaturated polyesters. The cross-linking reaction, presumably a Diels-Alder type, was claimed to yield products that possessed an attractive combination of mechanical, electrical, and adhesive properties (22).

Bis- and poly(maleimido) compounds have been patented for curing polyolefin copolymers to rubbery compositions (12).

Bis(fulvenes) polymerize with bis(maleimides) to yield very high molecular weight polymers. The polymer [22] formed from the reactants in Eq. (III-8) possessed an inherent viscosity of 0.82. It was prepared in dimethylformamide at room temperature (20). This polymerization is thermally reversible at steambath temperatures. Cast films of the polymer were tough and flexible. Other examples with even higher molecular weights are described in Table III.1 (see pp. 106–118).

[20]   [21]

(III-8)

[22]

The self-polymerization of [23] was attempted but did not yield polymer (17). Probably, the increased resonance stabilization of the fulvene moiety and steric hindrance were responsible for this result.

(III-9)

[23]

Instead of using a bis(diene), several Diels-Alder polymerizations have been performed with trienes (6). An example is shown in Eq. (III-10). Initially the reactants form an intermediate that possesses both the diene and dienophile groups. Self-polymerization of this intermediate yields the polymer. The cyclic oligomeric ester from maleic acid and 1,4-butanediol described earlier

[13] also polymerizes with 2-vinyl-1,3-butadiene [24] (7). Thermogravimetry and hydrolysis studies on this "ladder" polymer showed enhanced thermal and hydrolytic stability over related single-chain polymers.

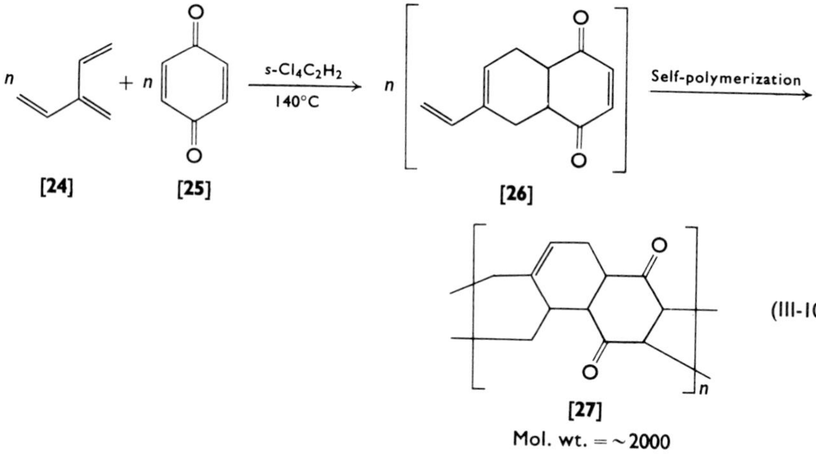

[24]   [25]

[26]

(III-10)

[27]
Mol. wt. = ~2000

The azine of benzaldehyde functions as a bis(diene) when polymerized with bis(maleimides). Moderately high molecular weight polymers are obtained (26). Although both solution and bulk procedures were attempted, only the latter gave polymer. Temperatures of 180°–190°C for 10 to 15 minutes gave best results. Model compound studies supported the structure assigned to the polymer repeat unit in Eq. (III-11).

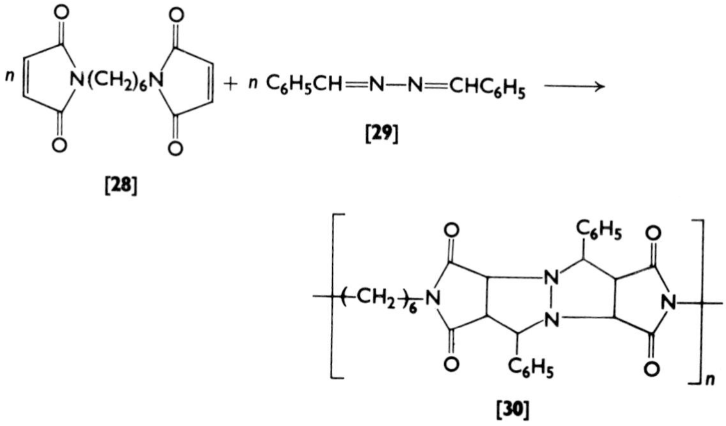

[28]   [29]

(III-11)

[30]

METHOD 2. POLYMERIZATION OF BIS(DIENOPHILES) WITH PSEUDOBIS(DIENES)

The polymerization of bis(dienophiles) with cyclopentadienones, α-pyrones, and thiophene dioxides has yielded some very high molecular weight

Diels-Alder polymers. This type of polymerization differs from Method 1 in that a bis(diene) is not employed. Rather, a dienophile reacts with a diene to yield an intermediate that can be converted to another diene by heating. These intermediates ([32] and [33]) are not isolated, but are formed and react *in situ*. Equation (III-12) depicts the course of the reaction of N,N'-hexamethylenebis(maleimide) with 2,5-dimethyl-3,4-diphenylcyclopentadienone (*13*). Peroxide-catalyzed cross-linking of these substituted cyclopentadienone derived polymers has been patented (*8*). Polymers treated in this way exhibited improved toughness, better stress cracking, and chemical resistance.

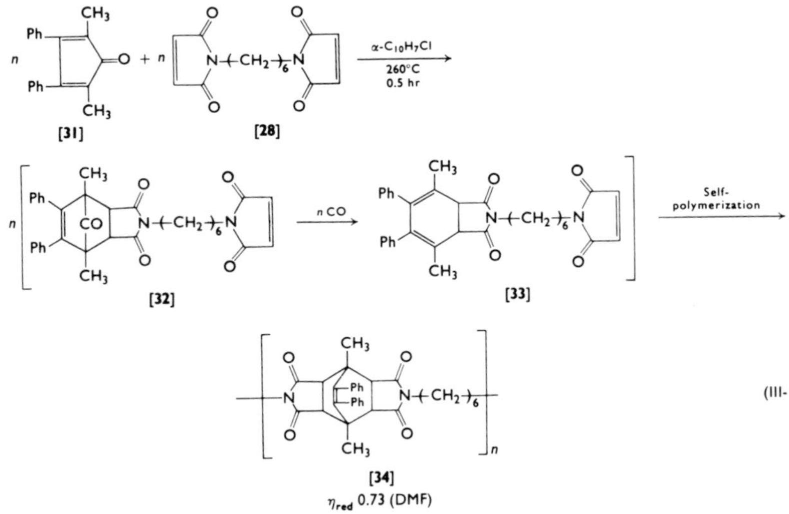

$$(III-12)$$

An example of the polymerization of an α-pyrone derivative is shown in Eq. (III-13) (*9, 14*).

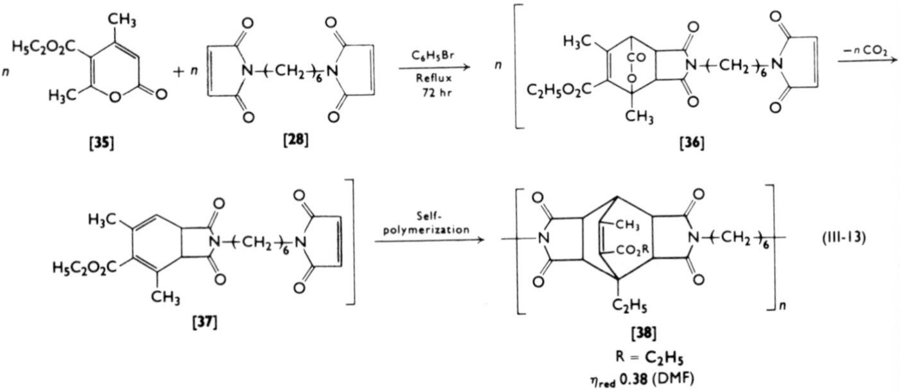

$$(III-13)$$

Thiophene dioxides are also useful monomers for this polymerization method (*10*).

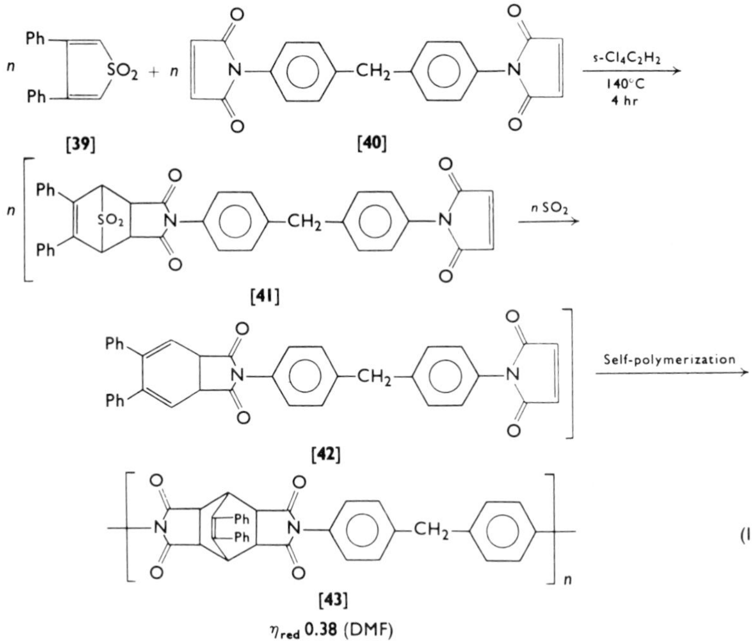

Ph⌐
n SO_2 + n [chemical scheme] $\xrightarrow[140°C\,4\,hr]{s\text{-}Cl_4C_2H_2}$
Ph⌐

[39]   [40]

n [chemical scheme with Ph, SO₂] $\xrightarrow{n\,SO_2}$

[41]

[chemical scheme with Ph] $\xrightarrow{\text{Self-polymerization}}$

[42]

[chemical scheme with Ph, Ph, CH₂]   (III-14)

[43]

η_{red} 0.38 (DMF)

The evolution of the gaseous product in this polymerization makes the initial Diels-Alder reaction irreversible. This factor probably contributes to the ease with which high molecular weight polymers are obtained. Recently, two groups of workers have described the polymerization of diacetylenes with bis(cyclopentadienones) (*19, 21, 27*). An example is shown in Eq. (III-15). The reactants were heated together in a sealed tube at 300°C for 50 hours with toluene as a solvent. Relatively high molecular weight products were obtained (*27*). The polymers were also notable in that they possessed decomposition temperatures of 470°–550°C in air (*27*). Other examples are listed in Table III.1.

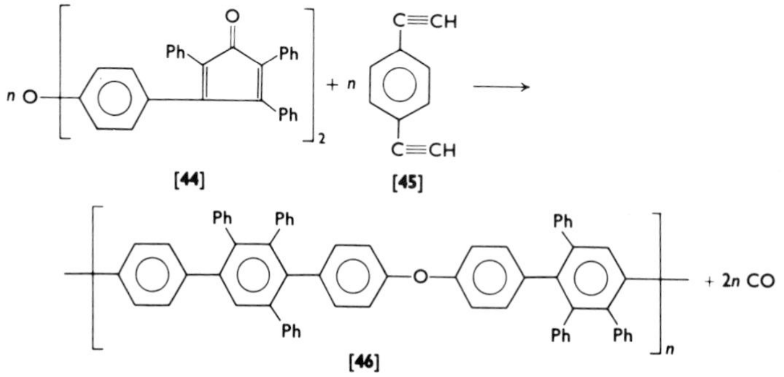

n O [chemical scheme with Ph, Ph, Ph]$_2$ + n [chemical scheme C≡CH / C≡CH] $\longrightarrow$

[44]   [45]

[chemical scheme with Ph, Ph, Ph, O, Ph, Ph, Ph]$_n$ + $2n$ CO   (III-15)

[46]

TABLE III.1

Diels-Alder Polymers

No.	Monomers	Method	Molecular weight	Solubility	T_m (°C)	Remarks and property data	References
1	Homopolymer from 2-vinylbutadiene [24]	1	—	—	130–165	Yellow solid	5, 6
2	Homopolymer from 1,6-bis(cyclopentadienyl)-hexane	1	η_{lnh} 0.042	Benzene, other aromatic hydrocarbons	—	Viscous oil. Cross-links upon exposure to atmosphere	29
3	Homopolymer from α,α'-bis(cyclopentadienyl)p-xylene	1	η_{lnh} 0.12	Benzene, other aromatic hydrocarbons	160 d	Cross-links on exposure to atmosphere	29
4	Homopolymer from 1,9-bis(cyclopentadienyl)-nonane	1	—	Aromatic hydrocarbons	—	Viscous oil. Cross-links upon exposure to atmosphere	29
5	(a) 2-Vinylbutadiene [24] (b) Benzoquinone [25]	1	440 (Rast cryoscopy)	s-Tetrachloro-ethane, camphor	170–200 340–400	Polymerization yielded soluble(mol. wt. = 440, T_m = 170°–200°C) and an insoluble fraction (T_m = 340°–400°C). The latter was believed to have a molecular weight of ~2000	5, 6
6	(a) 2-Vinylbutadiene [24] (b) N,N′-Methylenediacrylamide	1	[η] 0.05	DMF	—	Brown, glassy solid	5, 6
7	(a) 2-Vinylbutadiene [24] (b) Ethylene diacrylate	1	—	Acetone	—	A translucent glass	5, 6
8	(a) 2-Vinylbutadiene [24] (b) N,N′-p-Phenylenebis(maleimide) [9]	1	—	—	—	—	5, 6

9	(a) 2-Vinylbutadiene [24] (b) N,N'-m-Phenylenebis(maleimide) [21]	1	—	Insoluble	>400	—	4
10	(a) 2-Vinylbutadiene [24] (b) N,N'-Benzidinebis(maleimide)	1	—	—	—	—	5, 6
11	(a) 2,5-Dimethylthiophene dioxide (b) N,N'-Hexamethylenebis(maleimide) [28]	2	η_{red} 0.37	Phenol/s-tetra-chloroethane (3/2), chlorinated naphthalenes	250	—	10
12	(a) 2,5-Dimethylthiophene dioxide (b) N,N'-(4,4'-Diphenylmethane)bis-(maleimide) [40]	2	η_{red} 0.31	Phenol/s-tetra-chloroethane (3/2), chlorinated naphthalenes	400	A film cast from phenol/s-tetra-chloroethane (3/2) had the following properties: Tensile strength, 8850 psi; Tensile modulus, 250,000 psi (at 25°C) and 150,000 psi (at 350°C); Elongation = 9.2%	10
13	(a) 4,6-Dimethyl-5-carbethoxy-α-pyrone [35] (b) N,N'-Hexamethylenebis(maleimide) [28]	2	η_{red} 0.38	DMF, bromo-benzene, other chlorinated hydrocarbons	195	—	14
14	(a) 4,6-Dimethyl-5-carbethoxy-α-pyrone [35] (b) N,N'-[4,4'-(3,5,3',5'-Tetramethyl-diphenylmethane)]bis(maleimide)	2	η_{red} 0.15	DMF, bromo-benzene	>300	—	14

TABLE III.1—*continued*

Diels-Alder Polymers

No.	Monomers	Method	Molecular weight	Solubility	T_m (°C)	Remarks and property data	References
15	(a) Bis(2-butadienylmethyl) acetal 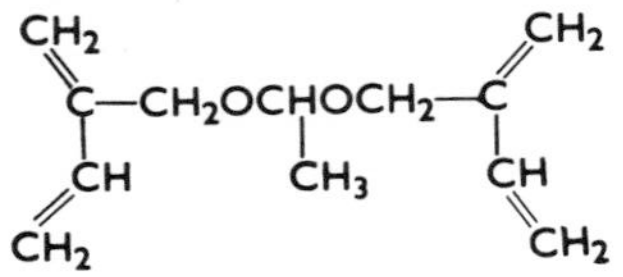 (b) Benzoquinone [25]	1	$[\eta]$ 0.28	DMF	130–140	—	5, 6
16	(a) Bis(2-butadienylmethyl) acetal (b) N,N′-p-Phenylenebis(maleimide) [9]	1	$[\eta]$ 0.08	DMF, acetone	185–194	—	5, 6
17	(a) Bis(2-butadienylmethyl) acetal (b) N,N′-Benzidinebis(maleimide)	1	$[\eta]$ 0.19	DMF	170–174	—	5, 6
18	(a) 3,4-Diphenylthiophene dioxide [39] (b) N,N′-Hexamethylenebis(maleimide) [28]	2	η_{red} 0.21	DMF, aliphatic and aromatic chlorinated hydrocarbons	210	—	10
19	(a) 3,4-Diphenylthiophene dioxide [39] (b) N,N′-(4,4′-Diphenylmethane)bis-(maleimide) [40]	2	η_{red} 0.38	DMF, chlorinated aliphatics and aromatics	400	Film of polymer cast from DMF had the following properties: Tensile strength = 9900 psi; Tensile modulus = 330,000 psi (25°C)	10

109

No.	Compound		Viscosity	Solvent	Temp.	Remarks	Refs.
20	(a) 1,6-Bis(cyclopentadienyl)hexane (b) Benzoquinone [25]	1	η_{inh} 0.13	Benzene, xylene	125	& 130,000 psi (350°C); Elongation = 13.6%. Polymer was resistant at room temp. toward aq. NaOH (10%) and aq. HCl (10%)	28, 29
21	(a) 1,6-Bis(cyclopentadienyl)hexane (b) N,N'-Hexamethylenebis(maleimide) [28]	1	η_{inh} 0.10	Benzene	140	—	29
22	(a) α,α'-Bis(cyclopentadienyl)-p-xylene  (b) Benzoquinone [25]	1	η_{inh} 0.11	Benzene	180	—	29
23	(a) α,α'-Bis(cyclopentadienyl)-p-xylene (b) N,N'-Hexamethylenebis(maleimide) [28]	1	η_{inh} 0.22	DMF	240	—	29
24	(a) Bis(2-butadienylmethyl)-m-xylylene dicarbamate 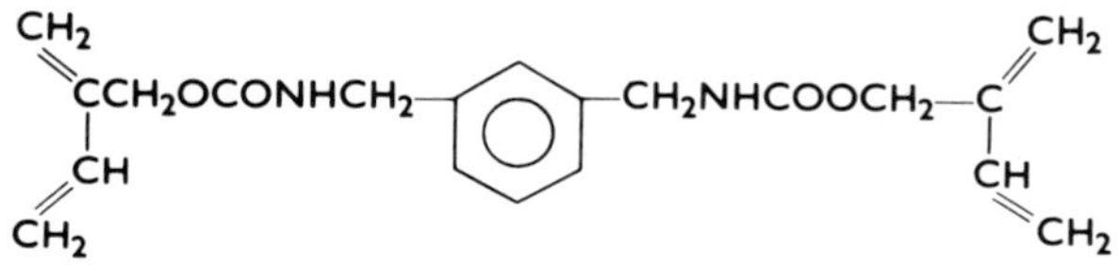 (b) N,N'-p-Phenylenebis(maleimide) [9]	1	$[\eta]$ 0.05	DMF	90–95	—	5, 6

TABLE III.1—continued

Diels-Alder Polymers

No.	Monomers	Method	Molecular weight	Solubility	T_m (°C)	Remarks and property data	References
25	(a) Bis(2-butadienylmethyl)-m-xylylene dicarbamate (b) N,N′-Benzidinebis(maleimide)	1	[η] 0.15	DMF	145–150	—	5, 6
26	(a) Bis(2-butadienylmethyl)hexamethylene dicarbamate [8] 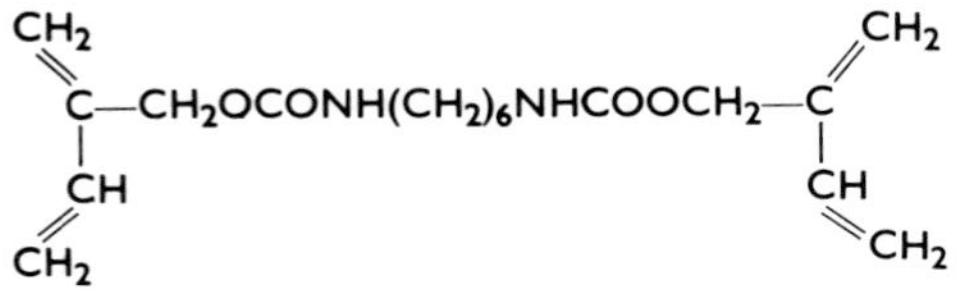 (b) N,N′-p-Phenylenebis(maleimide) [9]	1	[η] 0.20	DMF	74–78	—	5, 6
27	(a) Bis(2-butadienylmethyl)hexamethylene dicarbamate [8] (b) N,N′-Benzidinebis(maleimide)	1	[η] 0.19	DMF	133–137	—	5, 6
28	(a) 2,5-Dimethyl-3,4-diphenyl-cyclopentadienone [31] (b) N,N′-Hexamethylenebis(maleimide) [28]	2	η_{red} 0.73	DMF, CHCl₃, other chlorinated hydrocarbons	235	Amorphous (X-ray). A compression-molded film (250°C) had the following properties: Tensile strength = 6000 psi; Tensile modulus = 160,000 psi; Elongation = 6%; Modulus of elasticity = 396,000 psi; Flexural	8, 13

For compound 26, the structure shown:

CH₂
‖
C—CH₂OCONH(CH₂)₆NHCOOCH₂—C—CH
| |
CH CH₂
‖ ‖
CH₂

	(a) / (b)		η_{red}	Solvents		Properties	Ref.
						strength = 16,100 psi; Heat distortion temperature (ASTM) = 186.5°C; H_2O absorption = 0.51%; Arc resistance = 79 sec. Dielectric strength: short time = 366 volts/mil; step by step = 429 volts/mil	13
29	(a) 2,5-Dimethyl-3,4-diphenyl-cyclopentadienone [31] (b) N,N'-(2,4-Tolylene)bis(maleimide) 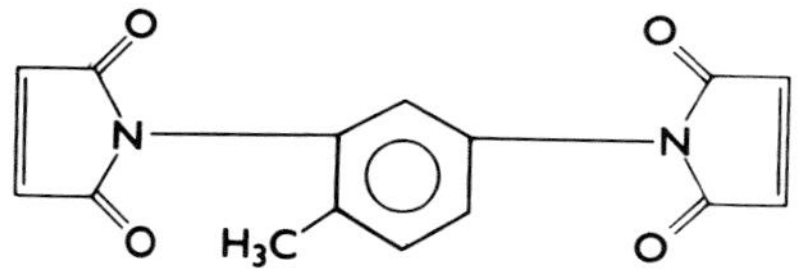	2	η_{red} 0.12	DMF, halogenated aromatics	>300	—	13
30	(a) 2,5-Dimethyl-3,4-diphenyl-cyclopentadienone [31] (b) N,N'-Benzidinebis(maleimide)	2	η_{red} 0.53	DMF, bromobenzene, α-chloronaphthalene	300	T_s claimed >400°C. A film of this polymer had the following properties: Tensile strength = 11,800 psi; Tensile modulus = 240,000 psi (room temp.) and 150,000 psi (200°C); Elongation = 17%. Dielectric strength: Short time = 273 volts/mil; step by step = 234 volts/mil	8, 13

TABLE III.1—*continued*

Diels-Alder Polymers

No.	Monomers	Method	Molecular weight	Solubility	T_m (°C)	Remarks and property data	References
31	(a) 2,5-Dimethyl-3,4-diphenyl-cyclopentadienone [31] (b) N,N'-(4,4'-Diphenylmethane)-bis(maleimide) [40]	2	η_{red} 0.67	DMF, bromo-benzene, α-chloro-naphthalene	>300	A film of this polymer had the following properties: Tensile strength = 10,400 psi; Tensile modulus = 240,000 psi (room temp.) and 110,000 psi (200°C); Elongation = 18%. Dielectric strength: Short time = 167 volts/mil; step by step = 226 volts/mil. T_g >300°C	8, 13
32	(a) 2,5-Dimethyl-3,4-diphenyl-cyclopentadienone [31] (b) N,N'-[4,4'-bis(o-tolylene)]bis(maleimide) 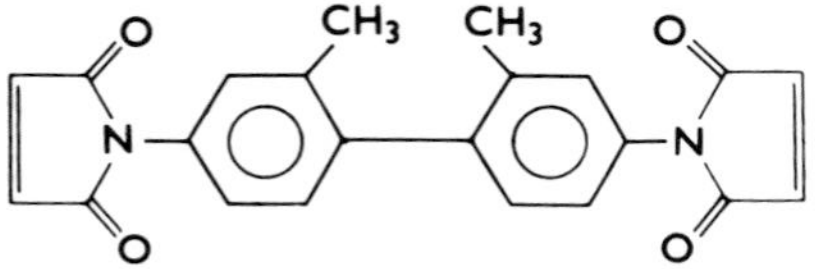	2	η_{red} 2.05	DMF, halo-genated aromatics	>300	—	13, 15
33	(a) 2,5-Dimethyl-3,4-diphenyl-cyclopentadienone [31] (b) N,N'-[4,4'-(3,3'-Dimethylbiphenyl)]bis-(maleimide) 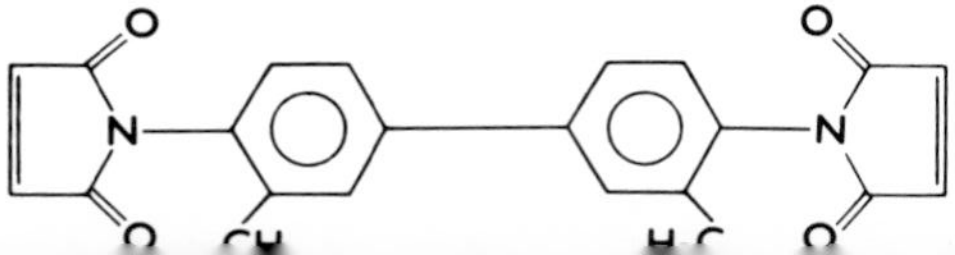	2	η_{red} 1.61	DMF, halo-genated aromatics	>300	A film of this polymer had the following properties: T_g >360°C; Tensile strength = 15,800 psi; Tensile modulus = 390,000 psi (room temp.) and 210,000 psi (200°C); Elongation = 4.5%. Dielectric strength: Short time = 207 volts/mil; step by step = 197 volts/mil	13

34	(a) 2,5-Dimethyl-3,4-diphenyl-cyclopentadienone [31] (b) N,N'-[4,4'-(3,3'-Dimethyldiphenyl-methane)]bis(maleimide) 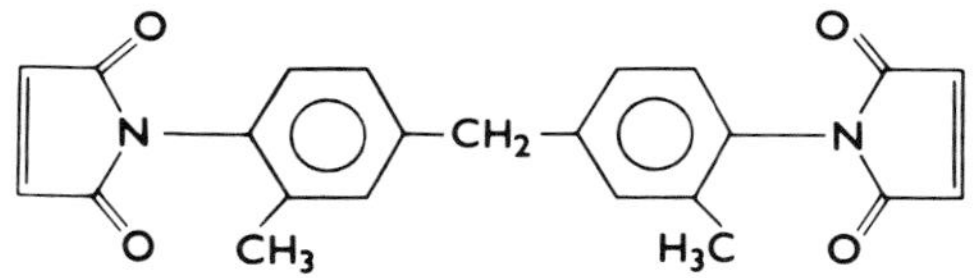		2	η_{red} 0.36	DMF, bromo-benzene, α-chloro-naphthalene	>300	—	13
35	(a) 2,5-Dimethyl-3,4-diphenyl-cyclopentadienone [31] (b) N,N'-[4,4'-(3,5,3',5'-Tetramethyldiphenyl-methane)]bis(maleimide) 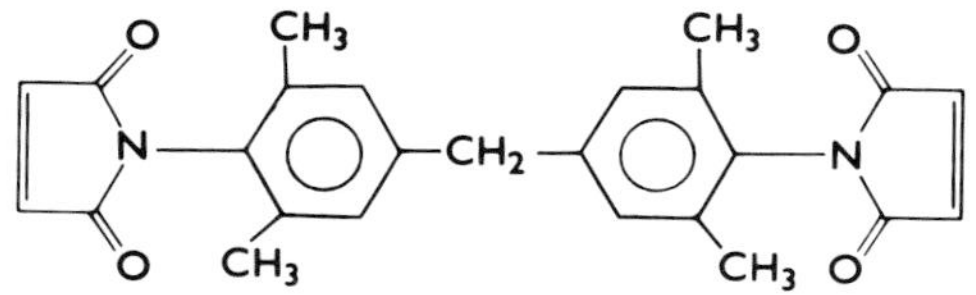		2	η_{red} 0.34	DMF, halo-genated aromatics	>300	—	13
36	(a) 2,5-Dimethyl-3,4-diphenyl-cyclopentadienone [31] (b) N,N'-[4,4'-(2,5,2',5'-Tetramethyldiphenyl-methane)]bis(maleimide) 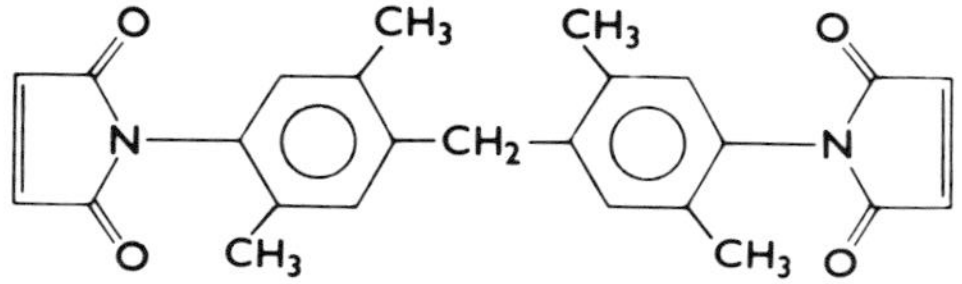		2	η_{red} 0.27	DMF, bromo-benzene, α-chloro-naphthalene	>300	—	13

TABLE III.1—*continued*

Diels-Alder Polymers

No.	Monomers	Method	Molecular weight	Solubility	T_m (°C)	Remarks and property data	References
37	(a) 1,9-Bis(cyclopentadienyl)nonane (b) Benzoquinone [25]	1	η_{inh} 0.13	Benzene	110	—	29
38	(a) 1,9-Bis(cyclopentadienyl)nonane (b) N,N'-Hexamethylenebis(maleimide) [28]	1	η_{inh} 0.18	Benzene	120	—	29
39	(a) 2-Methyl-3,4-diphenyl-5-n-propyl-cyclopentadienone (b) N,N'-m-Phenylenebis(maleimide) [21]	2	η_{red} 0.28	DMF, halogenated aromatics	>300	—	13
40	(a) 2-Methyl-3,4-diphenyl-5-n-propyl-cyclopentadienone (b) N,N'-Hexamethylenebis(maleimide) [28]	2	η_{red} 0.45	DMF, halogenated hydrocarbons	250	—	13
41	(a) 2-Methyl-3,4-diphenyl-5-n-propyl-cyclopentadienone (b) N,N'-(2,4-Tolylene)bis(maleimide)	2	η_{red} 0.13	DMF, halogenated aromatics	>300	—	13

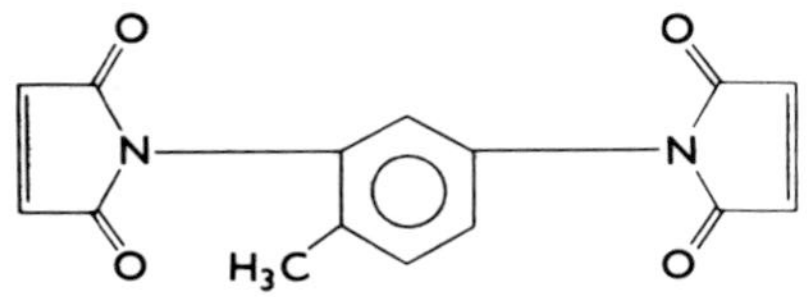

42   (a) 2-Methyl-3,4-diphenyl-5-n-propyl-cyclopentadienone
(b) N,N'-(4,4'-Bis-o-tolylene)bis(maleimide)

(a)

(b)

[45]

No.	R		Viscosity	Solvent	Thermal		Ref.
42		2	η_{red} 0.89	DMF, halogenated aromatics	>300	—	13
43	R = —	2	—	—	—	—	21
44	R = —S—	2	η_{sp} 0.40	Toluene	550 d (TGA)	—	19, 27
45	R = $+CH_2+_3$	2	η_{sp} 0.17	Toluene	490 (TGA)	—	19, 27
46	R = $+CH_2+_4$	2	η_{sp} 0.36	Toluene	490 (TGA)	—	19, 27

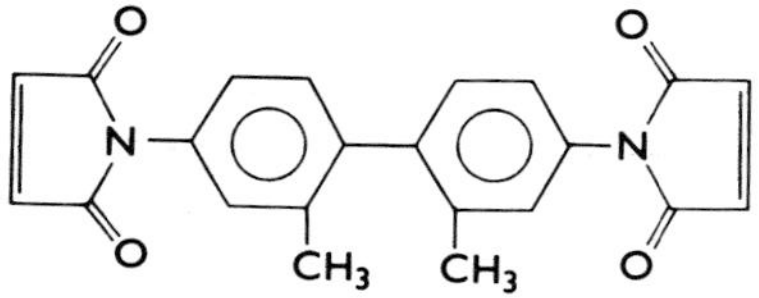

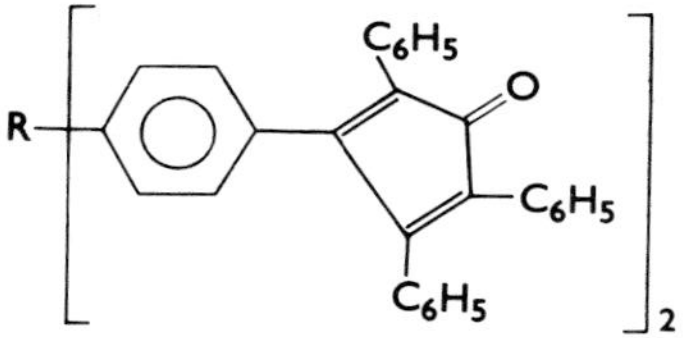

TABLE III.1—*continued*

Diels-Alder Polymers

No.	Monomers	Method	Molecular weight	Solubility	T_m (°C)	Remarks and property data	References
47	R = —O—; (b) 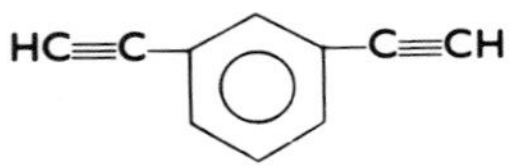 HC≡C—[structure]—C≡CH [44]	2	η_{sp} 0.31	Toluene	550 (TGA)	—	19, 27
48	R = —S—; (b) 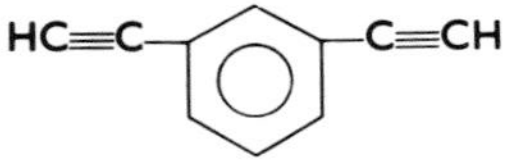 HC≡C—[structure]—C≡CH	2	η_{sp} 0.26	Toluene	550 (TGA)	—	19, 27
49	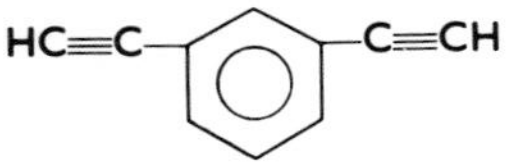 R = (CH₂)₃; (b) HC≡C—[structure]—C≡CH	2	η_{sp} 0.16	Toluene	490 (TGA)	—	19, 27
50	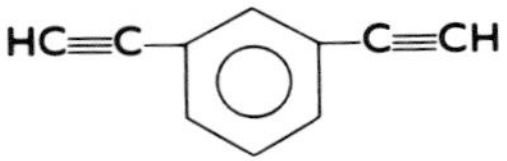 R = (CH₂)₄; (b) HC≡C—[structure]—C≡CH	2	η_{sp} 0.14	Toluene	470 (TGA)	—	19, 27
51	(a) Perchlorocoumalin (b) N,N'-Hexamethylenebis(maleimide) [28]	2	η_{red} 0.15	DMF	—	—	9

* * *

117

No.	Reactants		Viscosity / $\overline{M}_n$	Solvent	mp (°C)	Properties	Ref.
52	(a) Perchlorocoumalin (b) 4,4′-Diphenylmethanebis(maleimide) [40]	2	η_{red} 0.15	DMF	—	—	9
53	(a) 2-Vinyl-1,3-butadiene [24] (b) Maleic acid/1,4-butanediol cyclic oligomer [13]	1	3640	Acetone, CHCl$_3$, DMF	143–150 (soft)	—	7
54	(a) Benzalazine [29] (b) N,N′-p-Phenylenebis(maleimide) [9]	1	η_{inh} 0.30	DMF	>300	—	26
55	(a) Benzalazine [29] (b) N,N′-m-Phenylenebis(maleimide) [21]	1	η_{inh} 0.13	DMF	>300 (soft)	—	26
56	(a) Benzalazine [29] (b) N,N′-o-Phenylenebis(maleimide)	1	η_{inh} 0.20	DMF	>300 (soft)	—	26
57	(a) Benzalazine [29] (b) N,N′-Hexamethylenebis(maleimide) [28]	1	η_{inh} 0.20; 3400	DMF	238 (soft)	—	26
58	(a) Dimeric, cyclic carbonate of 2,3-bis(hydroxymethyl)butadiene-1,4 [14] (b) p-Benzoquinone [25]	1	$\overline{M}_n$ 2000	Acetone, CHCl$_3$, DMF	>400	—	7
59	(a) Dimeric, cyclic carbonate of 2,3-bis(hydroxymethyl)butadiene-1,4 [14] (b) Maleic acid/1,4-butanediol cyclic oligomer [13]	1	1850	Acetone, CHCl$_3$, DMF	300 d	—	7
60	(a) 4,6-Diphenyl-2-pyrone (b) 4,4′-Diphenylmethanebis(maleimide) [40]	2	η_{red} 0.44	s-Tetrachloroethane	—	Tensile strength = 10,000 psi. Tensile modulus = 300,000 psi (25°C); 20,000 psi (325°C). Elongation = 20%	9

TABLE III.1—*continued*

Diels-Alder Polymers

No.	Monomers	Method	Molecular weight	Solubility	T_m (°C)	Remarks and property data	References
61	(a) 1,1′-Bis(dimethyl-1-isoprenylsilyl)-ferrocene (b) 1,3-Divinyldisiloxane	1	4000 (ebulli-oscopy)	—	61–68	—	*11*
62	(a) 1,1′-Bis(dimethyl-1-isoprenylsilyl)-ferrocene (b) 1,1′-Bis(dimethylvinylsilyl)ferrocene	1	4080 (ebulli-oscopy)	Xylene	87–95	—	*11*
63	(a) 2,5-Dimethyl-3,4-diphenyl-cyclopentadienone (b) N,N′-Heptamethylenebis-(maleimide)	2	—	—	—	—	*8*
64	(a) 6,6′-p-Phenylenebis(6-methyl-fulvene) [20] (b) N,N′-m-Phenylenebis(maleimide) [21]	1	η_{inh} 1.14	DMF	—	Yellow, tough, cast films	*20*
65	(a) 6,6′-p-Phenylenebis(6-methyl-fulvene) [20] (b) N,N′-Hexamethylenebis-(maleimide) [28]	1	η_{inh} 0.46	CHCl₃	—	—	*20*
66	(a) 6,6′-p-Phenylenebis(6-methyl-fulvene) [20] (b) N,N′-(4,4′-Diphenylmethane)bis-(maleimide) [40]	1	η_{inh} 0.62	—	—	—	*20*
67	(a) 6,6′-(Oxydi-p-phenylene)bis-(6-phenylfulvene) (b) N,N′-m-Phenylenebis(maleimide) [21]	1	η_{inh} 0.42	—	—	Yellow, tough films	*20*

REFERENCES

1. Alder, K., and Stein, G., *Ann. Chem.* **485**, 223 (1931).
2. Alder, K., and Stein, G., *Ann. Chem.* **496**, 204 (1932).
3. Alder, K., and Stein, G., *Chem. Ber.* **67**, 613 (1934).
4. Bailey, W. J., and Economy, J., *Abstr. 126th Meeting Am. Chem. Soc., New York* p. 19S (1954).
5. Bailey, W. J., Economy, J., and Hermes, M. E., *Am. Chem. Soc., Div. Polymer Chem., Preprints*, **1** (2), 1 (1960).
6. Bailey, W. J., Economy, J., and Hermes, M. E., *J. Org. Chem.* **27**, 3295 (1962).
7. Bailey, W. J., and Feinberg, B. D., *Am. Chem. Soc., Div. Polymer Chem., Preprints* **8**, No. 1, 165 (1967).
8. Baum, B. O., U.S. Patent 3,097,189 (Union Carbide Corp.) (1963).
9. Chow, S. W., U.S. Patent 3,074,915 (Union Carbide Corp.) (1963).
10. Chow, S. W., and Whelan, J. M., Jr., U.S. Patent 2,971,944 (Union Carbide Corp.) (1961); *Chem. Abstr.* **55**, 12941 (1961).
11. Greber, G., and Hallensleben, M. L., *Makromol. Chem.* **104**, 90 (1967).
12. Kehn, J. T., U.S. Patent 3,334,075 (Esso Research and Engineering Co.) (1967).
13. Kraiman, E. A., U.S. Patent 2,890,206 (Union Carbide Corp.) (1959); *Chem. Abstr.* **53**, 17572 (1959).
14. Kraiman, E. A., U.S. Patent 2,890,207 (Union Carbide Corp.) (1959); *Chem. Abstr.* **53**, 17572 (1959).
15. Kraiman, E. A., *Macromol. Syn.* **2**, 110 (1966); *Chem. Abstr.* **65**, 18698 (1966).
16. Kraiman, E. A., *Encyl. Polymer Sci. Technol.* **5**, 23 (1966); *Chem. Abstr.* **66**, 5285, 55764v (1967).
17. Meek, J. S., and Argabright, P. A., *J. Org. Chem.* **22**, 1708 (1957).
18. Meek, J. S., Argabright, P. A., and Stacy, R. D., *Abstr. 134th Meeting Am. Chem. Soc., Chicago* p. 23P (1958).
19. Mukamal, H., Harris, F. W., Rakutes, R. O., and Stille, J. K., *Am. Chem. Soc., Div. Polymer Chem., Preprints* **8**, 496 (1967).
20. Reeder, J. A., U.S. Patent 3,334,071 (E. I. duPont de Nemours & Co.) (1967).
21. Reid, W., and Freitag, D., *Naturwissenschaften* **53**, 306 (1966); *Chem. Abstr.* **65**, 13835 (1966).
22. Renner, A., Widmer, F., and von Schulthess, A., *Kunststoffe* **53**, 509 (1963).
23. Staudinger, H., *Ann. Chem.* **467**, 73 (1928).
24. Staudinger, H., and Bruson, H., *Ann. Chem.* **447**, 97 (1926).
25. Stille, J. K., *Fortschr. Hochpolymer.-Forsch.* **3**, 48 (1961); *Chem. Abstr.* **56**, 15653 (1962).
26. Stille, J. K., and Anyos, T., *J. Polymer Sci.* **A2**, 1487 (1964).
27. Stille, J. K., Harris, F. W., Rakutis, R. O., and Mukamal, H., *J. Polymer Sci.* **B4**, 791 (1966).
28. Stille, J. K., and Plummer, L., *Abstr. 136th Meeting Am. Chem. Soc., Atlantic City* p. 3T (1959).
29. Stille, J. K., and Plummer, L., *J. Org. Chem.* **26**, 4026 (1961).
30. Upson, R. W., U.S. Patent 2,726,232 (E. I. duPont de Nemours & Co.) (1955); *Chem. Abstr.* **50**, 6835 (1956).

CHAPTER IV

Polymerization of Diisopropenyl Monomers and Other Carbocyclic Ring-Forming Polymerizations

A. Polymerization of Diisopropenyl Monomers

METHOD 1. WITH BF_3 OR $SnCl_4/HCl$ CATALYSTS

Treatment of p-diisopropenylbenzene with boron trifluoride in s-tetrachloroethane yields a polyindane (8).

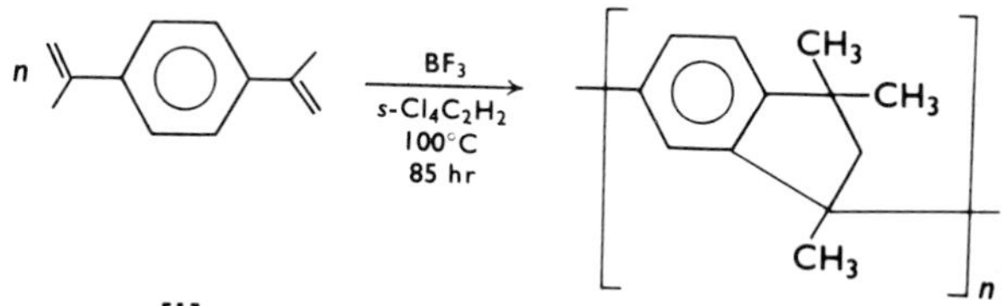

[1]   [2]

η_{red} 0.57   (IV-1)

The polymerization probably proceeds through the steps shown in (IV-3). Boron trifluoride and stannic chloride/hydrogen chloride are preferred catalysts (2, 25). The reaction can be performed in bulk (6) or in solution. The temperature at which the reaction is performed is very important: at below 80°C, a cross-linked insoluble polymer is obtained; saturated, linear, soluble polymers result at higher temperatures.

Other diisopropenyl derivatives were also polymerized to polyindanes. Linear, soluble polymers were obtained from m-diisopropenylbenzene and from the series of monomers represented by [7].

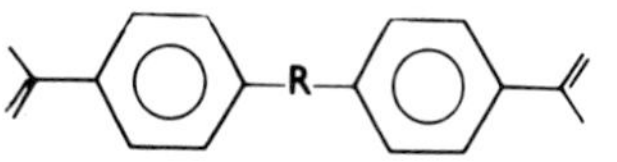

[7]   (IV-2)

$R = SO_2, CH_2, +CH_2)_2^-$

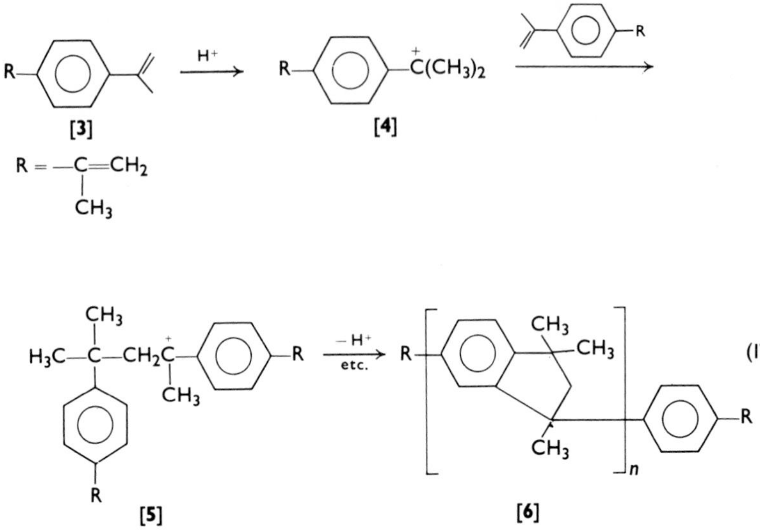

$$R = -\underset{\underset{CH_3}{|}}{C}=CH_2$$

(IV-3)

[5]   [6]

An interesting temperature effect was observed in the following reaction. At 80°C, the polyindane [9] was obtained (23). However, when the reaction was conducted at 200°C an unsaturated polymer resulted. It possessed structure [10].

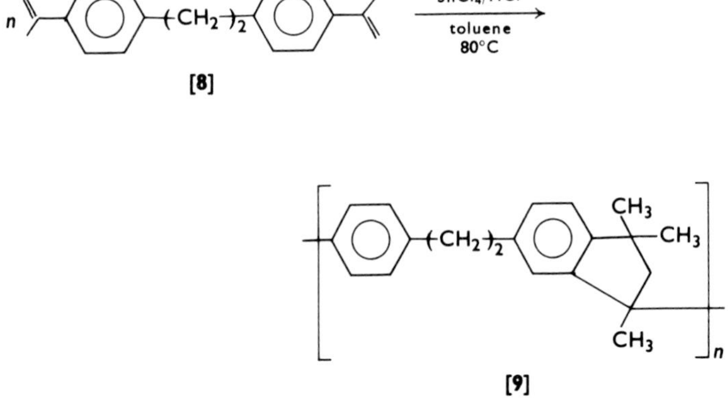

[8]

(IV-4)

[9]

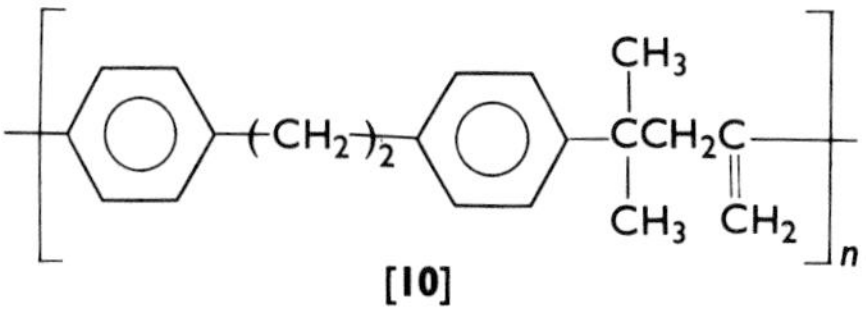

(IV-5)

[10]

Apparently, elimination to give the conjugated system is favored at higher temperatures.

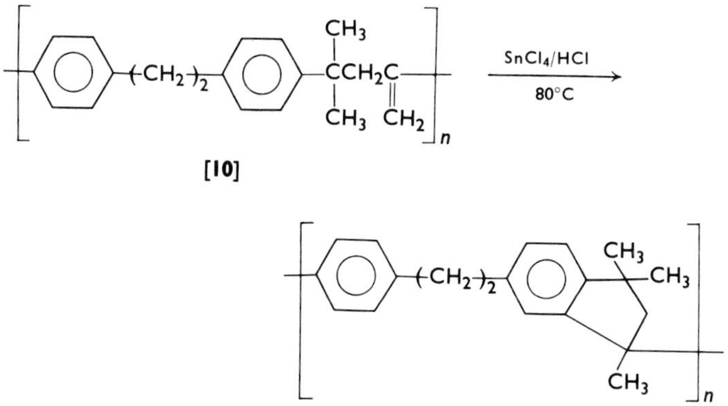

[10]

(IV-6)

[9]

A similar result was observed with the 4,4'-diisopropenyl derivative of diphenyl-methane (23, 25). Again, the structure of the polymeric product was governed by the reaction temperature employed, with ring formation being favored at temperatures below 100°C. Different results were obtained when R in [7] was oxygen, sulfur, or sulfone (24). Only unsaturated polymer resulted on treatment of [7; R = O or S] with $SnCl_4/HCl$ in toluene regardless of the polymerization temperature. On the other hand, with [7; R = SO_2], a polyindane was obtained at both 80° and 180°C. An explanation for this phenomenon was offered (24).

METHOD 2. WITH COMPLEX CATALYSTS

High molecular weight polyindanes were obtained from p-diisopropenyl-benzene using an insoluble complex catalyst of butyllithium/titanium tetra-chloride/hydrogen chloride (Li/Ti ratio of 1.0–2.0) in toluene (12). Polymers with reduced viscosities of 0.81 possessing less than 0.05% double bonds were obtained. Other complex catalysts, like triethylaluminum/tetrabutyltitanate/hydrogen chloride (Al/Ti ratio of 1.0–2.0) were also useful (12).

The polyindanes prepared from diisopropenyl monomers are listed in Table IV.1 (pp. 134–135).

B. Other Carbocyclic Ring-Forming Polymerizations

METHOD 1. POLYMERS FROM DIPHENYLDIACETYLENE

The thermal polymerization of diphenyldiacetylene *in vacuo* was claimed to yield a polymer possessing structure [12] with a molecular weight of approximately 1100 (*10*). It was soluble in solvents such as benzene, chloroform, ether, dioxane, and dimethylformamide and had excellent thermal stability. Its weight loss at 350°C was below 5% and no marked decomposition was observed even at 500°C. The material did not form peroxides with oxygen, and exhibited photoconductivity in the region of its optical absorption.

$$n\ C_6H_5C{\equiv}C{-}C{\equiv}CC_6H_5 \longrightarrow \qquad\qquad (\text{IV-7})$$

[11]

[12]

The polymerization of diphenyldiacetylene in the presence of vanadyl acetylacetonate and triethylaluminum gave an open-chain polymer (*10*) [13]. However, when tri(isobutyl)aluminum and titanium tetrachloride were used to catalyze polymerization of [11], the product was postulated to contain another type of repeat unit [14] (*35*). The soluble product from the latter polymerization possessed a cryoscopic molecular weight of 1270 and a softening point of 255°–260°C. It also had good heat resistance, losing only 3% of its weight after 6 hours at 250°C in argon. Definite catalytic activity toward the decomposition of nitrous oxide was exhibited by this product [12, 14].

$$nC_6H_5C{\equiv}CC{\equiv}CC_6H_5 \xrightarrow[\substack{(C_2H_5)_3Al \\ C_6H_6}]{\text{Vanadyl acetylacetonate}} \qquad\qquad (\text{IV-8})$$

[11]

[13]

iso-(C₄H₉)₃Al / TiCl₄

[14]   and units of structure [12]

METHOD 2. POLYMERIZATION OF 1,2,4,5-TETRABROMOBENZENE

Treatment of 1,2,4,5-tetrabromobenzene [15] with a sodium–potassium alloy yielded a polymer that presumably possessed structure [16] (30). The polymer is a yellow-red solid, partially soluble in ethanol and benzene.

$$\text{[15]} \qquad \xrightarrow{\text{Na–K}} \qquad \text{[16]} \qquad \qquad \text{(IV-9)}$$

METHOD 3. POLY(METHYL VINYL KETONES)

The polymer obtained by the base-catalyzed polymerization of methyl vinyl ketone was shown to contain the cyclic units [19] and [20] as well as the 1,2-polymer [18]. Infrared analysis was used to determine this fact (36). Increasing the polymerization temperature resulted in an increase of structures [19] and [20] in the polymer chain.

$$n\,CH_3COCH{=}CH_2 \xrightarrow{\text{tert-BuONa}} \left[CH_2CH{-}\underset{COCH_3}{\ } \right]_n \qquad \text{(IV-10)}$$

$$\text{[17]} \qquad \qquad \text{[18]}$$

$$\text{[19]} \qquad \qquad \text{[20]} \qquad \qquad \text{(IV-11)}$$

METHOD 4. POLYMERIZATION OF DIACETYL AND p-PHENYLENEDIAMINE

The polycondensation of diacetyl with p-phenylenediamine yields a dark-brown, amorphous powder that is soluble in dimethylformamide, formic acid, and sulfuric acid. Its structure was thought to be a poly(Schiff base). However, ozonization and infrared studies demonstrated that the most probable structure of the polymer was [23] (33). Since diacetyl dimerizes to a product which yields p-xyloquinone in basic medium, the polymer [23] could have arisen from the reaction of p-xyloquinone with the diamine (33).

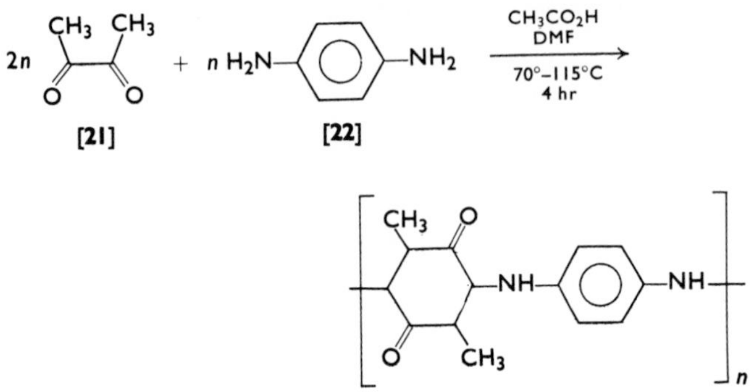

[21] [22]

[23]

(IV-12)

METHOD 5. FRIEDEL-CRAFTS POLYMERIZATIONS

The aluminum chloride-catalyzed condensation of methylene chloride with benzene yields several products (*19*).

$$\underset{[24]}{CH_2Cl_2} + \underset{[25]}{C_6H_6} \xrightarrow[\substack{40°–80°C \\ 4\ hr}]{AlCl_3} \begin{cases} \text{Diphenylmethane} \\ \text{Dibenzylbenzene} \\ \text{Polymeric residue} \end{cases} \qquad \text{(IV-13)}$$

The residue was identified as polybenzyl [**26**]. At a mole ratio of methylene chloride/benzene of 3.12/1 and in the presence of 4.3 % mole aluminum chloride (based on methylene chloride) the yield of polybenzyl was 64.9 %. The molecular weight of the polymer was 2970 and it was soluble in common organic solvents.

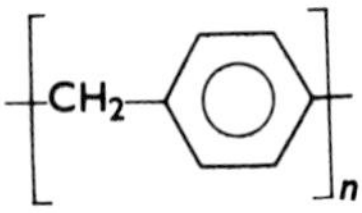

(IV-14)

[26]

A detailed study of the reaction and product has shown that some dihydroanthracene units are present in the chains (IV-15). Similar results were obtained from the condensation of halobenzenes with methylene chloride (*20*).

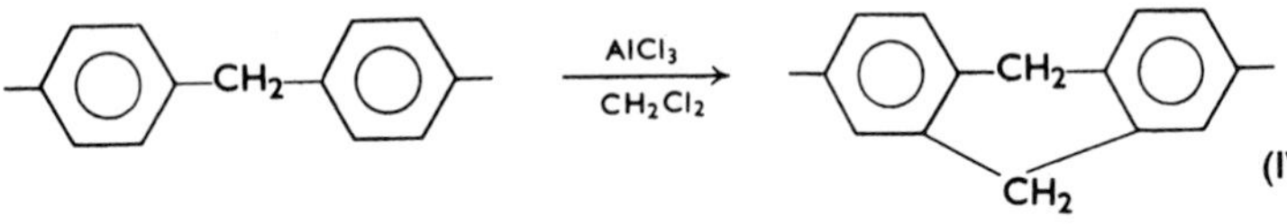

(IV-15)

[27] [28]

An interesting disproportionation of diphenylmethane has been reported (*21*).

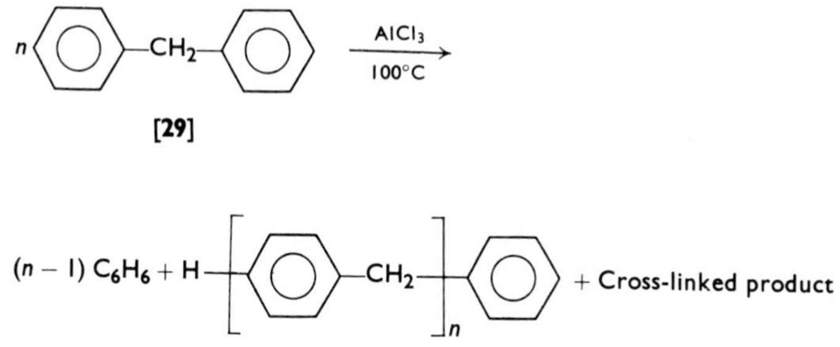

[29]

(IV-16)

$(n - 1)\ C_6H_6 + $ [25] [26] + Cross-linked product

Mol. wt. 2350

Dihydroanthracene units were also present in the polymer chain. Their formation was rationalized as follows:

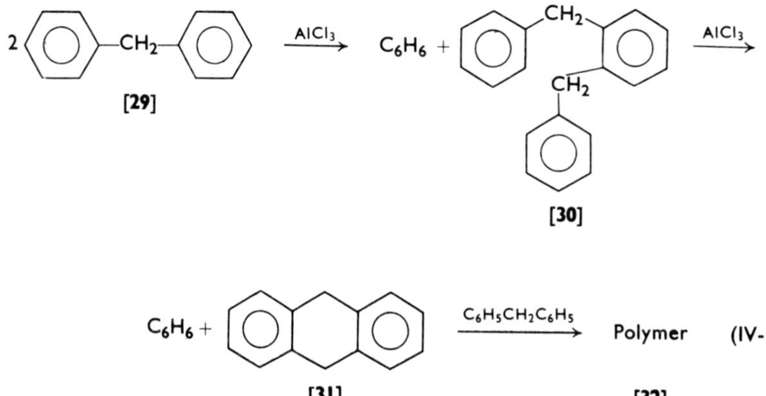

[29]   [30]

$C_6H_6 + $ [31] $\xrightarrow{C_6H_5CH_2C_6H_5}$ Polymer   (IV-17)

[32]

METHOD 6. POLYMERS FROM FERROCENE AND CARBONYL COMPOUNDS

A multicyclic soluble polymer was obtained from the zinc chloride-catalyzed condensation of ferrocene and acetone (IV-18) (*27, 28*). The polymer was a brown powder softening at 320°–360°C, and was soluble in benzene. Its molecular weight was determined cryoscopically and was about 3000. No crystallinity was detected by X-ray analysis. The material exhibits a signal in its ESR spectrum and has semiconducting properties. Its specific electroconductivity (50°C) was 1.23×10^{-12} ohm^{-1} cm^{-1} with an activation energy of 0.67 eV.

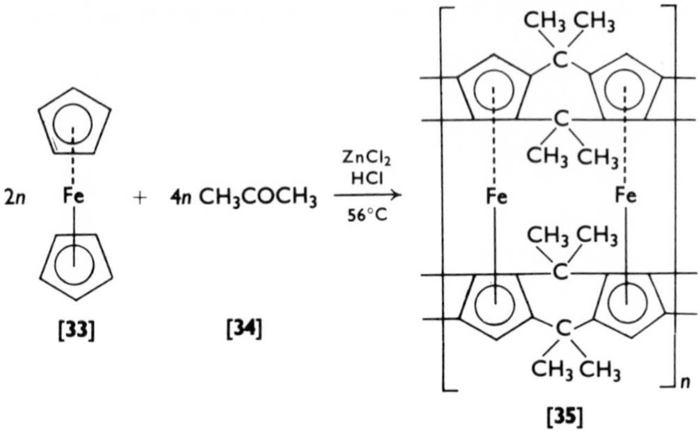

$$2n \quad [33] \quad + \quad 4n\ CH_3COCH_3 \quad \xrightarrow[56°C]{\underset{HCl}{ZnCl_2}} \quad [35] \qquad (IV\text{-}18)$$

[33]   [34]

[35]

o-Carboxybenzaldehyde and ferrocene polymerize to a polymer that contains phthalide structures in the repeat units. A soluble product is obtained when zinc chloride is used as catalyst at 115°C (*26*). The melting point of the product varies with its molecular weight. Fractions melting above 300°C possess number average molecular weight of 3000–6000. Brittle, transparent films could be cast from this product.

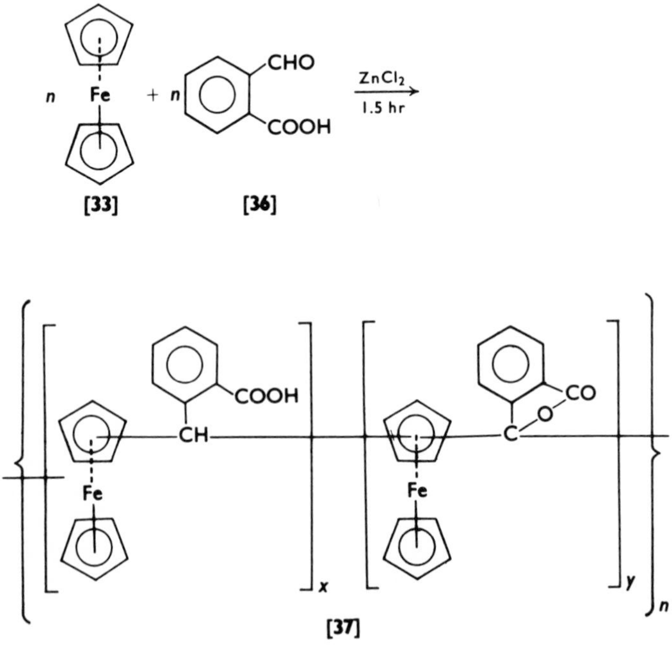

$$n \quad [33] \quad + \quad n \quad [36] \quad \xrightarrow[1.5\ hr]{ZnCl_2} \quad$$

[33]   [36]

$$[37] \qquad (IV\text{-}19)$$

[37]

The phthalide structure is felt to arise from condensation of [38] with ferrocene.

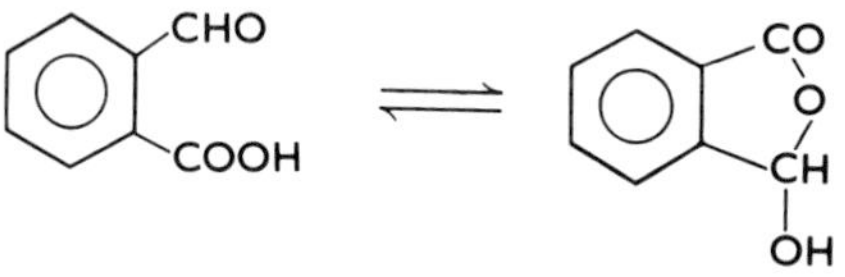

[36]   [38]

(IV-20)

METHOD 7. POLYMERS FROM POLYCYCLIC AROMATIC HYDROCARBONS AND ANHYDRIDES

The zinc chloride-catalyzed condensation of polycyclic aromatic hydrocarbons with pyromellitic dianhydride at temperatures of 250°–300°C yielded dark, insoluble, infusible polymers. Their structure was not unequivocally determined. Judging from what is known in the literature, they could possess either a quinone [39] or a lactone [40] type structure, with the former predominating (22, 30).

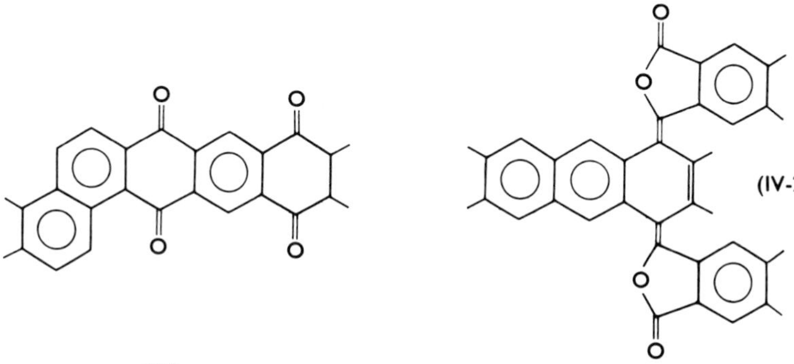

[39]   [40]

(IV-21)

The hydrocarbons used in this study included naphthalene, anthracene, phenanthrene, pyrene, chrysene, fluoranthene, perylene, dibenzopyrene, picene, biphenyl, and terphenyl. Polymers were also prepared from ferrocene (22, 30), acridine (22, 30), and anthraquinone (29). The polymers possessed semiconducting properties (1, 22, 29, 30). Room temperature resistivities are shown in the accompanying tabulation.

Resistivities of Polymers[a] from Aromatic Hydrocarbons and
Pyromellitic Dianhydride

Hydrocarbon	Resistivity (ohm cm) (25°C)	
	Polymerization at 253°C	Polymerization at 306°C
Naphthalene	9.7×10^6	1.4×10^6
Anthracene	8.3×10^5	3.2×10^5
Phenanthrene	1.0×10^5	9.2×10^4
Pyrene	1.6×10^4	7.6×10^3
Chrysene	1.6×10^5	2.1×10^4
Fluoranthene	4.4×10^5	3.5×10^5
Dibenzopyrene	—	9.5×10^2
Picene	—	1.6×10^4

[a] Molar ratios of hydrocarbon/pyromellitic dianhydride/zinc chloride = 1:1:2.

Condensation with phthalic anhydride also yielded polymeric materials. The structures of these products were not elucidated (*22, 30*). A somewhat different type of product was obtained from the condensation of pyromellitoyl chloride with polycyclic hydrocarbons in nitrobenzene with aluminum chloride (*22, 30*). Products varying in color from tan to purple-black resulted which were infusible and insoluble. Their room temperature resistivities were higher than those of the corresponding polymers prepared by the zinc chloride route. These higher resistivities may reflect lower molecular weights and/or a lower degree of conjugation. The room temperature resistivities for the two types of materials are shown in the second tabulation.

Effect of Catalyst on Resistivity of Aromatic Hydrocarbon–Anhydride Polymers

Hydrocarbon	Resistivity (ohm cm) (25°C)	
	$AlCl_3/C_6H_5NO_2$	$Zn\ Cl_2$
Naphthalene	1.6×10^{12}	1.4×10^6
Anthracene	1.5×10^8	3.2×10^5
Phenanthrene	7.8×10^{11}	1.0×10^5

METHOD 8. POLYMERS FROM BIS(KETENES)

Carbon suboxide can be considered to be the parent bis(ketene). It poly-merizes at room temperature in diethyl ether to yield yellow, red, or violet polymers. One recent structural study (*31*) on these soluble polymers concluded that the original structure proposed by Diels *et al.* (*11*) was correct. This structure is shown in Eq. (IV-22).

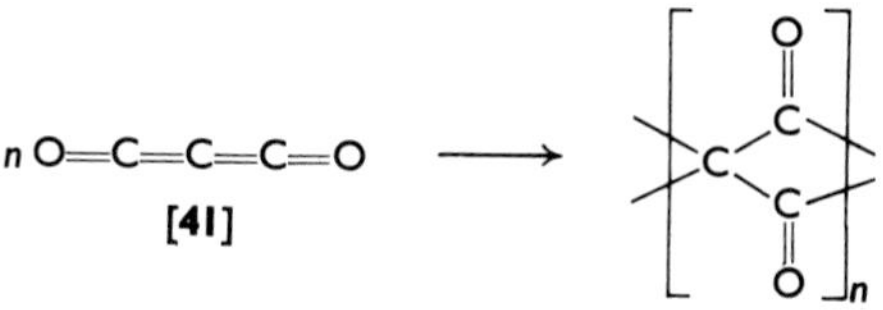

$$n\,O{=}C{=}C{=}C{=}O \longrightarrow \qquad\qquad\qquad (IV\text{-}22)$$

[41]

[42]

However, in the same year, another group concluded that the structure of the thermally initiated carbon suboxide polymer is [43] (*34*). Some resonance forms are also shown. X-ray data supported this planar, graphitic, hexagonal ring structure for the polymer. Polymers with different colors are produced by initiation at different temperatures and reflect molecular weight differences in the size of the conjugated system. Polymer produced at room temperature is water-soluble, but is insoluble in organic solvents. Thermally, poly(carbon suboxide) is reasonably stable up to 300°C, but turns to carbon at 500°C. A different polymer is produced when polymerization is initiated by ultraviolet light. Postulates about its structure are available (*34*).

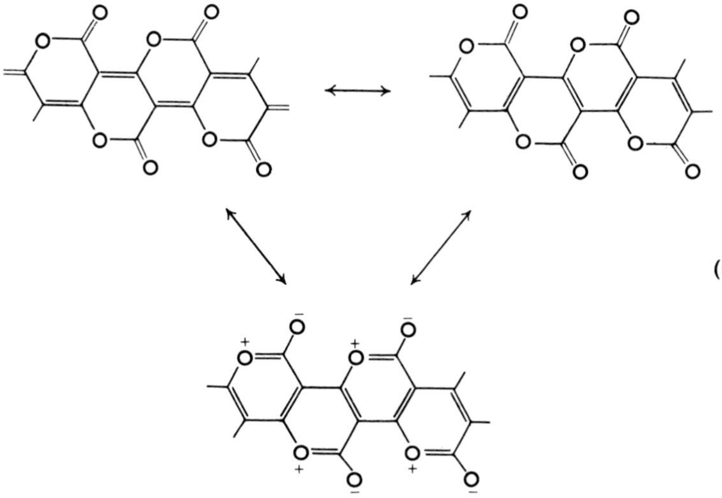

(IV-23)

[43]

The preparation of polymers from bis(ketenes) by the route shown in Eq. (IV-24) has been attempted (16–18, 37). Only ill-defined products resulted (3–5, 14, 16–18, 32, 37).

$$n \; \text{ClCOCH}_2\text{RCH}_2\text{COCl} \quad \xrightarrow[\text{solvent}]{\text{Base}} \quad n \; \text{O}{=}\text{C}{=}\text{CHRCH}{=}\text{C}{=}\text{O} \quad \longrightarrow$$

[44]   [45]

(IV-24)

[46]

METHOD 9. PHOTOINITIATED RING-FORMING POLYMERIZATIONS

A low yield of a polymer has been obtained from the phototelomerization of benzene in the presence of cyclooctene (9). The polymer was fractionated to yield fractions varying in molecular weight from less than 500 to 2000. Since the polymer possesses no aromatic NMR peaks or absorption in the ultraviolet, a saturated structure is indicated. The authors proposed structure [48] as being most probable, but did not rule out the presence of [49].

(IV-25)

[47]   [48]   [49]

Another interesting photoinitiated ring-forming polymerization is shown in Eq. (IV-26). Irradiation of dibenzylidenebenzene–diacetonitriles with incandescent light initiates their polymerization to cyclobutane ring-containing polymers. This can take place in the solid state and give soluble polymers. The product obtained from [50] possesses an intrinsic viscosity of 0.3 in sulfuric acid and melted at 320°C. Possible structures are shown in Eq. (IV-26). The polymers revert to monomer on heating with potassium hydroxide at about 300°C (15).

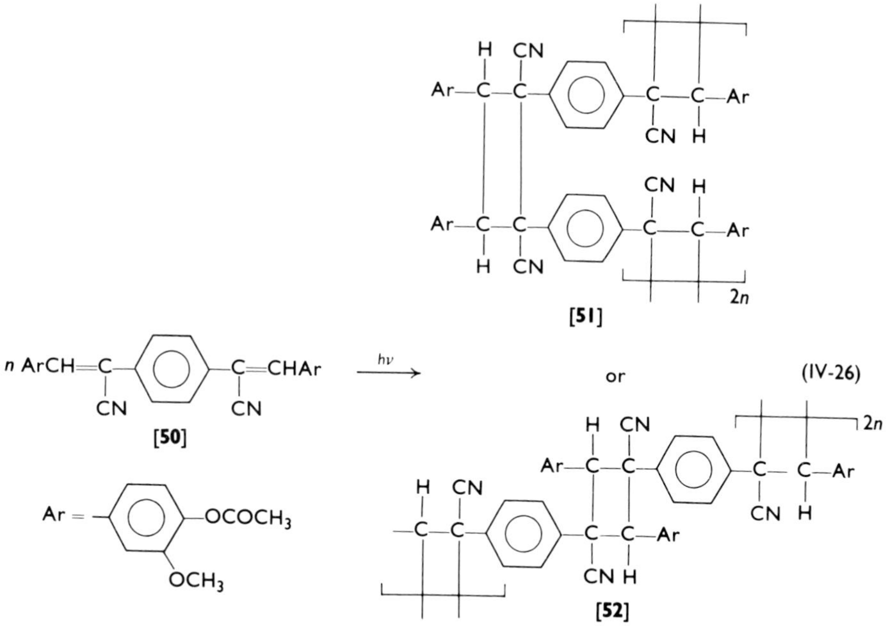

[51]

$$n \; ArCH{=}\underset{\underset{CN}{|}}{C} \overbrace{} \underset{\underset{CN}{|}}{C}{=}CHAr \xrightarrow{h\nu} \quad or \quad (IV\text{-}26)$$

[50]

$$Ar = \overbrace{} \begin{array}{l} OCOCH_3 \\ OCH_3 \end{array}$$

[52]

TABLE IV.1

Polymers from Diisopropenyl Monomers

No.	Monomers	Method	Molecular weight	Solubility	T_m (°C)	Remarks and property data	References
1	p-Diisopropenylbenzene [I]	A,1	η_{red} 0.57	Xylene, aliphatic hydrocarbons, s-tetrachloroethane	280–297	Structure supported by IR data	7, 8
		A,1	η_{red} >0.3	Xylene, aliphatic, aromatic hydrocarbons, CS_2, CCl_4	>240	Structure supported by IR data. Polymer claimed to be stable toward heat, oxidation, and hydrogenation	2, 6, 13, 25
		A,2	η_{red} 0.81	Benzene, toluene	280–290	Double-bond content in polymer <0.05% (Hanus IBr method)	12

2	*m*-Diisopropenylbenzene	A,1	η_{red} >0.3	Xylene, aliphatic hydrocarbons	—	—	*2, 6, 13*
3	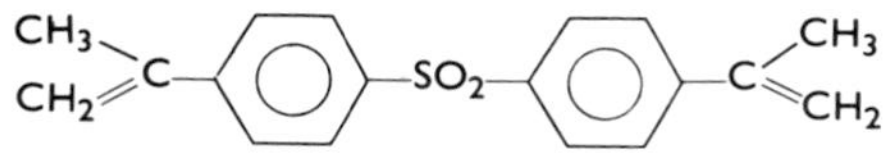	A,1	—	—	160	—	*24*
4	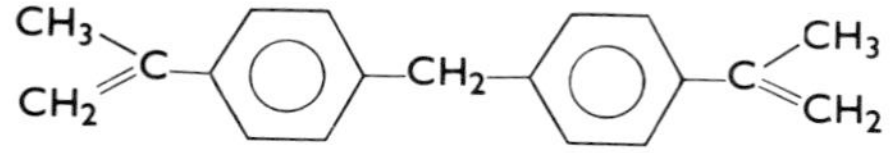	A,1	—	Aromatic hydrocarbons, CS_2, CCl_4	170	IR spectrum supports polymer structure. No residual unsaturation found in polymer	*24, 25*
5	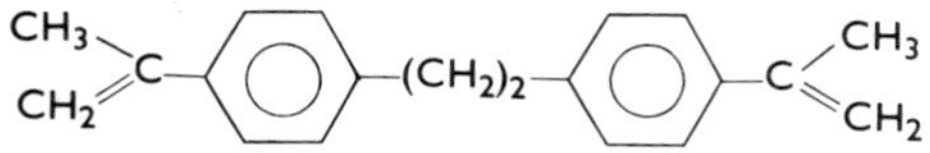	A,1	—	Aromatic hydrocarbons, CS_2, CCl_4	130	IR spectrum supports polymer structure. No residual unsaturation found in polymer	*23, 25*

REFERENCES

1. Baker, W. O., *J. Polymer Sci.* **C4**, 1633 (1964).
2. Belgian Patent 579,781 (issued to Imperial Chemical Industries) (1959).
3. Blomquist, A. T., and Meinwald, Y. C., *J. Am. Chem. Soc.* **79**, 2021 (1957).
4. Blomquist, A. T., and Spencer, R. R., *J. Am. Chem. Soc.* **69**, 472 (1947).
5. Blomquist, A. T., and Spencer, R. R., *J. Am. Chem. Soc.* **70**, 30 (1948).
6. Brunner, H., Palluel, A. L. L., and Walbridge, D. J., *J. Polymer Sci.* **28**, 629 (1958).
7. Brunner, H., and Walbridge, D. J., Australian Patent Appl. 25803/57 (1956).
8. Brunner, H., and Walbridge, D. J., British Patent 864,275 (Imperial Chemical Industries) (1961); *Chem. Abstr.* **55**, 17080 (1961).
9. Bryce-Smith, D., and Gilbert, A., *Chem. Commun.* No. 18, 643 (1966); *Chem. Abstr.* **65**, 18698 (1966).
10. Davydov, B. E., Demidova, G. N., Pirtskhalava, R. N., and Rozenshtein, L. D., *Elektrokhimiya* **1**, 876 (1965); *Chem. Abstr.* **63**, 14988 (1965).
11. Diels, O., Beckmann, R., and Tönnies, G., *Ann. Chem.* **439**, 76 (1924); *Chem. Abstr.* **19**, 40 (1925).
12. D'Onofrio, A. A., *J. Appl. Polymer Sci.* **8**, 521 (1964).
13. French Patent 1,172,725 (issued to Imperial Chemical Industries) (1959).
14. Hatchard, W. R., and Schneider, A. K., *J. Am. Chem. Soc.* **79**, 6261 (1957).
15. Holm, M. J., and Zienty, F. B., U.S. Patent 3,312,668 (Monsanto Co.) (1967); *Chem. Abstr.* **67**, 1174, 12151w (1967).
16. Kaye, H., Quart. Progr. Rept. No. 4, Contract No. AF33(657)-10889 (1964).
17. Kaye, H., Tech. Doc. Rept. ML-TDR-64-80, Part II, p. 33 (1965).
18. Kaye, H., *Dissertation Abstr.* **26**, 2475 (1965); *Chem. Abstr.* **64**, 6777 (1966).
19. Kolesnikov, G. S., Korshak, V. V., and Smirnova, T. V., *Bull. Acad. Sci. USSR, Div. Chem. Sci. (English Transl.)* p. 383 (1957).
20. Kolesnikov, G. S., Korshak, V. V., and Smirnova, T. V., *Bull. Acad. Sci. USSR, Div. Chem. Sci. (English Transl.)* p. 1498 (1957).
21. Kolesnikov, G. S., Korshak, V. V., Smirnova, T. V., and Fedorova, L. S., *Izv. Akad. Nauk SSSR, Otd. Khim. Nauk* p. 767 (1958).
22. Marschalk, C. M., *Bull. Soc. Chim. France* **9**, 400 (1942).
23. Mitin, Yu. V., *Vysokolmolekul. Soedin.* **6**, 484 (1964); *Polymer Sci. (USSR) (English Transl.)* **6**, 535 (1964); *Resins, Rubbers, Plastics* p. 545 (1965).
24. Mitin, Yu. V., and D'yachenko, T. D., *J. Gen. Chem. USSR (English Transl.)* **34**, 1098 (1964).
25. Mitin, Yu. V., and Glukhov, N. A., *Dokl. Akad. Nauk SSSR* **115**, 97 (1957); *Chem. Abstr.* **52**, 5341 (1958).
26. Neuse, E. W., and Koda, K., *J. Polymer Sci.* **A-1,4**, 2145 (1966); *Chem. Abstr.* **65**, 17055 (1966).
27. Paushkin, I. M., Polak, L. S., Vishnyakova, T. P., Patalakh, I. I., Machus, F. F., and Sokolinskaya, T. A., *J. Polymer Sci.* **C4**, 1481 (1964).
28. Paushkin, Ya. M., Vishnyakova, T. P., Patalakh, I. I., Sokolinskaya, T. A., and Machus, F. F., *Proc. Acad. Sci. USSR, Chem. Sect. (English Transl.)* **149**, 296 (1963).
29. Pohl, H. A., *Electro-Technol. (New York)* **67**, 85 (1961).
30. Pohl, H. A., and Engelhardt, E. H., *J. Phys. Chem.* **66**, 2085 (1962).
31. Porejko, S., Makurak, L., and Gabara, W., *Polimery* **8**, 293 (1963); *Chem. Abstr.* **66**, 338, 2924f (1967).
32. Sauer, J. C., *J. Am. Chem. Soc.* **69**, 2444 (1947).
33. Shirokova, M. N., and Yakubchik, A. I., *Vysokomolekul. Soedin.* **8**, 312 (1966); *Chem. Abstr.* **64**, 14291 (1966).

34. Smith, R. N., Young, D. A., Smith E. N., and Carter, C. C., *Inorg. Chem.* **2**, 829 (1963); *Resins, Rubbers, Plastics* 1029 (1964).
35. Teyssié, P., and Korn-Girard, A., *J. Polymer Sci.* **A2**, 2849 (1964).
36. Trossarelli, L., Guaita, M., and Priola, A., *Ric. Sci.*, *Rend.* [2] **A7**, 451 (1964); *Chem. Abstr.* **63**, 3045 (1965).
37. Witzel, J. M., Ph.D. Thesis, Cornell University.

CHAPTER V

Metallorganic Ring-Containing Polymers of Unsaturated Carbon Compounds

This chapter serves as an introduction to the fact that many polymeric materials in the literature were not made deliberately by synthetic polymer chemists. Rather, in the course of their characterization, they were found to be polymeric. In reviewing coordination polymers, Block (7) has described this type of material as a "natural coordination polymer." Natural is used here in the sense that they are polymeric because of the structure (crystalline, or otherwise) that they naturally assume to fulfill bonding requirements. Thus, in many of these cases, the assigned polymeric structures are existent only in the solid state because the materials are insoluble, or soluble only when they have reacted with the solvent or reagent under study. Members of this class of materials that possess rings formed during their preparation are discussed below. Since polymers of this type are frequently buried in nonpolymer publications, a comprehensive survey was not possible.

METHOD 1. REACTIONS OF UNSATURATED COMPOUNDS WITH INORGANIC SALTS

Alkyl- and arylethynyl copper [1] and silver compounds are a case in point (6, 14). These compounds are insoluble in solvents with which they do not react and are pictured to possess the structure shown. Substantial back-coordination from filled copper d orbitals to the antibonding orbitals of at least two acetylene groups bound to the metal is thought to account for three-membered ring formation. A strong donor with back-coordinating properties, like triethylphosphine, will readily dissolve propynyl copper to form $(C_2H_5)_3PCuC\equiv CCH_3$. It was unaffected by a variety of amines. The structure of the phosphine–metal acetylides has been investigated (8, 9). Trimethylphosphine–copper phenylacetylide was found to be a tetramer by a crystallographic study (9).

Recrystallization of silver perchlorate from benzene leads to formation of the complex $C_6H_6 \cdot AgClO_4$. The crystals are stable under a vapor pressure of

$$\begin{array}{c} R \\ \| \\ C \\ -Cu \leftarrow \| \| \\ C \\ Cu \\ \uparrow \\ RC\!\equiv\!CCu \leftarrow \end{array}$$

(V-1)

[1]

benzene but decompose rapidly in air. A detailed crystallographic study (16, 17) showed that this complex possessed structure [2]. Surprisingly, the benzene ring in the complex was found to be distorted since the C—C bonds nearest the silver ions were 0.08 Å shorter than the other four bonds in the ring. Comprehensive bond angle and bond distance data are available (17).

(V-2)

[2]

A very similar study has been performed on the complex formed from silver nitrate and cyclooctatetraene (12, 13). This polymeric complex is obtained by reaction of aqueous silver nitrate with cyclooctatetraene dissolved in petroleum ether. Like the benzene–silver perchlorate described above, this complex decomposes readily and hence was examined in an atmosphere of the ligand. Complete bond distance and angle data are available for its structure as shown in Table V.1 (13). The molecular structure of the 1 : 1 silver nitrate–cyclo-octatetraene dimer has been determined by X-ray crystallographic analysis (15).

Norbornadiene (NBD) forms two different complexes with silver nitrate, $NBD \cdot AgNO_3$ (18, 19) and $NBD \cdot 2AgNO_3$ (1, 18, 19). The latter complex, for which a crystal structure has recently been reported (2), can be obtained by adding NBD to an aqueous solution of silver nitrate. The crystals that separated were recrystallized from ethanol. Each double bond in the norbornadiene molecule is coordinated to a silver atom in a triangular-planar configuration. The NBD molecule then serves to cross-link two $AgNO_3$ chains.

(V-3)

[3]

Similar studies have been reported for the complexes of norbornadiene with cuprous chloride (3) and palladium chloride (4). A complex of 1,3- and 1,4-cyclooctadiene with palladium chloride has been reported to be a useful catalyst for the polymerization of olefins (5).

METHOD 2. REACTION OF METAL COMPLEXES OF POLYENES WITH POLYENES

The nickel(0) complex of cyclooctatetraene has been reported and adjudged to be polymeric, but of unknown molecular weight (20). Reaction of cyclo-dodecatrienenickel(0) with cyclooctatetraene gave a yellow intermediate that led to a black, metallic-appearing crystalline product of empirical formula C_8H_8Ni. The product was not sublimable without decomposition in vacuum, dissolved in benzene with a deep red color, and was hydrogenated to nickel and the corresponding amount of cyclooctane.

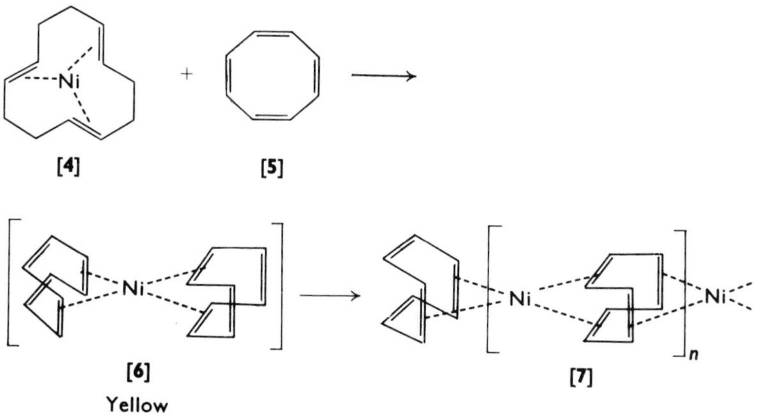

[4]   [5]

[6]   [7]   (V-4)

Yellow

METHOD 3. REACTION OF SODIOBIS(CYCLIC DIENES) WITH INORGANIC SALTS

Polymerization of some α,ω-bis(cyclopentadienyl)alkanes with iron salts has been reported (10, 11). Reaction of the disodio derivatives of the bis(cyclo-pentadienes) with ferrous chloride in tetrahydrofuran led to polymers and oligomers possessing the ferrocene structure. The polymers were qualitatively described as viscous, brown oils. No quantitative molecular weight data on the polymeric products were obtained.

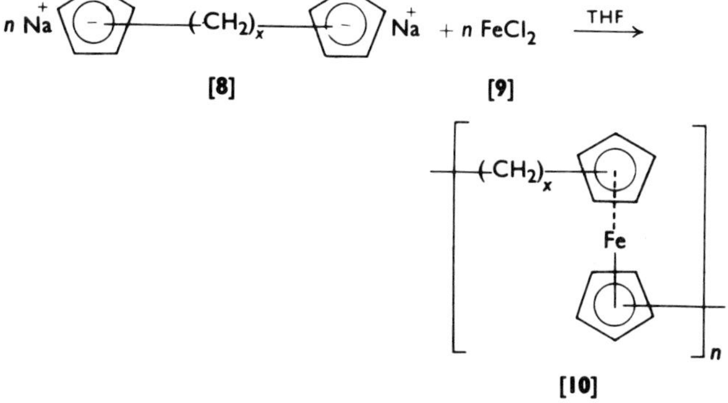

[8]   [9]

+ 2n NaCl   (V-5)

[10]

TABLE V.1

Coordination Polymers of Metals and Unsaturated Carbon Compounds

No.	Structure	Metal (M)	Method	Color	Solubility	References
1	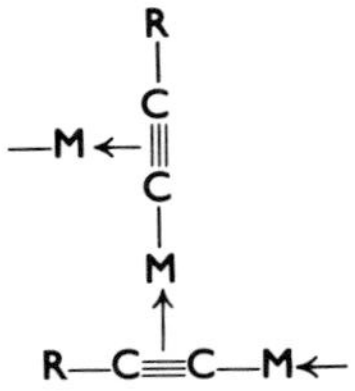 R = alkyl, aryl [1]	Cu(I)	1	Yellow, red	Insoluble	6, 14
2	ClO$_4^-$ [2]	Ag(I)	1	Colorless	Inert solvents, when R = tert-butyl	6, 14
	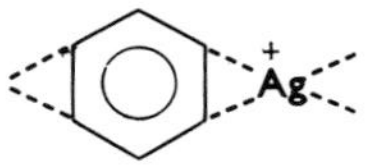	Ag(I)	1	—	—	16, 17
3	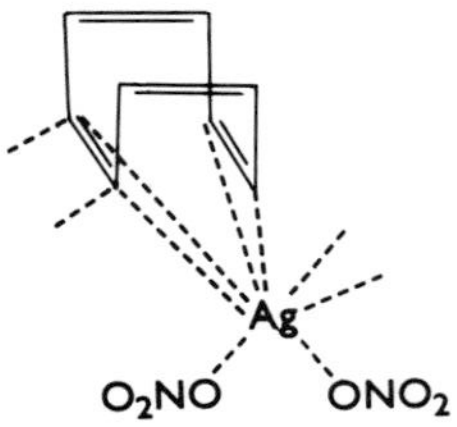	Ag(I)	1	Cream	—	12, 13

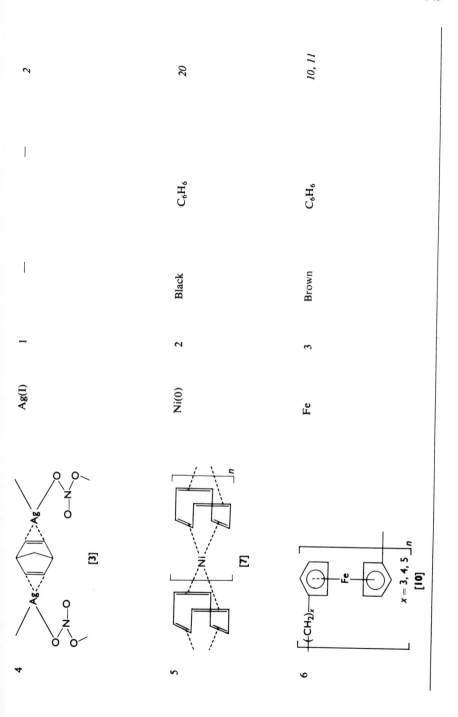

4	Ag(I)	1	—	—	2	[3]
5	Ni(0)	2	Black	C_6H_6	20	[7]
6	Fe	3	Brown	C_6H_6	10, 11	[10]

$x = 3, 4, 5$

REFERENCES

1. Abel, E. W., Bennett, M. A., and Wilkinson, G., *J. Chem. Soc.* p. 3178 (1959).
2. Baenziger, N. C., Haight, H. L., Alexander, R. J., and Doyle, J. R., *Inorg. Chem.* 5, 1399 (1966).
3. Baenziger, N. C., Haight, H. L., and Doyle, J. R., *Inorg. Chem.* 3, 1535 (1964).
4. Baenziger, N. C., Richards, G. F., and Doyle, J. R., *Acta Cryst.* 18, 924 (1965).
5. Belgian Patent 682,319 (issued to U.S. Rubber Co.) (1966).
6. Blake, D., Calvin, G., and Coates, G. E., *Proc. Chem. Soc.* p. 396 (1959).
7. Block, B. P., *in* "Inorganic Polymers" (F. G. A. Stone and W. A. G. Graham, eds.), p. 447. Academic Press, New York, 1962.
8. Coates, G. E., and Parkin, C., *J. Inorg. & Nucl. Chem.* 22, 59 (1961).
9. Corfield, P. W. R., and Shearer, H. M. M., *Acta Cryst.* 21, 957 (1966).
10. Luttringhaus, A., and Kullick, W., *Angew. Chem.* 70, 438 (1958).
11. Luttringhaus, A., and Kullick, W., *Makromol. Chem.* 44-46, 669 (1961).
12. Matthews, F. S., and Lipscomb, W. N., *J. Am. Chem. Soc.* 80, 4745 (1958).
13. Matthews, F. S., and Lipscomb, W. N., *J. Phys. Chem.* 63, 845 (1959).
14. Myl'nikov, V. S., *Russ. J. Phys. Chem. (English Transl.)* 40, 527 (1966).
15. Nyburg, S. C., and Hilton, J., *Acta Cryst.* 12, 116 (1959).
16. Rundle, R. E., and Goring, J. H., *J. Am. Chem. Soc.* 72, 5337 (1950).
17. Smith, H. G., and Rundle, R. E., *J. Am. Chem. Soc.* 80, 5075 (1958).
18. Traynham, J. G., *J. Org. Chem.* 26, 4694 (1961).
19. Traynham, J. G., and Olechowski, J. R., *J. Am. Chem. Soc.* 81, 571 (1959).
20. Wilke, G., *Angew. Chem.*, 72, 581 (1960).

CHAPTER VI

Metallorganic Ring Polymers from Nitrogen Chelate Ligands

A. Coordination Polymers of Metals and Nitrogenous Bases

Polymers formed from nitrogenous bases and metals are reminiscent of the metal–carbon ligand polymers discussed in Chapter V. In most instances, these products have also mainly attracted the interest of structural chemists. Physico-chemical data obtained from their studies supported the existence of polymeric structures in these materials.

METHOD 1. POLYMERIZATION OF IMIDAZOLES

Bis(imidazolato) metal polymers were obtained by reaction of imidazole with metal sulfates (20, 36). Temperatures near 100°C were used. The insolu-bility of the polymers prevented the determination of molecular weights. Several modifications of bis(imidazolato)copper(II) have been prepared and their magnetic properties studied in detail (36, 37). The magnetic behavior of the brown modification was interpreted to suggest the presence of the poly-meric structure (37). The cobalt- and zinc-containing materials possessed very high thermal stabilities, with weight loss being detectable at 500°–575°C in

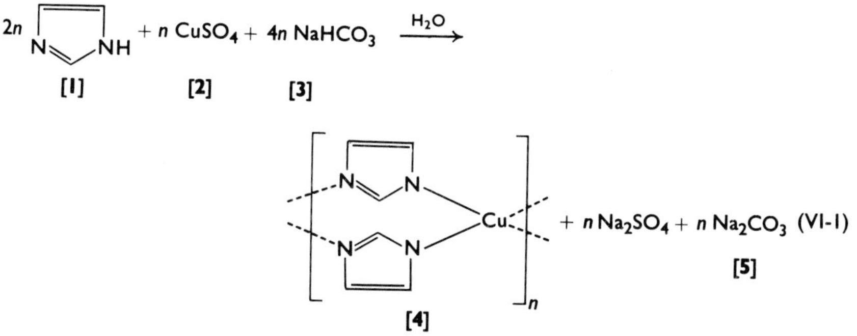

$$2n \left[\text{N} \diagup \text{NH} \right]_{[1]} + n\, CuSO_4 + 4n\, NaHCO_3 \xrightarrow{\ H_2O\ }$$

[1]   [2]   [3]

$$\left[\begin{array}{c} \text{N} = \text{N} \\ \text{N} = \text{N} \end{array} \text{Cu} \right]_{n} + n\, Na_2SO_4 + n\, Na_2CO_3 \quad (VI\text{-}1)$$

[4]   [5]

nitrogen. Electrical resistivities of these polymers were measured and found to be higher than that of imidazole itself. This result was contrary to expectations but plausible reasons were postulated to explain this fact.

The condensation of diamines with pyrazolyltetrazadiborines or triazolyl-tetrazadiborines yields polymers that are related to the imidazolato metal polymers (66). The product obtained from the polymerization in (VI-2) was described as being a solid resin.

METHOD 2. POLYMERS FROM METALS AND ALKYLENEDIAMINES, PYRIDINES, PYRAZINES, AND DINITRILES

Chromium(III) chloride has been polymerized with alkylenediamines, $H_2N(CH_2)_nNH_2$, under anhydrous conditions. When $n \geqslant 4$, polymeric complexes were obtained (63). They ($[Cr(diamine)_2Cl_2]Cl$) were thought to possess a polymeric sheet structure with octahedral coordination.

Pyridine forms complexes [9] with Mn(II), Co(II), and Cu(II) chlorides (27, 32, 56, 68). From magnetic measurements, a polymeric structure was postulated for these materials. Octahedral coordination with double chloride bridging between metal atoms (56) has been confirmed by subsequent crystallo-graphic structure determinations (27, 32). The heat of dissociation of the poly-meric, octahedral form of $Co(C_5H_5N)_2Cl_2$ to the monomeric tetrahedral form was only 3.2 kcal/mole (68). Thus, the backbone in polymers of this type is not very strong. Pyrazine, which is structurally similar to pyridine, also reacts with metal salts to produce polymers (50) for which sheetlike structures have been proposed [10]. The structure suggested consists of trans double halide-bridged octahedra linked together by pyrazine molecules, so that there is double bridging in one direction in the sheet and single bridging in the other. Thermochemical data for the decomposition of a large number of pyrazine and methylpyrazine complexes are available and support this structure (7).

[9]   [10]

(VI-3)

Polymeric complex cationic structures have been postulated for copper nitrate complexes of dinitriles, $[Cu(NC(CH_2)_nCN)_2]NO_3$. In the case of succinonitrile ($n = 2$) the dinitrile molecules act as double bridging groups between tetrahedral Cu(I) ions (44). Bond distances indicated substantial covalent character. For glutaronitrile, a two-dimensional polymeric cation based on tetrahedral copper(I) atoms and discrete nitrate anions was postulated (45). All of the copper atoms in planes perpendicular to the c axis are linked together by bridging glutaronitrile groups with the copper-to-nitrogen bond distances slightly less than the sum of the tetrahedral covalent radii. Thus, the addition of one carbon atom to the chain between the nitrile groups has led to an entirely different stereochemistry. In the case of the analogous adiponitrile complex, a three-dimensional four-connected network of copper atoms held together by dinitrile molecules was found (43).

B. Polymers from Bis(1,2-dioximes)

One of the best known chelate compounds is nickel dimethylglyoxime. Its formation and isolation represent a widely used specific analytical method for nickel. Structural studies (6) have shown the presence of a metal–metal interaction in the crystal that has been estimated at 10 kcal/mole. This fact has been suggested as the basis for its water insolubility and, of course, indicates that it is polymeric [11]. A study that varied the dioxime ligand and, hence, the metal–metal distance, was made to see if solubility were directly related to this feature (6). But the solubilities of the chelates that were prepared were found to be as dependent on the specific ligand as they were on the metal–metal distance. This was true in water and organic solvents.

$$
\left[
\begin{array}{c}
\text{H}_3\text{C} \diagdown \underset{\diagup}{\text{C}}{=}\text{N} \quad \overset{\text{O}\diagup\text{H}\cdots\text{O}}{\mid} \quad \text{N}{=}\underset{\diagdown}{\text{C}} \diagup \text{CH}_3 \\
\mid \text{-----Ni----} \mid \\
\text{H}_3\text{C} \diagup \underset{}{\text{C}}{=}\text{N} \quad \text{N}{=}\underset{}{\text{C}} \diagdown \text{CH}_3 \\
\text{O} \cdots\text{H}\diagup \text{O}
\end{array}
\right]_n
$$

(VI-4)

[11]

METHOD 1. POLYMERIZATION OF BIS (1,2-DIOXIMES) WITH METALS OR METAL SALTS

Bis(1,2-dioximes) have been polymerized with metals. Reaction of nickel acetate in methanol with or without sodium acetate yields high polymer (*39, 40*).

$$
n\,\underset{\text{[12]}}{\text{CH}_3\overset{\text{HON}}{\underset{\parallel}{\text{C}}}{-}\overset{\text{NOH}}{\underset{\parallel}{\text{C}}}{-}\text{R}{-}\overset{\text{HON}}{\underset{\parallel}{\text{C}}}{-}\overset{\text{NOH}}{\underset{\parallel}{\text{C}}}\text{CCH}_3} + n\,\underset{\text{[13]}}{\text{Ni}(\text{C}_2\text{H}_3\text{O}_2)_2} \longrightarrow
$$

$$
\left[
\begin{array}{c}
\text{R}{-}\text{C}{-}\text{C}{-}\text{CH}_3 \\
\parallel \quad \parallel \\
\text{O}{-}\text{N} \quad \text{N}{-}\text{O} \\
\text{H} \quad \text{Ni} \quad \text{H} \\
\text{O}{-}\text{N} \quad \text{N}{-}\text{O} \\
\parallel \quad \parallel \\
\text{H}_3\text{C}{-}\text{C}{-}\text{C}
\end{array}
\right]_n
\quad + 2n\,\text{CH}_3\text{CO}_2\text{H} \quad \text{(VI-5)}
$$

[14]   [15]

When R was

$$
-1,4\text{-C}_6\text{H}_4{-}\text{O}{-}1,4\text{-C}_6\text{H}_4-
$$

[16]

a polymer fraction that possessed an osmometric molecular weight of 20,000 was obtained. Metal bis(1,2-dioximates) have also been prepared in dimethyl formamide with or without added ammonia by the reaction shown in (VI-5). High molecular weights were not obtained even though several different bis-(1,2-dioximes) were used (*57*).

The reaction of a bis(1,2-dioxime) with elemental nickel to yield the chelate has been described (*39, 40*).

$$n \; C_6H_5\overset{\overset{\textstyle HON}{\|}}{C}\overset{\overset{\textstyle NOH}{\|}}{C} CH_2CH_2 \overset{\overset{\textstyle HON}{\|}}{C}\overset{\overset{\textstyle NOH}{\|}}{C} C_6H_5 + n \; Ni^0 \xrightarrow{\;C_5H_5N\;}$$

     [17]   [18]

$$\left[\begin{array}{c} CH_2CH_2C\!-\!C\!-\!C_6H_5 \\ \text{...} \\ O\!-\!N\quad N\!-\!O \\ H \quad Ni \quad H \\ O\!-\!N\quad N\!-\!O \\ H_5C_6\!-\!C\!-\!C \end{array} \right]_n \qquad (+\,2n\,H) \quad (VI\text{-}6)$$

     [19]   [20]

This reaction was not general, since the bis(1,2-dioximes) shown in Eq. (VI-5) with R being

$$-1,4\text{-}C_6H_4\!-\!X\!-\!1,4\text{-}C_6H_4\!-$$

     [21]

$$X = -\!; -CH_2\!-; -(CH_2)_2\!-; -(CH_2)_3\!-; -O\!-$$

did not react.

The bulk polymerization of 1,2-dioximes with metals has been described (35). A polymer containing 1,2-dioxime groups, prepared by nitrosating an ethylene/carbon monoxide copolymer, was cross-linked by exchange at 200°C with tris(ethyl acetoacetato)aluminum to yield tough, insoluble films.

$$\left[CH_2\!-\!\overset{\overset{\textstyle}{}}{C}\!-\!\overset{\overset{\textstyle}{}}{C}\! \right]_n + \; Al \!\!\left[\begin{array}{c} CH_3 \\ O\!=\!C \\ CH \\ O\!-\!C \\ OC_2H_5 \end{array} \right]_3 \longrightarrow$$

    (structure [22] with HON NOH)   [23]

[22]   [23]

$$\left[\begin{array}{c} CH_2\!-\!C\!-\!C \\ H\!\cdots\!O\!-\!N\quad N\!-\!O\!\cdots\!H \\ O\quad Al \quad O \\ N \qquad N \\ -C \qquad C- \end{array} \right]_n + \; CH_3\overset{\overset{\textstyle O}{\|}}{C}CH_2\overset{\overset{\textstyle O}{\|}}{C}OC_2H_5 \quad (VI\text{-}7)$$

     [24]

Pyridine is the most general solvent for metal bis(1,2-dioximates). The possibility that its solvent power was due to its coordination with the Ni(II) in the polymer was investigated ($39, 40$). However, recovery of polymer from pyridine solutions free of coordinated pyridine did not substantiate this possibility. The melting data that are available for poly[metal bis(1,2-dioximates)] show that they are infusible. The cases for which decomposition temperatures are listed in Table VI.2 (p. 162) are only temperatures at which color changes were observed. No melting or visible decomposition was observed. Crystallinity has been detected in some of these polymers by X-ray diffraction.

The formation of cyclic monomers and dimers was offered to explain the failure of the ligands in (VI-8) to yield high polymer. The absence of infrared absorptions characteristic of oxime end groups and the low ebullioscopic molecular weights of the products supported this theory (57).

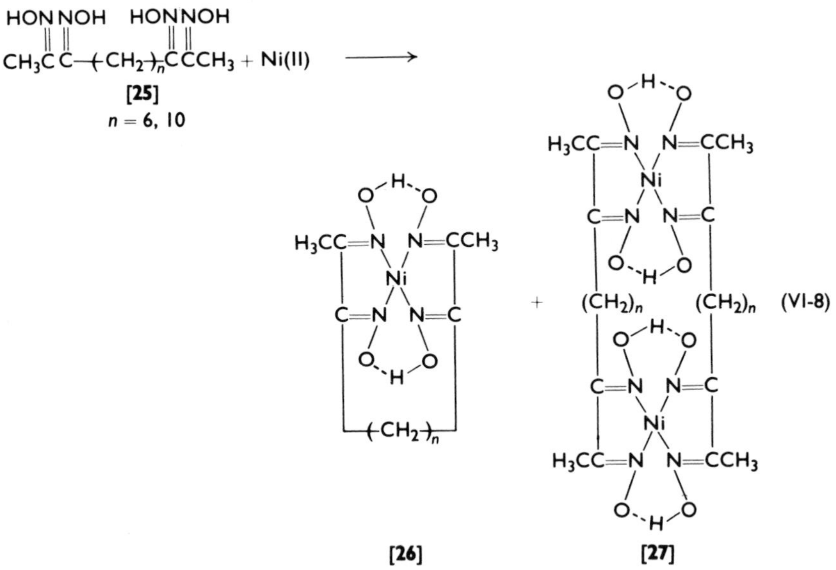

Polymerization of the dioxime of resorcinol-2,4-dialdehyde with Cu(II) has been reported (60).

C. Metal–Tetracyanoethylene Polymers

METHOD 1. POLYMERIZATION OF TETRACYANOETHYLENE AND RELATED TETRANITRILES WITH METALS, METAL SALTS, OR METAL CHELATES

A unique class of metal-containing polymers prepared by a ring-forming polymerization is derived from the reaction of tetracyanoethylene with metals

(8). The structures that have been postulated for the products resemble metal phthalocyanines, but are unique in that they contain no hydrogen. Heating powdered metals or their salts with tetracyanoethylene (TCNE) in bulk or with solvents at temperatures up to 300°C yields polymers as black, infusible products. Simultaneous preparation of the polymer and a fabricated part by heating the reactants in a mold has been described (12).

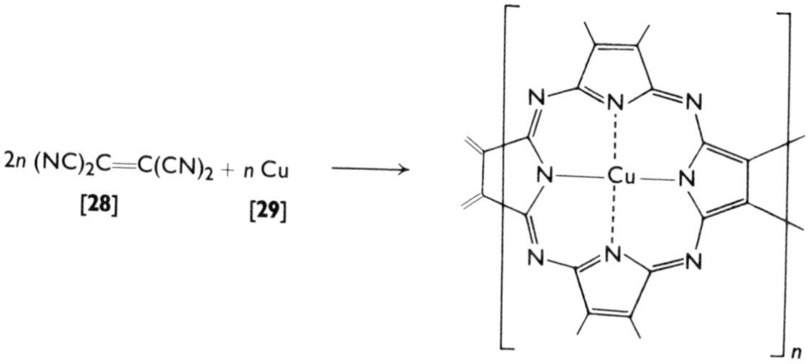

$$2n \ (NC)_2C{=\!\!=}C(CN)_2 + n \ Cu \longrightarrow$$

[28]   [29]

(VI-9)

[30]

Copolymers derived from substituting phthalonitrile for part of the TCNE are thought to possess structure [32]. The functionality of the reactants should lead to the rodlike structure [32] versus the sheetlike structure of the TCNE–metal homopolymer.

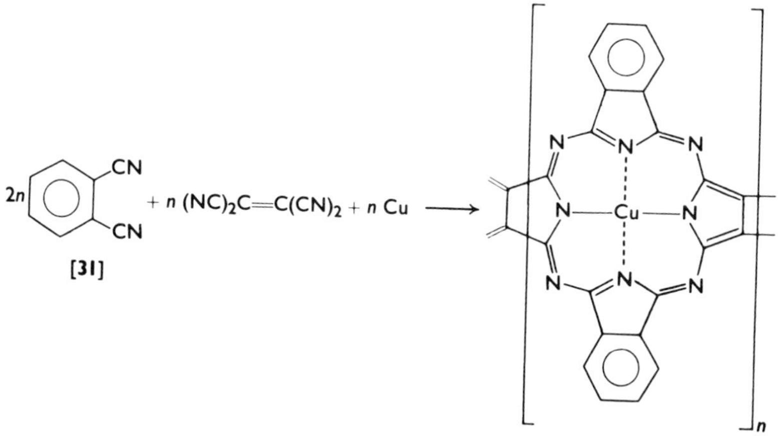

$$2n \ \begin{array}{c} CN \\ CN \end{array} + n \ (NC)_2C{=\!\!=}C(CN)_2 + n \ Cu \longrightarrow$$

[31]

(VI-10)

[32]

Ligand exchange between metal acetylacetonates and TCNE has also been used to prepare these polymers (VI-11). Reaction in bulk (42) as well as with solvents like cyclohexanone, nitrobenzene, and quinoline has been described (16).

Polymerization temperatures that were used were similar to those used in (VI-9). One difference in the product obtained from reaction (VI-11) was attributed to the presence or absence of a solvent. The bulk reaction was claimed to yield a crystalline polymer, while use of cyclohexanone for the same reaction yielded an amorphous product (*16*).

(VI-11)

[33] **[34]** **[35]**

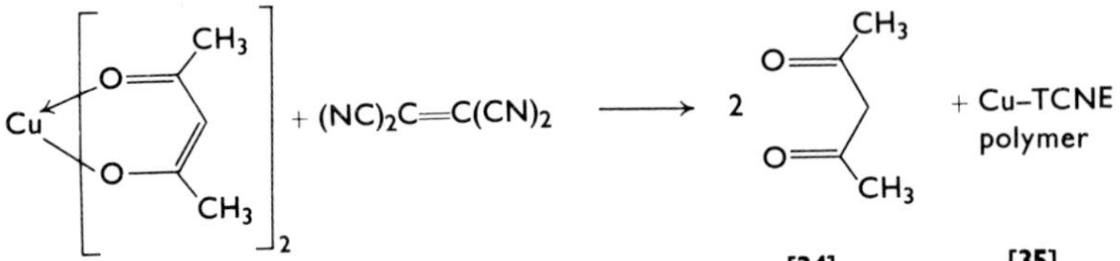

The polymerization of a large number of tetracyano compounds that bear a structural resemblance to tetracyanoethylene has been reported. Polymers possessing electrical conductivities of 5×10^{-5}–8×10^{-5} ohm^{-1} cm^{-1} were obtained by ligand exchange with copper acetylacetonate in bulk or in cyclohexanone. The cyano compounds that were studied included [**36**] through [**42**] (*52, 53*).

[36]

[37]

[38]

[39]

(VI-12)

[40]

[41]

[42]

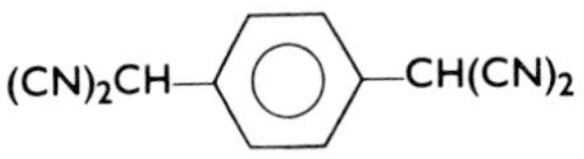

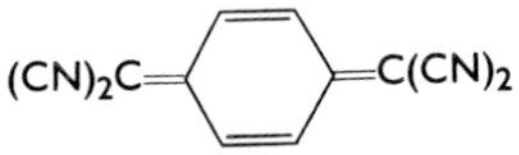

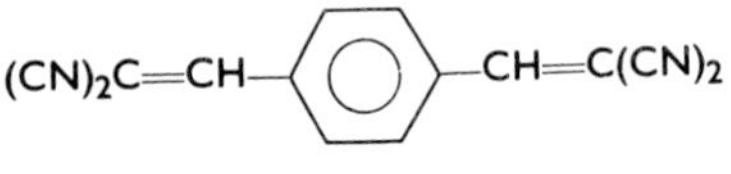

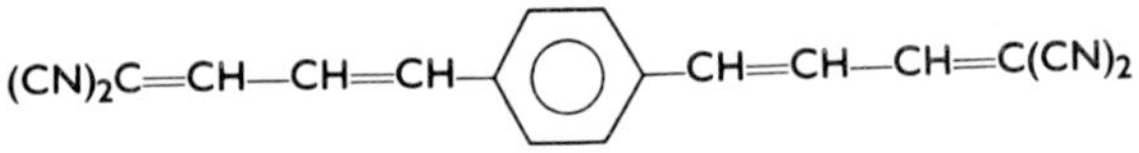

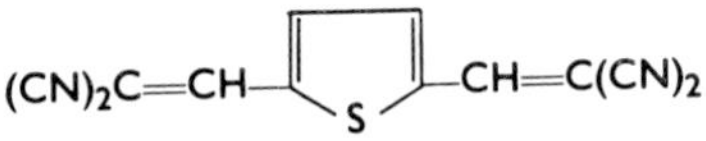

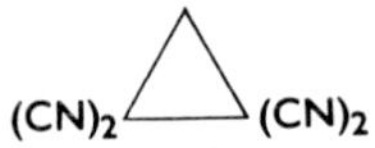

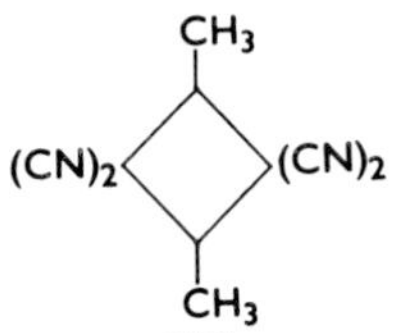

METHOD 2. FILM-FORMING POLYMERIZATION OF TETRACYANOETHYLENE ON METALS

Another interesting method of carrying out the synthesis of these polymers has been reported. Direct preparation of otherwise inaccessible polymer films on the surface of metallic copper, iron, and nickel was effected by heating the metals in vapors of TCNE from 150°–400°C for 5–20 hours at 10^{-5} mm Hg. Film thicknesses ranged from 5×10^{-6} to 3×10^{-5} cm. All were insoluble and infusible (9).

The mechanism by which these products are formed could be via the metal ion–radical salt that is formed from TCNE and metals in acetonitrile (64). When the salt [43] was heated with additional TCNE a product was formed that was identical to that obtained from direct reaction of the metal with TCNE.

$$(NC)_2C{=}C(CN)_2 \ + \ Cu \ \longrightarrow \ \overset{+}{Cu}[(NC)_2C{=}C(CN)_2]^{\,\overset{-}{}}$$

$$[28] \qquad\qquad [29] \qquad\qquad\qquad [43]$$

$$\overset{+}{Cu}[(NC)_2C{=}C(CN)_2]^{\,\overset{-}{}} + (NC)_2C{=}C(CN)_2 \ \longrightarrow \ \text{Polymer}$$

$$[43] \qquad\qquad\qquad\qquad\qquad\qquad [44]$$

$$(VI\text{-}13)$$

Tetracyanoethylene is polymerizable to a black, powdery, infusible material (17) without added metal by heating in nitrobenzene at 210°C for 10 hours under argon (13, 14). Comparison of this product with the product obtained by removal of magnesium from the magnesium–tetracyanoethylene poly-chelate indicated a close similarity. This was interpreted as evidence for the interrelationships shown in VI-14 (17).

Little evidence has appeared that allows a choice among the synthetic methods described above. The only molecular weight data available are re-duced viscosities in concentrated sulfuric acid, which were as high as 0.8. However, some anomalous behavior was noted (16). The polymers were insoluble in all other solvents, except for some partial solubility in some amines. Crystallinity was detected in at least one instance (16). The products were repeatedly described as being black and infusible. Thermal stability was quite good but depended to a degree on the preparative method and prior heating history. Although statements like "they could be heated at 500°C without decomposition" were noted (8), they were not supportable by the evidence (16). The products did appear to possess interesting electrical proper-ties. Conductivities of 10^{-5} to 10^{-12} ohm^{-1} cm^{-1} were reported (16). The iron-containing polymer had an initial dielectric constant of 7 at 3000 cps. Heating this product or changing the temperatures at which the polymer was prepared yielded samples of polymer with a dielectric constant as high as 70 (9).

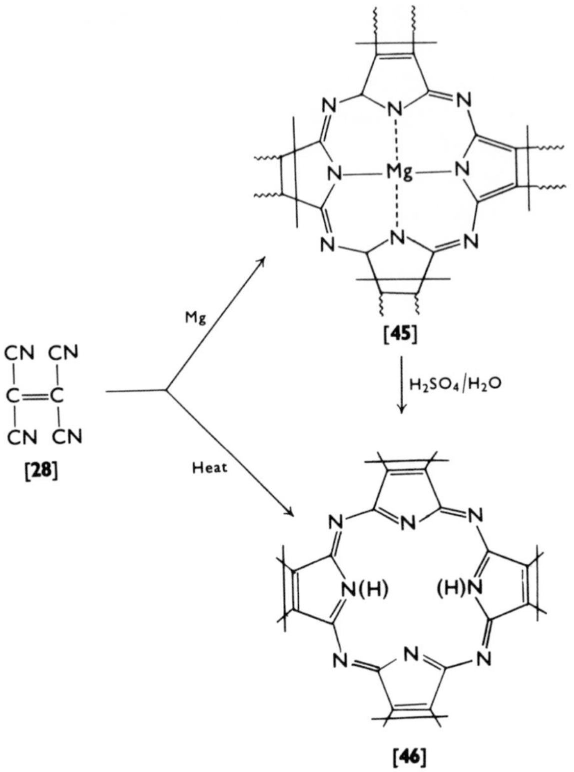

(VI-14)

D. Metal Phthalocyanine Polymers

The impetus for the preparation of polymeric metal phthalocyanines is repeatedly traced to an early report on the thermal stability of copper phthalocyanine (24). Dent and Linstead (24) described it to be "exceptionally resistant to heat and at about 580°C it may be sublimed at low pressure in an atmosphere of nitrogen or carbon dioxide." This description served to suggest to several groups that incorporation of a metal phthalocyanine structure into a polymeric repeat unit would yield polymers of exceptional thermal stability.

METHOD 1. POLYMERIZATION OF DIANHYDRIDES WITH UREA AND METALS

Heating bis(1,2-dicarboxylic acids) or the corresponding dianhydrides with a nitrogen source (like urea) and a metal or metal salt has been used most frequently to prepare polymeric metal phthalocyanines (VI-15). Ammonium molybdate is mentioned frequently as being a useful promoter for this reaction. Reaction in bulk at temperatures of >180°C is generally employed (4, 26, 55). The effect of certain reaction variables on the polymer molecular weight was reported (4), but since the methods used to determine molecular weight were questionable, their worth is doubtful. The polymers are only soluble in concentrated sulfuric acid and dimethylformamide, and all molecular weight measurements carried out in solution indicated that the polymers were of low molecular weight.

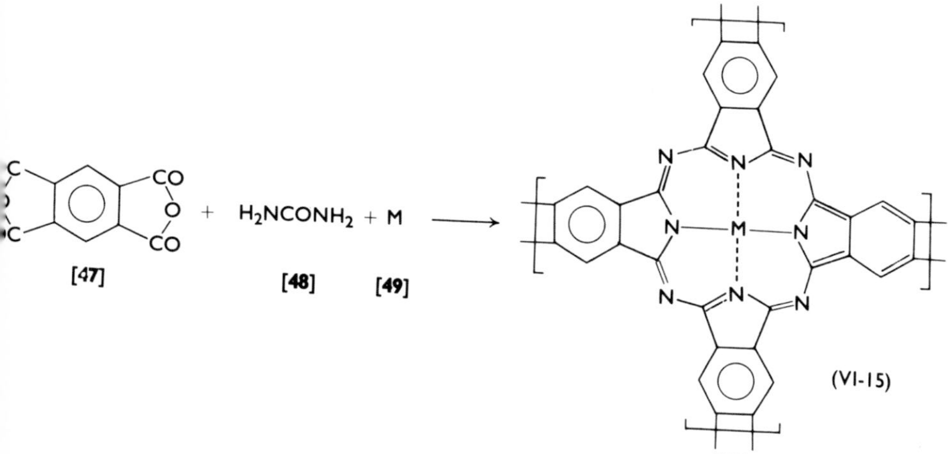

$$[47] \qquad H_2NCONH_2 + M \longrightarrow \qquad (VI\text{-}15)$$

$$[48] \qquad [49] \qquad\qquad [50]$$

Addition of a monofunctional anhydride to the polymerization in various mole ratios has been reported. An example of the effect on structure of this variation is shown in Eq. (VI-16). Although the products should be more linear and maybe more tractable, no large differences in properties were noted.

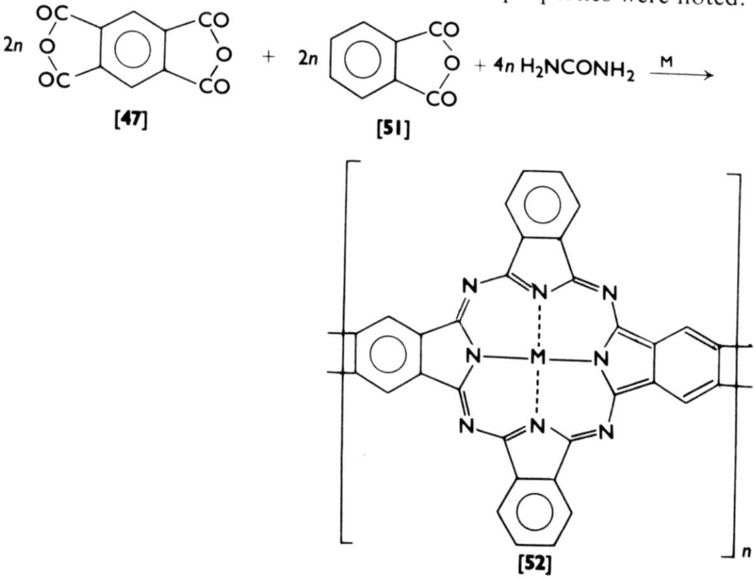

$$2n \quad [47] \quad + \quad 2n \quad [51] \quad + \quad 4n\, H_2NCONH_2 \xrightarrow{\ M\ }$$

$$(VI\text{-}16)$$

$$[52]$$

METHOD 2. POLYMERIZATION OF TETRANITRILES WITH METALS OR METAL SALTS

An example of this polymerization is given in Eq. (VI-17). An added nitrogen source is not necessary although they have been used (11, 30). This synthesis has also been carried out under pressure (23, 67).

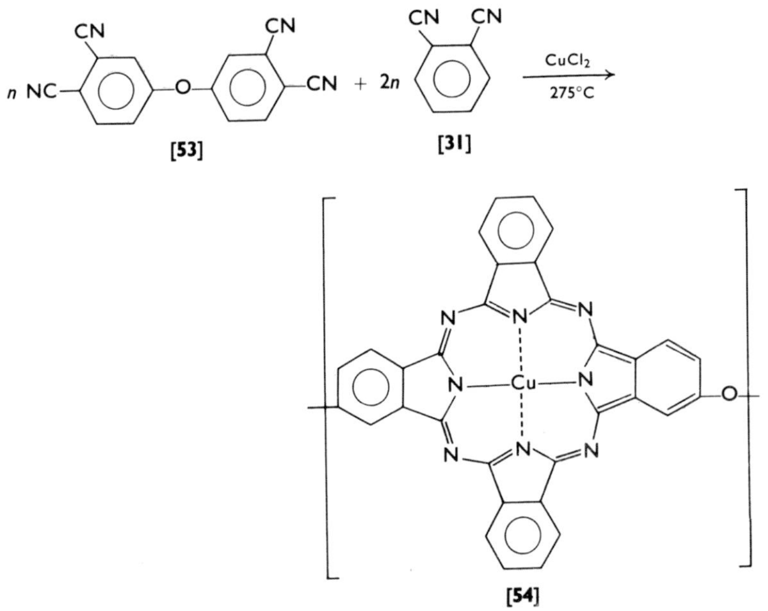

$$(VI-17)$$

[53]   [31]

[54]

Pyromellitonitrile has been used as a reactant in this synthesis (34, 67). Heating this tetranitrile with metal salts at 150°–200°C in ethylene glycol or dimethylformamide yields polymeric metal phthalocyanines (34). The direct preparation of thin films of metal phthalocyanines on a substrate has been patented (64). In this method, pyromellitonitrile vapors are heated in the presence of the substrate which can either be a metal or an inert substrate possessing a metal coating. Films 10–300 microns thick are obtainable and are valuable for their semiconduction properties. Additionally, surfaces can be coated by immersing an object in a hot solution of pyromellitonitrile in an inert solvent.

Polymers that are closely related to the metal phthalocyanines have been prepared from 2,3,4,5-tetracyanothiophene and 2,3,4,5-tetracyanofuran (52, 53). Polymerization with copper acetylacetonate in bulk or in cyclohexanone solution gave polymers whose electrical conductivities ranged from 5×10^{-5} to 8×10^{-5} ohm^{-1} cm^{-1}.

METHOD 3. POLYMERIZATION OF DIFUNCTIONAL SILICON AND TITANIUM PHTHALOCYANINES

Another route to polymeric metal phthalocyanines that has been described for those containing silicon (2, 51, 59) or titanium (18) as the central atom employs [57] and [58] as monomers.

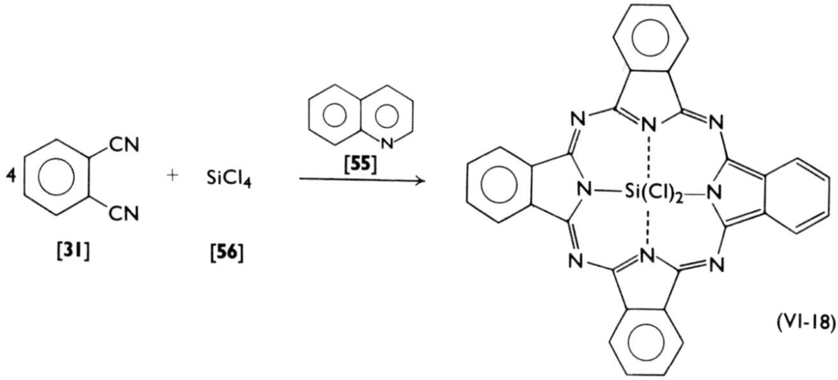

(VI-18)

[57]
(PcSiCl$_2$)

$$PcSiCl_2 \xrightarrow[H_2O]{H_2SO_4} PcSi(OH)_2 \qquad (VI-19)$$

[57]   [58]

Polymerization of the dichlorosilyl phthalocyanine monomer [57] with resorcinol gave low polymer. Thermal dehydration of the silanediol [58] gave the polysiloxane [61] for which evidence was obtained indicating an appreciable degree of polymerization. Because of the thickness of the phthalocyanine planes, this polymer is felt to contain 180°—O—Si—O—angles. The analogous titanium polymers were intractable and not exceptionally stable (18).

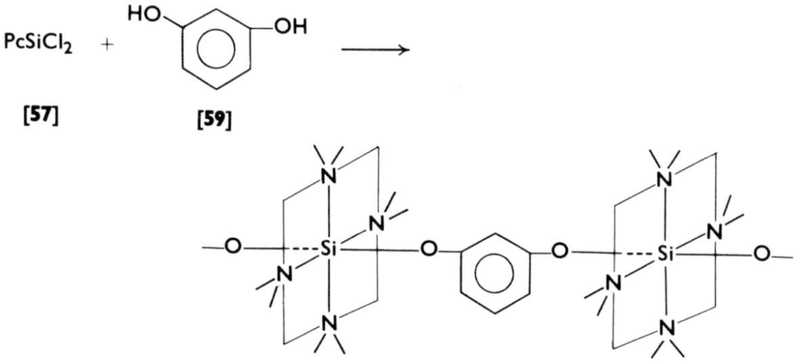

(VI-20)

[60]

$$PcSi(OH)_2 \xrightarrow{\text{Heat}}$$

(VI-21)

[58]   [61]

Polymeric metal phthalocyanines are insoluble, dark-colored materials. Some of the initial work (3) claimed molecular weights of 30,000–40,000 based on elemental analytical data, but the meaning of these results has been questioned. When viscosity data have been reported on soluble products, only low values were found. The material's insolubility prevents obtaining a definitive answer. Electrolysis of metal polyphthalocyanines has been successful in removing excess metal from the polymer (70). Crystallinity has been detected in these materials and its extent is reportedly influenced by the pressure employed during synthesis (23). Using Method D,2 with copper gave an amorphous product at 240 atmospheres. Lower pressures gave a product that was 50% crystalline.

It was mentioned earlier that the reported thermal stability of monomeric copper phthalocyanine served to generate interest in its polymeric relatives as thermally stable materials (24, 28, 29, 41). The fact that the monomeric copper phthalocyanine was sublimable *in vacuo* at 580°C was interpreted to be indicative of excellent thermal stability. One would not expect to use this same criterion of thermal stability for polymers, but somehow stability at this temperature was apparently anticipated. Subsequent work with the monomer (48, 49) showed that it could be heated at 800°C for 1 hour *in vacuo* with no change. However, more detailed examination of its thermal stability at 800°C led to the suggestion that its thermal stability was due to a very slow rate, i.e., high activation energy of decomposition, and was not a measure of the intrinsic thermal stability of the compound. Generally, the polymeric metal phthalocyanines are reported to decompose in the 250°–450°C range *in vacuo* or in air, and hence are less "stable" than the monomeric copper phthalocyanines. Among the more stable polymers, those derived from the dianhydride of 3,3′,4,4′-tetracarboxybenzophenone were reported to show a weight decrease by thermogravimetry at 450°C (46). The polymeric siloxanyl phthalocyanine shown in Eq. (VI-20) was reported to be stable in vacuum at 520°C for several hours and to require temperatures greater than 550°C for decomposition (59). These values do approach the range that was initially anticipated on the basis of data for monomeric copper phthalocyanine.

The electrical properties of polymeric metal phthalocyanines are receiving rather extensive attention. There is general agreement that they are typical semiconductors (*5, 8, 10*). A resistivity of 40 ohm-cm (25°C) was reported for poly(copper phthalocyanine) (*8, 30, 34, 58*). It has been reported that poly-(copper phthalocyanines) prepared by Method D,1 had poorer conductivity than those prepared by Method D,2. This difference was attributed (*11, 33*) to the presence of acid side groups in the polymers prepared by Method D,1. Correlations between electroconductivity and EPR signals (*10*) and between degree of crystallinity and conductivity activation energy (*23*) have been described for polymeric phthalocyanines. The two most thorough studies of the electrical properties of poly(copper phthalocyanine) were not in complete agreement (*30, 33*).

Poly(copper phthalocyanine) was unaffected by exposure to 10^8 r.e.p. from a ^{60}Co source.

Some of the earliest work with poly(metal phthalocyanines) was aimed at their use as dyes (*21, 65*). The polymers were sulfonated to impart water solubility.

Another interesting application area for metal polyphthalocyanines is their behavior as catalysts for organic reactions. A mixed copper–iron polyphthalocyanine was studied as a catalyst for the oxidation of acetaldehyde ethylene acetal (*38*). The use of the mixed metal polymer stems from a biological analogy where synergism has been noted when these two metals are present. Selective oxidation of benzaldehyde ethylene acetal and cumene was also investigated with this catalyst (*38*). Other work of this type has been reported using poly(copper phthalocyanine) as a catalyst for the oxidation of cumene and cyclohexene (*62*), the decomposition of hydrogen peroxide (*61*), and the exchange reaction between hydrogen and deuterium (*1*).

TABLE VI.1

Coordination Polymers of Metals and Nitrogenous Bases

No.	Structure	Metal (M)	Methods	Color	Solubility	T_m (°C)	Remarks and property data	References
1	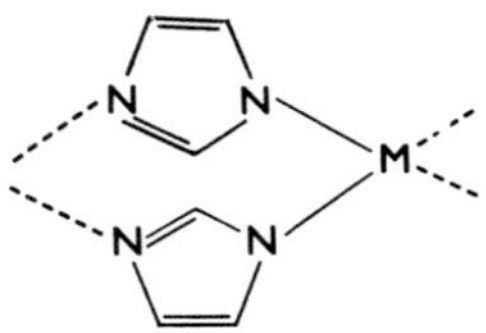 [4]	Cu(II)	A,1	Blue	Insoluble	279	Crystalline. TGA and resistivity data in (20)	20, 36, 37
		Zn(II)	A,1	—	Insoluble	>360	Crystalline. TGA and resistivity data	20
		Co(II)	A,1	—	Insoluble	>360	Crystalline. TGA and resistivity data	20
		Hg(II)	A,1	—	—	—	—	19
2	$Cu(NCCH_2CH_2CN)_2{}^+NO_3{}^-$		A,2	—	—	—	—	44
3	$Cu(NC(CH_2)_4CN)_2{}^+NO_3{}^-$		A,2	—	—	—	—	43
4	$Cu(NC(CH_2)_3CN)_2{}^+NO_3{}^-$		A,2	—	—	—	—	45
5	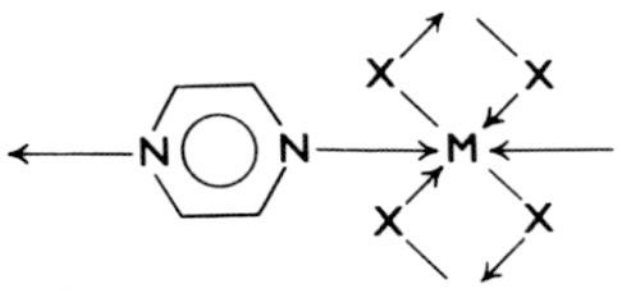 [10]	Ni(II) (X = Cl)	A,2	Green	—	—	Magnetic properties reported	7, 50
		Ni(II) (X = Br)	A,2	Green	—	—	Magnetic properties reported	7, 50

Metal	Type	Color	Solubility		Magnetic	References
Ni(II) (X = I)	A,2	Yellow	—	—	Magnetic properties reported	50
Co(II) (X = Br)	A,2	Violet	—	—	Magnetic properties reported	7, 50
Co(II) (X = Cl)	A,2	Violet	—	—	Magnetic properties reported	7, 50

6 Dipyridine chlorides (see structure [9])

Metal	Type	Color	Solubility		Magnetic	References
Mn(II)	A,2	—	—	—	—	27, 32, 56
Co(II)	A,2	—	—	—	—	27, 32, 56, 68
Cu(II)	A,2	—	—	—	—	27, 32, 56
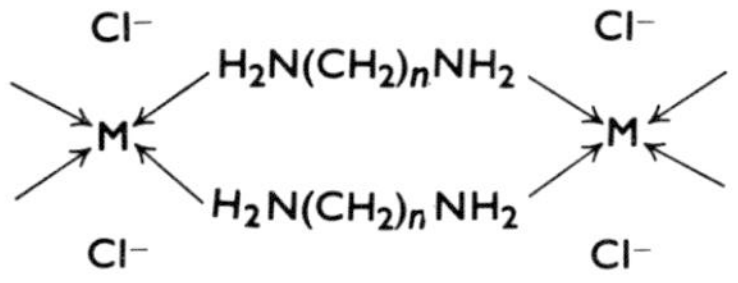 Cr(III) n = 4	A,2	Red-violet	Insoluble	—	—	63
Cr(III) n = 5	A,2	Red-violet	Insoluble	—	—	63
Cr(III) n = 6	A,2	Red-violet	Insoluble	—	—	63
Cr(III) n = 7	A,2	Red-violet	Insoluble	—	—	63

7

Cl^-, $H_2N(CH_2)_nNH_2$, M, Cl^-, $H_2N(CH_2)_nNH_2$, Cl^-, M, Cl^- (bridged dipyridine chloride structure)

TABLE VI.2

Polymers from Bis(1,2-dioximes)

No.	Structure	Metal (M)	Method	Color	Solubility	Molecular weight	T_m (°C)	Remarks and property data	References
1	R = $\text{+(CH}_2)_6$; R' = CH₃	Ni(II)	B,1	Orange	Pyridine	400–600	300 d	Crystalline	57
		Cu(II)	B,1	Black	—	—	—	—	57
		Co(II)	B,1	Brown	—	—	—	—	57
		Fe(II)	B,1	Brown	—	—	—	—	57
2	R = $\text{+(CH}_2)_{10}$; R' = CH₃	Ni(II)	B,1	Orange	Pyridine	560–620	220 d	Amorphous	57
		Cu(II)	B,1	Black	—	—	—	—	57
		Co(II)	B,1	Brown	—	—	—	—	57
		Fe(II)	B,1	Brown	—	—	—	—	57
3	R = p-C₆H₄; R' = CH₃	Ni(II)	B,1	Orange	Insoluble	—	300 d	Crystalline	57
		Cu(II)	B,1	Black	—	—	—	—	57
		Co(II)	B,1	Brown	—	—	—	—	57
		Fe(II)	B,1	Brown	—	—	—	—	57
4	R = p-C₆H₄—p-C₆H₄; R' = CH₃	Ni(II)	B,1	Brick	Pyridine	—	>360	—	39, 40
5	R = p-C₆H₄CH₂—p-C₆H₄; R' = CH₃	Ni(II)	B,1	Brick	Pyridine	—	>360	—	39, 40
6	R = p-C₆H₄(CH₂)₂—p-C₆H₄; R' = CH₃	Ni(II)	B,1	Brick	Pyridine	—	>360	—	39, 40
7	R = p-C₆H₄(CH₂)₃—p-C₆H₄; R' = CH₃	Ni(II)	B,1	Brick	Pyridine	—	>360	—	39, 40
8	R = p-C₆H₄O—p-C₆H₄; R' = CH₃	Ni(II)	B,1	Brick	Pyridine	20,000 (osmometry)	>360	—	39, 40
9	R = $\text{+(CH}_2)_2$; R' = C₆H₅	Ni(II)	B,1	Red	—	—	360	—	39, 40

TABLE VI.3

Metal–Tetracyanoethylene Polymers

No.	Structure	Metal (M)	Method	Color	Solubility	Molecular weight	T_m (°C)	Remarks and property data	References
1	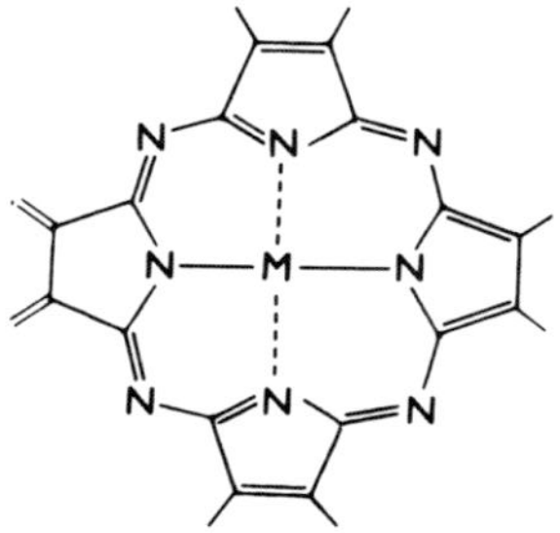	Cu(II) [30]	C,1	Black	H_2SO_4, partly in DMF, pyridine	—	Infusible	—	16, 17, 64
		Cu(II) [30]	C,1	Black	H_2SO_4	η_{red} 0.8	Infusible	Crystalline and amorphous	8, 15, 16
		Cu(II) [30]	C,2	Black	H_2SO_4	—	Infusible	—	9
2		Fe(II)	C,1; C,2	Black	H_2SO_4	—	Infusible	—	9, 16, 17
3		Mg(II)	C,1	Black	H_2SO_4	—	Infusible	—	16, 17
4		Ni(II)	C,2	Black	H_2SO_4	—	Infusible	—	9
5	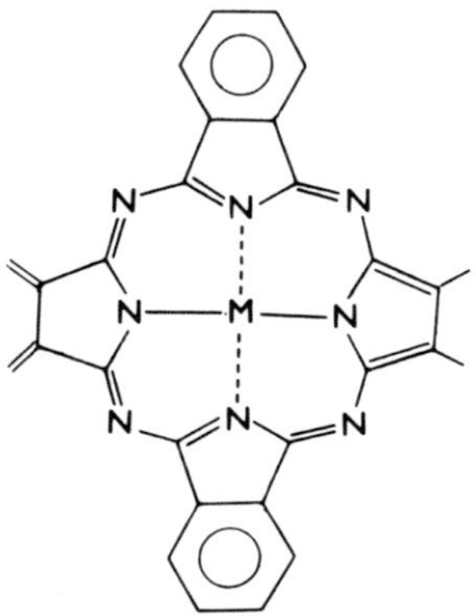	Cu(II) [32]	C,1	Black	H_2SO_4	—	Infusible	—	8, 15

TABLE VI.4

Metal Phthalocyanine Polymers

No.	Structure	Metal (M)	Method	Color	Solubility	Molecular weight	Remarks and property data	References
1	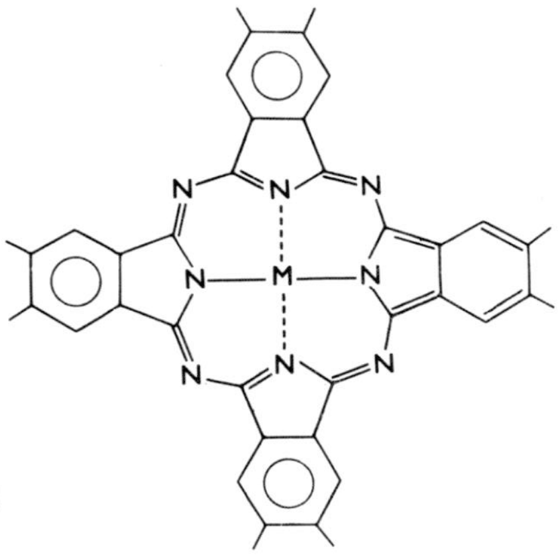	Cu(II)	D,1	Blue	H_2SO_4	20,000	Crystalline	3, 4, 10, 25, 26, 31, 48, 58
2	[50]	Cu(II)	D,2	Violet	DMF	—	Crystalline (50%)	8, 11, 23, 30, 34, 58, 67, 69
		Fe(II)	D,2	—	DMF	—	—	8
3		Co(II)	D,1; D,2	—	—	—	Electrical properties, ref. (34)	4, 25
4		Ni(II)	D,1	—	—	—	Electrical properties, ref. (34)	4, 25
5		Mg(II)	D,2	—	—	—	—	22

6	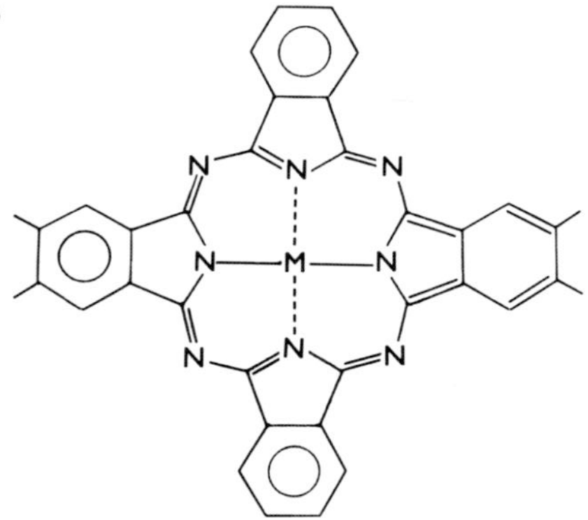 Cu(II)	D,1	Blue	DMF	—	$T_m = 350°C$ d	10, 55
	Cu(II)	D,2	Violet	H_2SO_4	η_{red} 0.05	Various compositions were prepared	11, 67

[52]

R = —O—

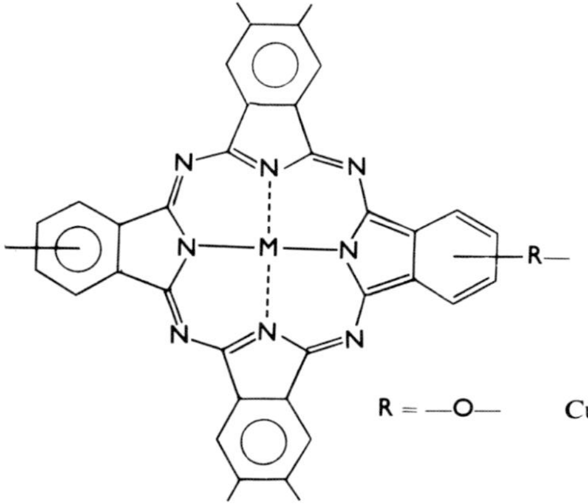 7	Cu(II)	D,1	—	H_2SO_4	—	—	10

TABLE VI.4—continued

Metal Phthalocyanine Polymers

No.	Structure	Metal (M)	Method	Color	Solubility	Molecular weight	Remarks and property data	References
8	R = —|—	Cu(II)	D,2	—	—	—	—	8
9	R = —|—	Fe(II)	D,2	—	DMF	—	—	8
10	R = —O— [54]	Cu(II)	D,1	Gray	DMF	4000	T_m, 350°C d	10, 55
		Cu(II)	D,2	—	DMF, H_2SO_4	η 0.12	—	8, 54
11	R = >C=O	Cu(II)	D,l; D,2	Blue	H_2SO_4	"Low"	—	21, 46, 47
12	R = >C=O	Co(II)	D,1	Violet	H_2SO_4	"Low"	—	46, 47

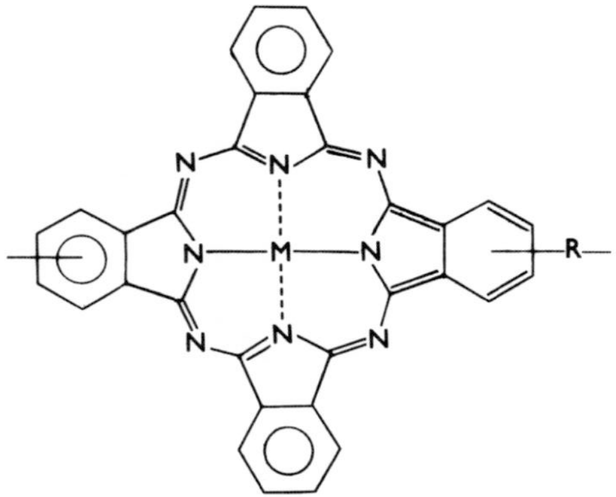

	R							
13	R = $>$C=O	Ni(II)	D,1	Blue	H$_2$SO$_4$	"Low"	—	46, 47
14	R = —SO$_2$—	Cu(II)	D,1	Green	—	—	—	21

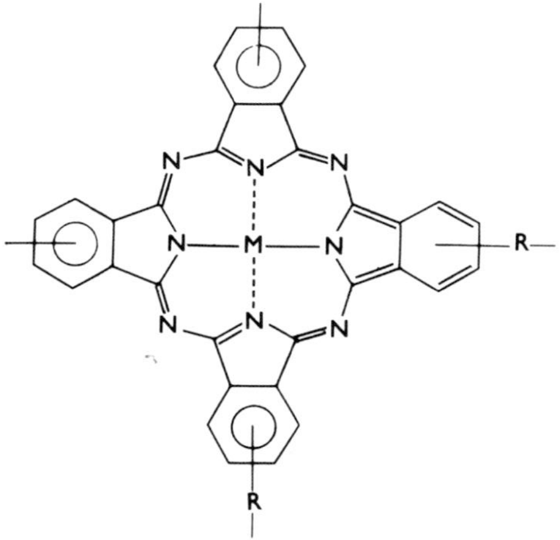

	R							
15	R = —O—	Cu(II)	D,1; D,2	—	H$_2$SO$_4$	[η] 0.06	—	10, 54
16	R = $>$C=O	Cu(II)	D,1; D,2	—	—	—	—	21
17	R = —SO$_2$—	Cu(II)	D,1; D,2	—	—	—	—	21

TABLE VI.4—*continued*

Metal Phthalocyanine Polymers

(PcMCl₂)

No.	Structure	Metal (M)	Method	Color	Solubility	Molecular weight	Remarks and property data	References
18	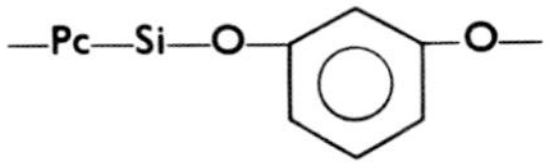 —Pc—Si—O— (with phenylene-O)	Si(IV)	D,3	—	—	—	—	*51*
19	—Pc—Ti—O—	Ti(IV)	D,3	—	Insoluble	—	—	*18*

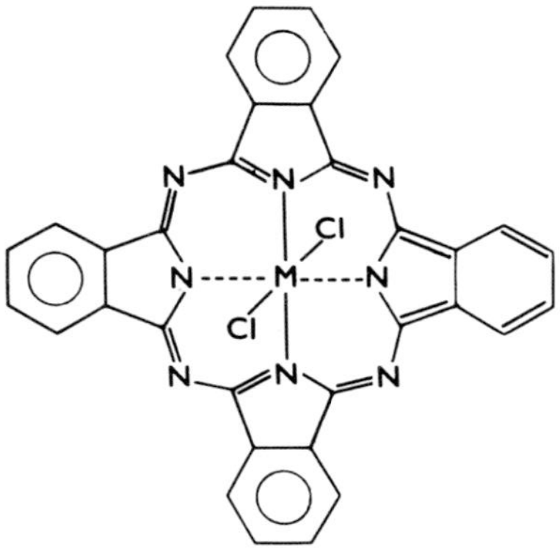

REFERENCES

1. Acres, G. J. K., and Eley, D. D., *Trans. Faraday Soc.* **60**, 1157 (1964).
2. AD 477,800, Research Center, Aerospace Group. General Precision, Inc. Little Falls, N.J. (1966).
3. Bailar, J. C., Jr., WADC Tech. Rept. No. 57-657, p. 35 (1958).
4. Bailar, J. C., Jr., Martin, K. V., Judd., M. L., and McLean, J. A., Jr., WADC Tech. Rept. No. 57-391, Part I (1957).
5. Balabanov, E. I., Berlin, A. A., Parini, V. P., Tal'roze, V. L., Frankevich, E. L., and Cherkashin, M. I., *Dokl. Akad. Nauk SSSR* **134**, 1123 (1960); *Chem. Abstr.* **55**, 12977 (1961).
6. Banks, C. V., and Barnum, D. W., *J. Am. Chem. Soc.* **80**, 3579 (1958).
7. Beech, G., and Mortimer, C. T., *J. Chem. Soc., A, Inorg., Phys., Theoret.* p. 1115 (1967).
8. Berlin, A. A., *J. Polymer Sci.* **55**, 621 (1961).
9. Berlin, A. A., Boguslavski, L. I., Burshtein, R. K., Matveeva, N. G., Sherle, A. I., and Shurmovskaya, N. A., *Dokl. Akad. Nauk SSSR* **136**, 1127 (1961); *Chem. Abstr.* **56**, 4198 (1962).
10. Berlin, A. A., Cherkashina, L. G., and Balabanov, E. I., *Vysokomolekul. Soedin.* **4**, 376 (1962); *Resins, Rubbers, Plastics* p. 2359 (1962).
11. Berlin, A. A., Cherkashina, L. G., Frankevich, E. L., Balabanov, E. M., and Aseyev, Yu. G., *Vysokomolekul. Soedin.* **6**, 832 (1964); *Polymer Sci. (USSR) (English Transl.)* **6**, 915 (1964).
12. Berlin, A. A., and Matveeva, N. G., Russian Patent 126,612 (1959); *Chem. Abstr.* **54**, 16917 (1960).
13. Berlin, A. A., and Matveeva, N. G., *Proc. Acad. Sci. USSR, Chem. Sect. (English Transl.)* **167**, 283 (1966).
14. Berlin, A. A., and Matveeva, N. G., *Vysokomolekul. Soedin* **8**, 736 (1966).
15. Berlin, A. A., Matveeva, N. G., and Sherle, A. I., *Izv. Akad. Nauk SSSR, Otd. Khim. Nauk* **12**, 2261 (1959); *Chem. Abstr.* **54**, 10854 (1960).
16. Berlin, A. A., Matveeva, N. G., Sherle, A. I., and Kostrova, N. D., *Vysokomolekul. Soedin.* **4**, 860 (1962); *Polymer Sci. (USSR) (English Transl.)* **4**, 260 (1963); *Resins, Rubbers, Plastics*, p. 2095 (1962).
17. Berlin, A. A., Sherle, A. I., Belova, G. V., and Boreyev, O. M., *Vysokomolekul. Soedin.* **7**, 88 (1965); *Polymer Sci. (USSR) (English Transl.)* **7**, 92 (1965).
18. Block, B. P., and Meloni, E. G., NASA Accession No. N65-13167, Rept. No. AD 449,580, Avail. CFSTI (1964) from *Sci. Tech. Aerospace Rept.* **3**, 389 (1965); *Chem. Abstr.* **63**, 11708 (1965).
19. Brooks, P., and Davidson, N., *J. Am. Chem. Soc.* **82**, 2118 (1960).
20. Brown, G. P., and Aftergut, S., *J. Polymer Sci.* **A2**, 1839 (1964).
21. Bucher, A., U.S. Patent 2,492,732 (Ciba Ltd.) (1949); *Chem. Abstr.* **44**, 7556 (1950).
22. Cherkashina, L. G., and Berlin, A. A., *Vysokomolekul. Soedin.* **8**, 627 (1966); *Polymer Sci. (USSR) (English Transl.)* **8**, 687 (1966).
23. Cherkashina, L. G., Frankevich, E. L., Eremina, I. V., Balabanov, E. I., and Berlin A. A., *Vysokomolekul. Soedin.* **7**, 1264 (1965).
24. Dent, C. E., and Linstead, R. P., *J. Chem. Soc.* p. 1027 (1934).
25. Drinkard, W. C., Jr., *Dissertation Abstr.* **17**, 499 (1957).
26. Drinkard, W. C., Jr., and Bailar, J. C., Jr., *J. Am. Chem. Soc.* **81**, 4795 (1959).
27. Dunitz, J. D., *Acta Cryst.* **10**, 307 (1957).
28. Elvidge, J. A., and Lever, A. B. P., *Proc. Chem. Soc.* p. 195 (1959).
29. Elvidge, J. A., and Lever, A. B. P., *J. Chem. Soc.* p. 1257 (1961).
30. Epstein, A., and Wildi, B. S., *J. Chem. Phys.* **32**, 324 (1960).

31. Felmayer, W., and Wolf, I., *J. Electrochem. Soc.* **105**, 141 (1958); *Chem. Abstr.* **52**, 8738 (1958).
32. Ferroni, E., and Bondi, E., *J. Inorg. & Nucl. Chem.* **8**, 458 (1958).
33. Frankevich, E. L., Busheva, L. I., Balabanov, E. I., and Cherkashina, L. G., *Polymer Sci. (USSR) (English Transl.)* **6**, 1132 (1964).
34. Hanke, W., East German Patent 51,432 (1966); *Chem. Abstr.* **66**, 7196, 76488y (1967).
35. Hoover, F. W., and Miller, H. C., British Patent 791,325 (E. I. duPont de Nemours & Co.) (1958); *Chem. Abstr.* **52**, 14193 (1958).
36. Inoue, M., Kishita, M., and Kubo, M., *Inorg. Chem.* **4**, 626 (1965).
37. Inoue, M., Kishita, M., and Kubo, M., *Bull. Chem. Soc. Japan.* **39**, 1352 (1966).
38. Inoue, H., Kida, Y., and Imoto, E., *Bull. Chem. Soc. Japan* **40**, 184 (1967).
39. Jones, M. E. B., Thornton, D. A., and Webb, R. F., *Makromol. Chem.* **49**, 62 (1961); *Resins, Rubbers, Plastics* p. 1159 (1962).
40. Jones, M. E. B., Thornton, D. A., and Webb, R. F., *Makromol. Chem.* **49**, 69 (1961); *Resins, Rubbers, Plastics* p. 1163 (1962).
41. Joyner, R. D., and Kenney, M. E., *J. Am. Chem. Soc.* **82**, 5790 (1960).
42. Katon, J. E., U.S. Patent 3,267,115 (Monsanto Co.) (1966).
43. Kinoshita, Y., Matsubara, I., Hibuchi, T., and Saito, Y., *Bull. Chem. Soc. Japan* **32**, 1221 (1959); *Chem. Abstr.* **54**, 16982 (1960).
44. Kinoshita, Y., Matsubara, I., and Saito, Y., *Bull. Chem. Soc. Japan* **32**, 741 (1959); *Chem. Abstr.* **54**, 12715 (1960).
45. Kinoshita, Y., Matsubara, I., and Saito, Y., *Bull. Chem. Soc. Japan* **32**, 1216 (1959); *Chem. Abstr.* **54**, 16983 (1960).
46. Korshak, V. V., Rogozhin, S. V., and Vinogradov, M. G., *Izv. Akad. Nauk SSSR, Otd. Khim. Nauk* p. 1473 (1962); *Resins, Rubbers, Plastics* p. 2871 (1962).
47. Korshak, V. V., Rogozhin, S. V., and Vinogradov, M. G., *Bull. Acad. Sci. USSR, Div. Chem. Sci. (English Transl.)* p. 1384 (1962); *Resins, Rubbers, Plastics* p. 2871 (1962).
48. Lawton, E. A., *J. Phys. Chem.* **62**, 384 (1958).
49. Lawton, E. A., and McRitchie, D. D., WADC Tech. Rept. No. 57-642 (1957); *Chem. Abstr.* **55**, 18166 (1961).
50. Lever, A. B. P., Lewis, J., and Nyholm, R. S., *Nature* **189**, 58 (1961).
51. Luloff, J., and Vogel, C., AD 608,263, Avail. CFSTI (1964); *U.S. Govt. Res. Develop. Rept.* **40**, 19 (1965); *Chem. Abstr.* **63**, 740 (1965).
52. Manecke, G., and Wöhrle, D., *Makromol. Chem.* **102**, 1 (1967).
53. Manecke, G., Wöhrle, D., and Kossmehl, G., *Intern. Symp. Macromol. Chem., Preprints, 1966* p. 1. Brussels, 1967.
54. Marvel, C. S., and Martin, M. M., *J. Am. Chem. Soc.* **80**, 6600 (1958).
55. Marvel, C. S., and Rassweiler, J. H., *J. Am. Chem. Soc.* **80**, 1197 (1958).
56. Mellor, D. P., and Coryell, C. D., *J. Am. Chem. Soc.* **60**, 1786 (1938).
57. Murahashi, S., and Kubota, H., *Bull. Chem. Soc. Japan.* **35**, 1465 (1962); *Resins, Rubbers, Plastics* p. 345 (1963).
58. Novikov, G. F., and Frankevich, E. L., *Vysokomolekul. Soedin.* **A9**, 588 (1967).
59. Owen, J. E., Joyner, R. D., and Kenney, M. E., *Abstr. 139th Meeting Am. Chem. Soc., St. Louis*, p. 17M (1961).
60. Ramaswamy, K. K., and Sen, D. N., *Indian J. Chem.* **4**, 142 (1966); *Chem. Abstr.* **65**, 2094 (1966).
61. Roginskii, S. Z., Berlin, A. A., Golovina, O. A., Dokukina, E. S., Sakharov, M. M., and Cherkashina, L. G., *Kinetika i Kataliz* **4**, 431 (1963).
62. Roginskii, S. Z., Berlin, A. A., Kutseva, L. N., Aseeva, R. M., Cherkashina, L. G., Sherle, A. I., and Matveeva, N. G., *Dokl. Akad. Nauk SSSR* **148**, 118 (1963).
63. Schäfer, H. L., and Kling, O., *Z. Anorg. Allgem. Chem.* **309**, 245 (1961).

64. Sherle, A. I., Aseev, Y. G., Frankevich, E. L., Berlin, A. A., and Kasatochkin, V. I., *Bull. Acad. Sci. USSR, Div. Chem. Sci. (English Transl.)* p. 1053 (1964).
65. Swiss Patent 263,655 (issued to Ciba, Ltd.) (1949); *Chem. Abstr.* **44**, 9158 (1950).
66. Trofimenko, S., French Patent 1,466,118 (E. I. DuPont de Nemours & Co.) (1967); *Chem. Abstr.* **67**, 4122, 43814u (1967).
67. Tuemmler, W. B., U.S. Patent 3,245,965 (Monsanto Co.) (1966).
68. Wendlandt, W. W., *Chemist-Analyst* **53**, 71 (1964).
69. Wildi, B. S., U.S. Patent 3,293,075 (Monsanto Co.) (1966).
70. Wildi, B. S., U.S. Patent 3,300,399 (Monsanto Co.) (1967).

CHAPTER VII

Metallorganic Ring Polymers from Nitrogen : Oxygen Chelate Ligands

A. Polymers from Bis(amino acids) and Bis(aminophenols)

Chelates of amino acids, particularly those of α-aminocarboxylic acids, have been known for many years. Polymers containing this structural feature were unwittingly prepared as early as 1913 (62). Bis(α-aminocarboxylic acids) were intentionally polymerized with transition metals in attempts to prepare useful paint pigments (17). Colored, insoluble, and highly cross-linked materials were obtained, but the colors were not of high enough a quality to be useful. Recent work with this class of ligand had as its objective the synthesis of heat-stable materials (2, 4, 5). The fact that Co(III)–amino acid complexes exhibited excellent stability toward heat and chemical reagents served as a stimulus.

METHOD 1. POLYMERIZATION OF BIS(AMINO ACIDS) WITH METAL SALTS AND/OR METAL CHELATES

Polymerization of a metal salt with the bis(ligand) is employed in this method. Equation (VII-1) shows an example with an aminosulfonic acid (4, 5).

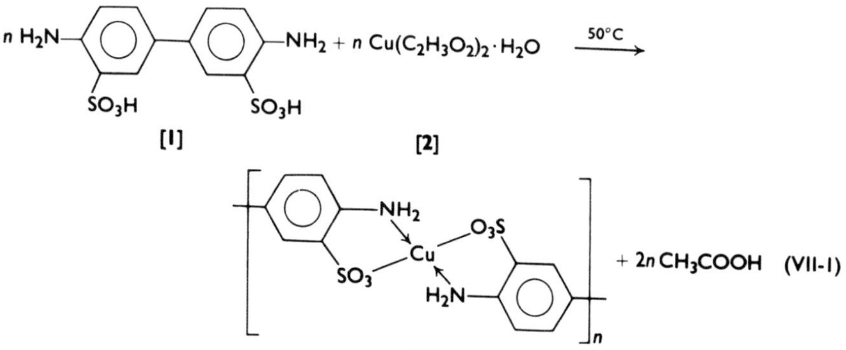

$$n\ H_2N-\underset{\underset{[1]}{SO_3H}}{\bigcirc}-\underset{SO_3H}{\bigcirc}-NH_2 + \underset{[2]}{n\ Cu(C_2H_3O_2)_2\cdot H_2O} \xrightarrow{50°C}$$

$$\underset{[3]}{\left[\cdots \right]_n} + \underset{[4]}{2n\ CH_3COOH} \quad (VII\text{-}1)$$

173

Bulk reaction with cupric nitrate, reaction in aqueous and organic solvents at reflux, and mixing aqueous solutions of the reactants via slow diffusion processes are among the reaction conditions that are reported (5). No evidence was presented that indicated success in obtaining high molecular weight products. The original work with this system (17) did claim the preparation of a silklike product, the visible nature of which could be indicative of a high molecular weight.

Ligand exchange has been attempted for the polymerization of α,α'-diaminosebacic acid (4). The reaction shown in Eq. (VII-2) did not proceed until ammonia was added. However, complete exchange did occur under these conditions, leading to a cross-linked Co(III)–α,α'-diaminosebacic acid polymer. The successful use of this reaction to prepare linear, high molecular weight polymers has not been reported.

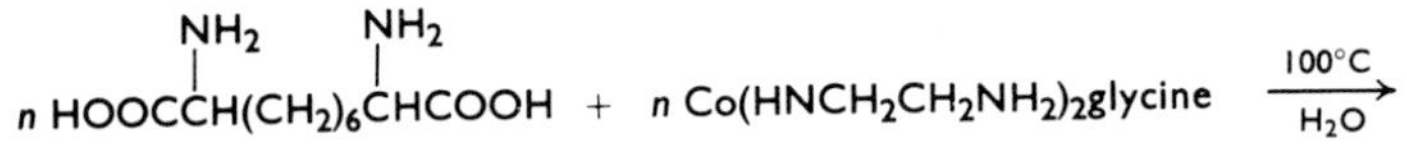

[5]   [6] 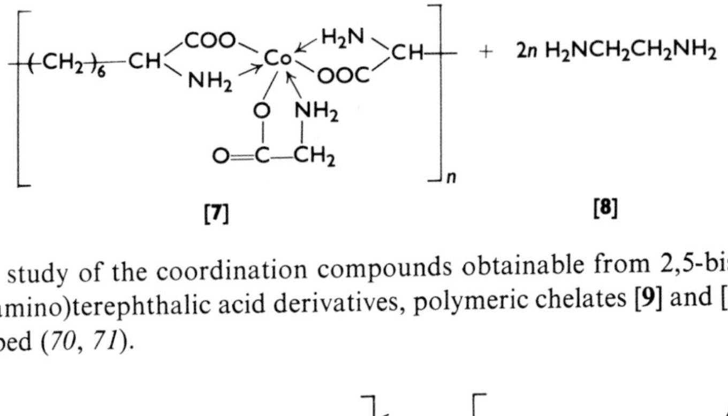   (VII-2)   [7]   [8]

In a study of the coordination compounds obtainable from 2,5-bis(substituted amino)terephthalic acid derivatives, polymeric chelates [9] and [10] were described (70, 71).

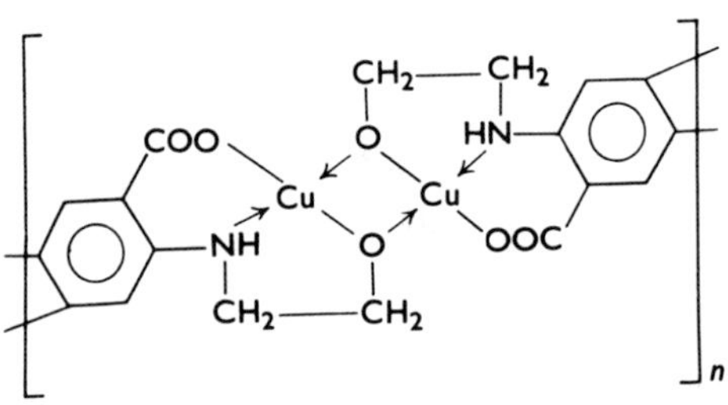

[9] 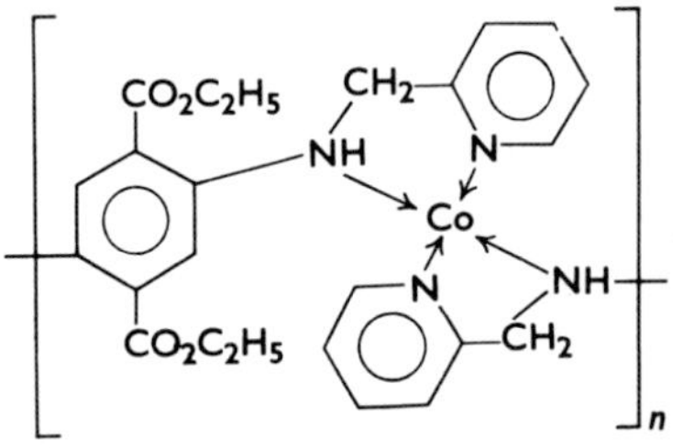   [10]   (VII-3)

Coordination of p-(1,3-butanedione)-N-phenylglycine with a variety of metal ions yielded a number of mixed chelate polymers [13] (53). This study is described in added detail under polymeric bis(β-diketonates) (Chapter IX).

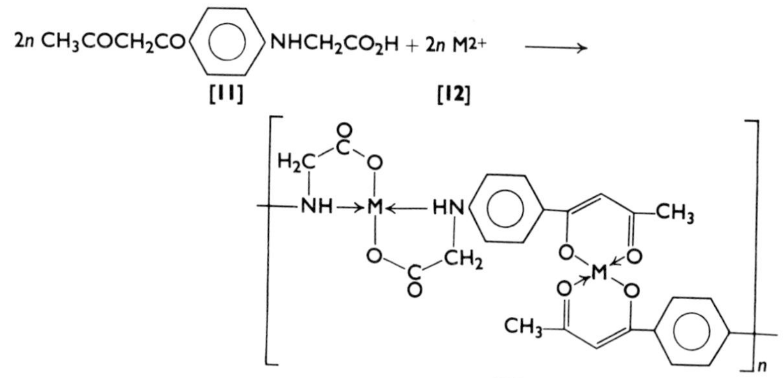

$2n$ CH$_3$COCH$_2$CO — ⟨○⟩ — NHCH$_2$CO$_2$H + $2n$ M^{2+} ⟶

[11]   [12]

(VII-4)

[13]

Bis(o-aminophenols) have been polymerized with metal ions (4, 5, 36). Evidence indicative of high molecular weight products was not presented.

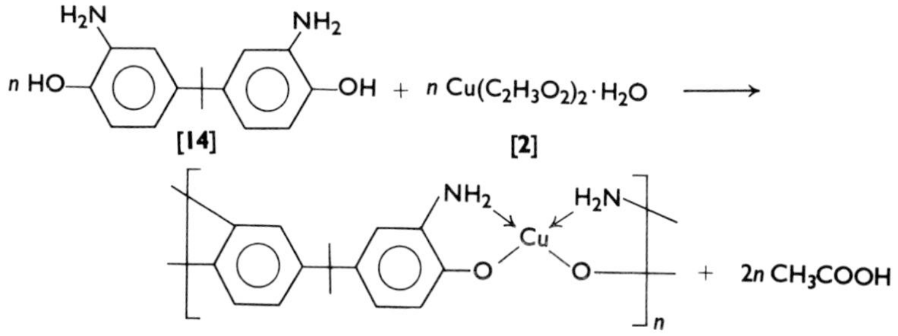

n HO — ⟨○⟩(H$_2$N) — ⟨○⟩(NH$_2$) — OH + n Cu(C$_2$H$_3$O$_2$)$_2$·H$_2$O ⟶

[14]   [2]

+ $2n$ CH$_3$COOH   (VII-5)

[15]

B. Metal Bis(8-hydroxyquinolinates) and Related Types

8-Hydroxyquinoline has found wide utility in analytical chemistry as a ligand for various metal ions (48). Bifunctional ligands possessing this same

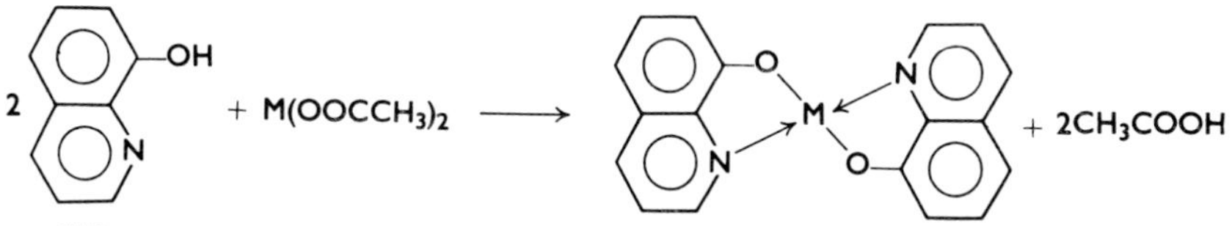

2 ⟨quinoline⟩—OH + M(OOCCH$_3$)$_2$ ⟶ [complex] + 2CH$_3$COOH

[16]   [17]   [18]   (VII-6)

structural feature include 5,8-dihydroxyquinoxaline [19], 1,4- [21] and 1,5-dihydroxyphenazines [20]. These latter "bifunctional 8-hydroxyquinolines" have also been studied as chelating agents for the analytical determination of metal ions (1, 37, 39, 43, 44). Although polymers were undoubtedly formed in this work, this was not the prime objective. Hence, no characteristics of the products other than color were described.

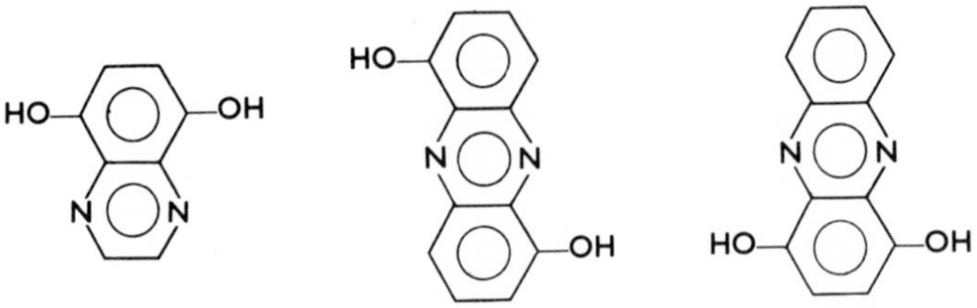

[19]   [20]   [21]   (VII-7)

A similar situation exists for several bis(8-hydroxyquinolines) containing azo linkages that were synthesized and investigated as dyes. A few examples ([22], [23]) are shown. More recently, the polymerization of both of these bis(ligands) has been studied (69).

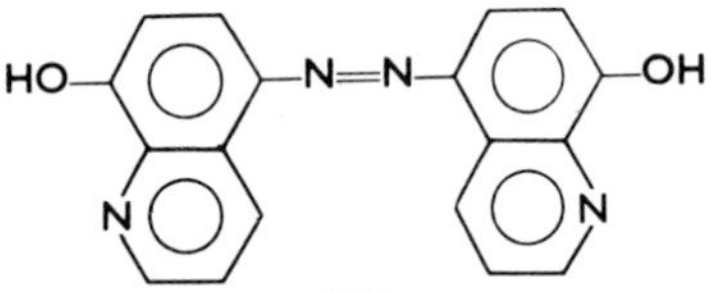

[22]
(4, 5, 22)   (VII-8)

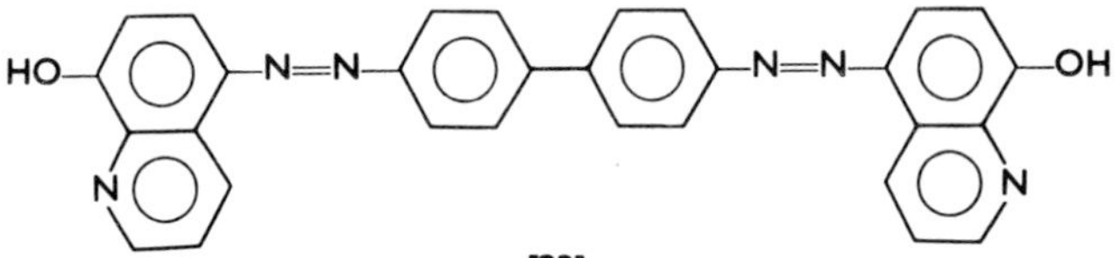

[23]
(12, 60)

METHOD 1. POLYMERIZATION OF BIS(8-HYDROXYQUINOLINES) WITH METAL
SALTS OR METAL CHELATES

Intentional polymerization of bis(8-hydroxyquinolines) has been studied rather extensively in recent years. As is true with many classes of chelate polymers that have been studied, thermal stability has been the most sought after property. Dimethylformamide is useful as a solvent for the polymerization of bis(8-hydroxy-5-quinolyl) derivatives with divalent metal acetates (VII-9). However, even at reflux (150°C) in this powerful solvent, the products precipitated early and possessed low molecular weights (9, 27–29, 32, 69). Dimethyl sulfoxide has also been used for the polymerization (31). Interfacial polymerization of benzene solutions of the ligand and ammonium complexes of the metal has been described. No advantage was apparent (31). Metal acetylacetonates in dimethylformamide have also been employed (47).

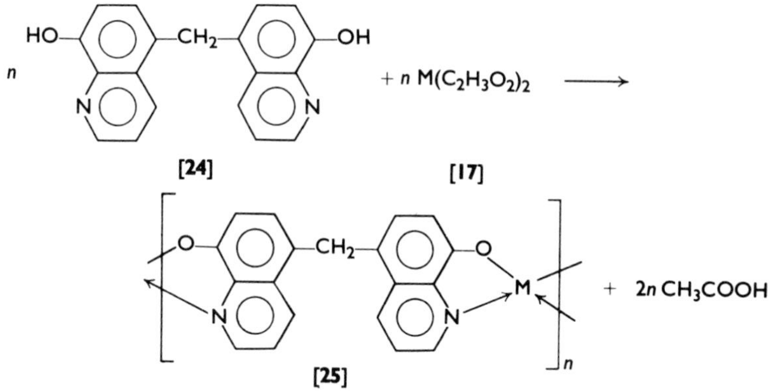

$$\text{[24]} + n\ \text{M(C}_2\text{H}_3\text{O}_2)_2 \longrightarrow \text{[25]} + 2n\ \text{CH}_3\text{COOH} \qquad \text{(VII-9)}$$

Melt polymerization of bis(8-hydroxy-5-quinolyl) derivatives with metal acetylacetonates has been described. The initial stages of the reaction can be carried out in solution (32, 69) followed by removal of the solvent and acetylacetone. Reaction temperatures up to 290°C with an emphasis on fast reaction times gave better results (27). Since the products are not fusible to stable melts, this is not a true melt procedure.

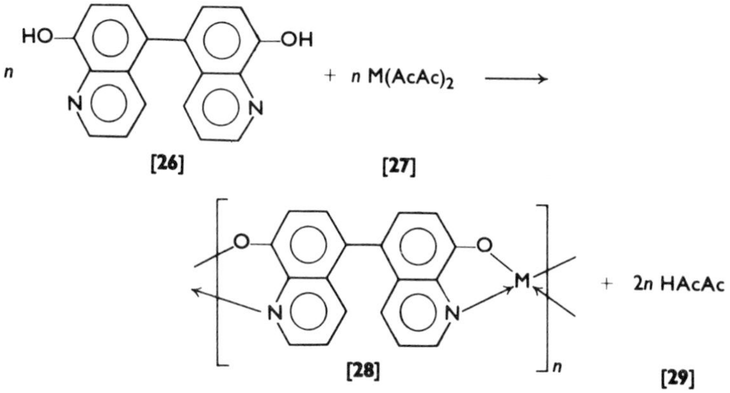

$$\text{[26]} + n\ \text{M(AcAc)}_2 \longrightarrow \text{[28]} + 2n\ \text{HAcAc} \qquad \text{(VII-10)}$$

Tris(o-hydroxyphenyl)triazine possesses structural features similar to 8-hydroxyquinoline. Linear polymers can be prepared by reaction of this trifunctional ligand with divalent metal salts in solution (32, 34). Reaction in bulk leads to the formation of cross-linked network polymers. Exactly how the difference in polymer structures [31] and [32] was determined was not made clear because both products were insoluble and infusible. It was postulated that the linear structure was obtainable because it precipitated from the reaction solvent before reaction with a third metal ion. Dimethylformamide was used in conjunction with an alcohol, such as methanol or ethanol, for the solution reaction. Temperatures up to 330°C were used for the bulk reaction.

[17] + n M(C$_2$H$_3$O$_2$)$_2$

[30]

[31]

+ 2n HOOCCH$_3$

[32]

+ 2n HOOCCH$_3$

Solution

Bulk

(VII-11)

Products that possessed similar structures were also prepared from salicy-lonitrile and its metal salts. A reaction of this type was run in an extreme high pressure apparatus at high temperature. Reaction of zinc-salicylonitrile with added salicylonitrile was performed at 14,000 kg/cm^2 and 300°C in a Bridgman apparatus (34). Trimerization of the nitrile groups to yield triazine nuclei was postulated to have occurred. This type of polymerization procedure has been extended to many other nitriles with salts of salicylonitrile (35). Nitriles that have been "copolymerized" include terephthalonitrile, acrylonitrile, adipo-nitrile, and 2-phenoxybenzonitrile. In all cases, the products were obtained from the pressure apparatus as hard moldings possessing high melting tem-peratures. Temperatures of from 125°–500°C and pressures of 3500–40,000 kg/cm^2 were used.

A patent (33) describes the reaction of tris(2-hydroxyphenyl)triazine with boric and phenyboronic acids. Products that were thermally stable to 440° and 380°C, respectively, were obtained.

The thermal stability of polymers prepared from bis(8-hydroxy-5-quinolyl) derivatives has been of continuing interest to the workers in this field. A recent series of papers (27–29) represents the definitive work on this property. Some decomposition temperatures obtained by thermogravimetry in vacuum are shown in Fig. VII.1 for three series of polymers. The trend in thermal stability for the Ni > Cu < Zn polymers is unmistakable, and is in agreement with other bis(8-hydroxyquinoline) coordination polymers containing these metals (31). By studying the volatile products arising as a result of the thermal degradation of these polymers, information about the mechanism has been obtained. No metal or metal-containing compounds were volatilized. Rather, only organic materials formed by bond cleavages within the polymers were found. However, rupture of the metal–ligand bonds is also probably occurring. If this is a major occurrence, a minimum of three chemical bonds must be broken before volatile organic fragments are generated. Hopefully, additional studies by these workers (29) will serve to pinpoint the sequence of bond rupture on thermolysis.

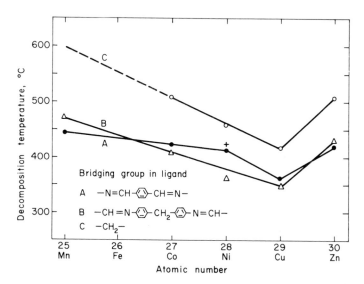

FIG. VII.1. Relationship between the thermal stability (decomposition temperature) of the coordination polymer and atomic number of the metal for bis(8-hydroxyquinoline) ligands containing different bridging groups (29).

Magnetic properties of the polymeric chelates derived from bis(8-hydroxy-5-quinolyl)methane were used to aid in structure determination. The magnetic moments of the Co(II) and Mn(II) polymers were 4.4 and 5.8 bohr magnetons, respectively. In both cases these values were suggestive of tetrahedral bond arrangements based on sp^3 hybridization (46). More extensive studies with this bis(ligand) have been reported (61). Narrow EPR signals in the polymers of bis(8-hydroxy-5-quinolyl)methane with Mg(II), Zn(II), Cd(II), and Hg(II) have been described (8). Their origin in the presence of these metals was not explainable. Electrical properties have been measured for polymeric metal chelates derived from 1,5-dihydroxyphenazine (31) and bis(8-hydroxy-5-quinolyl)methane (61). With the latter ligand, semiconductors were obtained. A mechanism of conduction via charge-transfer complexes was described (61).

An attempt to measure glass transition temperatures of a series of these polymers by "thermomechanical curves" was complicated by simultaneous thermal decomposition (*47*).

C. Metal-Containing Poly(Schiff Bases)

The reaction product of an aldehyde or ketone with an amine is commonly called a Schiff base. The distinguishing structural feature of a Schiff base is a carbon–nitrogen double bond. Although the majority of polymers that will be discussed in this section are chelated Schiff bases, several similar materials are included. Polymeric Schiff bases are one of the oldest known classes of condensation polymers. Perhaps for this reason, many of the recent polymeric metal–Schiff bases have been prepared by coordinating a polymeric Schiff base with the metallic ion (*14, 15, 21, 51, 52*). Although this work is pertinent, it has not been considered in detail because it falls outside the main theme of this book, namely, ring-forming polymerization in which the ring is actually formed during the propagation step.

METHOD 1. REACTION OF DICARBONYL COMPOUNDS AND DIAMINES WITH METAL SALTS OR METAL CHELATES

Polymerization of a dicarbonyl compound, a diamine, and a metal salt, is the most direct route to polymeric metal–Schiff bases (VII-12). One of the earliest uses of this reaction was as a colorimetric analytical method for metal ions (*16*). This reaction has been carried out in aqueous media, dimethylformamide (*50*), and mixed solvents incorporating benzene (*50, 75*). As with most chelate polymers, insolubility hampers obtention of high molecular weight. Molecular weights of 2000–11,000 were reported for the products obtained from some halogen-substituted bis(salicylaldehyde)–diamine–uranyl complexes (*75*).

[33]   [8]   [34]

[35]   [36]   (VII-12)

A variant in the synthesis of this class of chelate polymer employs the reaction of a metal chelate with a diamine. Bulk polymerization at 80°C *in vacuo* was used for the reaction shown in Eq. (VII-13) (*14*). Metal acetylacetonates have been reacted with methylenedianiline in attempts to get analogous reactions but only charred residues were obtained (*15*). A polymeric chelate failed to exchange with a diamine to give polymer in one case (*4*).

[37] [38] [39] (VII-13)

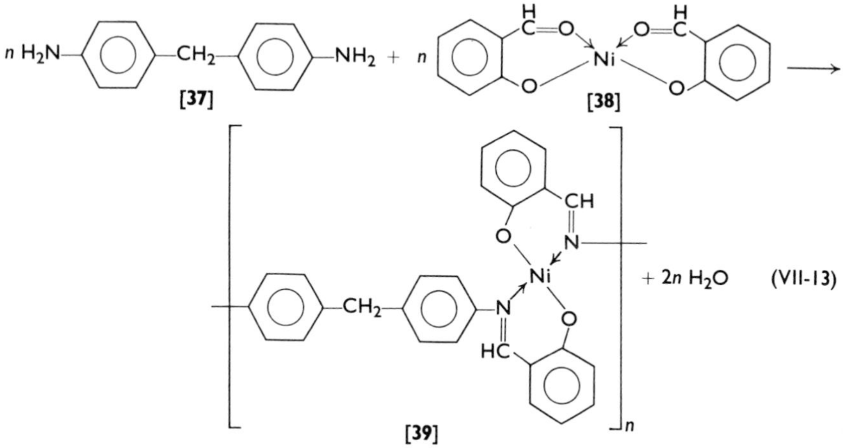

METHOD 2. POLYMERIZATION OF BIS(SCHIFF BASES) WITH METAL SALTS OR METAL CHELATES

A simplification in Method C,1 occurs when a preformed bis(ligand) is polymerized with a metal ion (*18*).

[40] [41] [42] (VII-14)

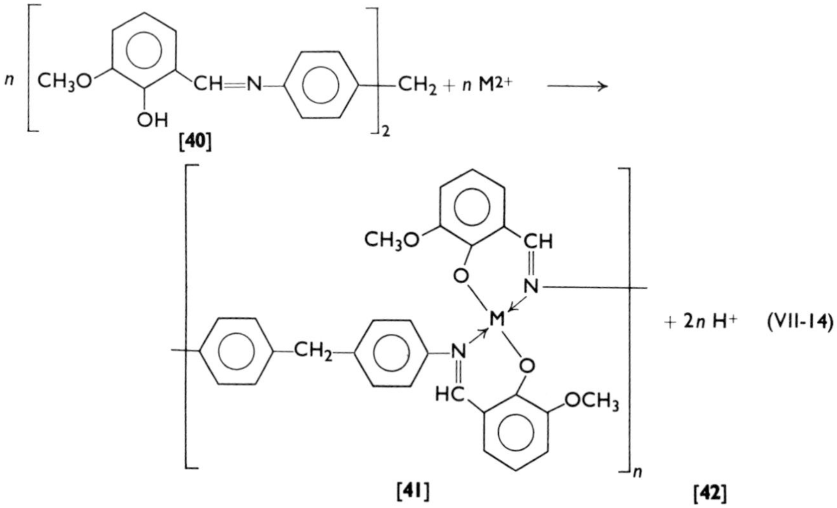

Metal acetylacetonates have been used as the metal source (*18*) in addition to more ordinary salts. In certain instances, the chelation reaction was carried out in the presence of ammonium hydroxide (*57–59*). This modification was used to prepare some unique materials from the nicotinic acids. The polymer [46] shown in Eq. (VII-15) was reported to be thermally stable at 350°C, and to resist boiling alkali.

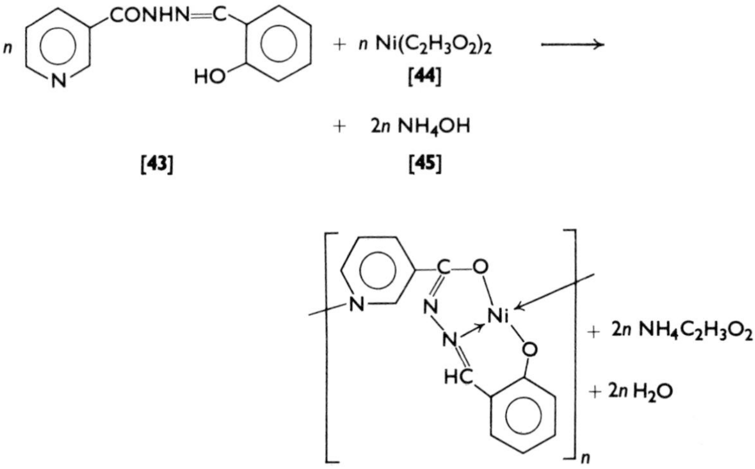

Good resistance to boiling alkali was reported for the polymer [48] prepared from dibenzaloxalhydrazimidine and nickel acetate (*59*), viz.,

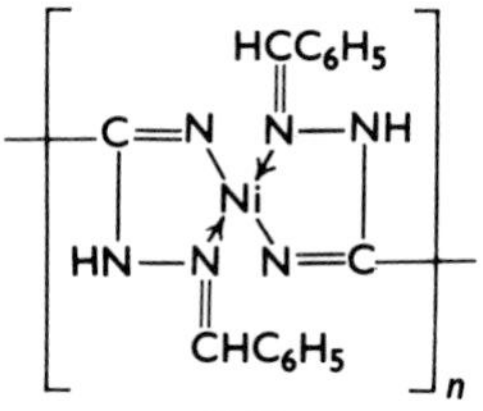

Multifunctional, polymeric Schiff bases were converted to coatings by chelate exchange with monomeric chelates (*24–26*). Although not specifically polymer-oriented, other studies have been reported that dealt with reactants that could have formed polymers (*30, 55*).

A unique method for determining the molecular weights of these polymers has been reported (*67*). Polymers prepared from $Cu^{82}Br_2$ were analyzed for their radioactivity, which was assumed to be present as end groups. Calculations using these data gave their molecular weights. Related studies using different physical data (*56, 66*) have concluded that two- and three-dimensional structures predominate in these and other classes of chelate polymers. X-Ray studies of several members of this polymer class indicate that they are amorphous (*56, 65, 72*).

The most recent investigations into this class of chelate polymer had as its aim the preparation of thermally stable materials. Monomeric analogs included the Cu, Ni, and Co complexes of acetylacetone–ethylenediamine which may be heated "almost to redness" without decomposition (*4*). Nevertheless, nothing exceptional in the way of thermal stability has been reported for this class of chelate polymer. Decomposition temperatures in the range of 250°–350°C are reported (*56, 65*). One relative order based on thermogravimetry was reported to be Ni(II) > Cd(II) > Cu(II) > Zn(II) > Co(II) > Fe(II) (*56*). Studies with related monomeric chelates have been described (*49, 52*).

Electron paramagnetic resonance studies have been reported for these chelate polymers (*7, 56*) and utilized in discussions of structure. Electrical conductivities in the 10^{-7}–10^{-13} ohm^{-1} cm^{-1} range were obtained on some of these materials (*68*).

The catalytic activity of certain polymers derived from 5,5′-methylenebis-(salicylaldehyde) for the decomposition of hydrazine (*11, 41*), isopropanol (*11*), formic acid (*11*), hydrogen peroxide (*42*), and the oxidation of cumene to its hydroperoxide (*40*) has been studied.

D. Polymers from Bis(*o*-hydroxyazo) Ligands

METHOD 1. POLYMERIZATION OF BIS(*o*-HYDROXYAZO) LIGANDS WITH METAL SALTS

The preparation of metal chelate polymers from bis(*o*-hydroxyazo) ligands has been reported. Bis[(*o*-hydroxyphenyl)azo]- [49] (*18–20*) and bis(3-hydroxy-4-azopyrazolone) [50] (*19, 20*) compounds are polymerizable. With both classes of ligands, black, intractable products were obtained on reaction with metal salts. Only Cu(II) polymers have been investigated. Dimethylformamide, dioxane, and dioxane-ethanol mixtures were used as solvents. The products were not characterized because of their insolubility.

[49]   [50]   (VII-17)

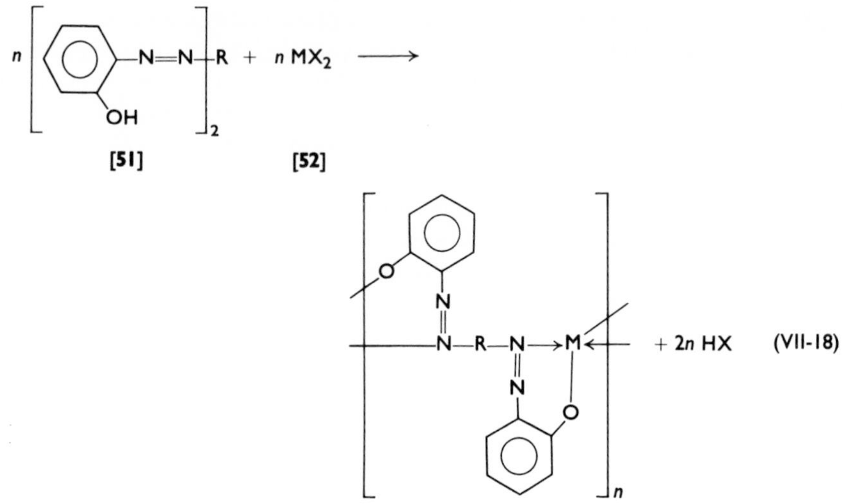

[51]   [52]

+ 2n HX   (VII-18)

[53]   [54]

E. Polymers from Miscellaneous Bis(N:O) Ligands

METHOD 1. POLYMERIZATION OF PYROMELLITIMIDE WITH METAL SALTS

The chelation of pyromellitimide with metals in dimethylformamide has been described (VII-19) (23). Yields vary depending on the specific metal ion and anion that are employed. The polymers were purported to be stable in boiling water and to be unchanged after heating for 3 hours in air at 300°C. The mercuric chelate decomposes at 510°C in air. Electrical properties were also measured.

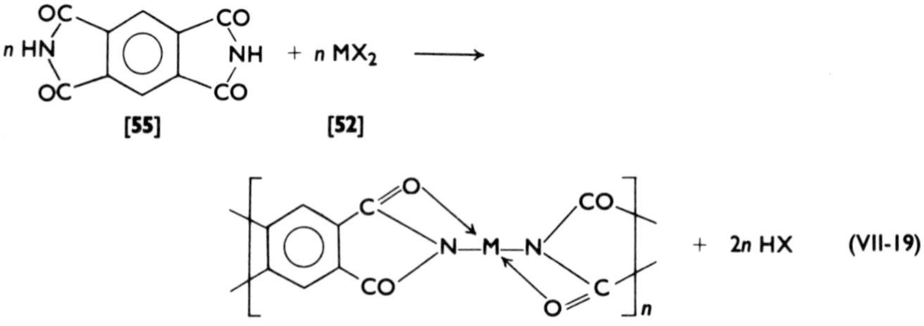

[55]   [52]

+ 2n HX   (VII-19)

[56]

METHOD 2. POLYMERIZATION OF N,N'-BIS(β-BENZOYLVINYL)DIAMINES AND 2,5-BIS(ARYLAMINOQUINONES) WITH METAL SALTS

N,N'-Bis(β-benzoylvinyl)diamines polymerize with copper acetate to yield polymeric powders that are insoluble in common organic solvents (VII-20) (54). Slight solubility in naphthalene and phenanthrene was reported. The polymers are thermally stable at 350°–400°C.

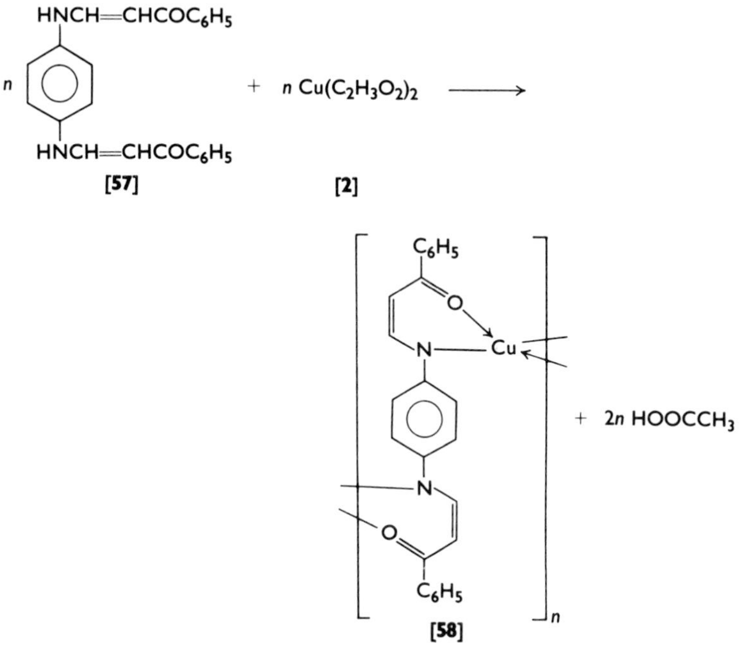

n

HNCH=CHCOC₆H₅

HNCH=CHCOC₆H₅

[57]

$+$ n Cu(C₂H₃O₂)₂ $\longrightarrow$

[2]

$$\text{[58]} \quad + \quad 2n \text{ HOOCCH}_3 \quad \text{(VII-20)}$$

2,5-Bis(arylaminoquinones) possess chelating sites that are similar to those in the bis(ligand) [57]. A series of these monomers polymerizes with Cu(II) and Co(II) ions yielding polymers whose structures were supported by analytical and infrared spectral data (10). In addition to [59], other bis(arylaminoquin-ones) possessing substituents on the quinone and N-phenyl rings were evalu-ated. Thermal stability, electrical conductivity, and ESR data for these polymers are available (10).

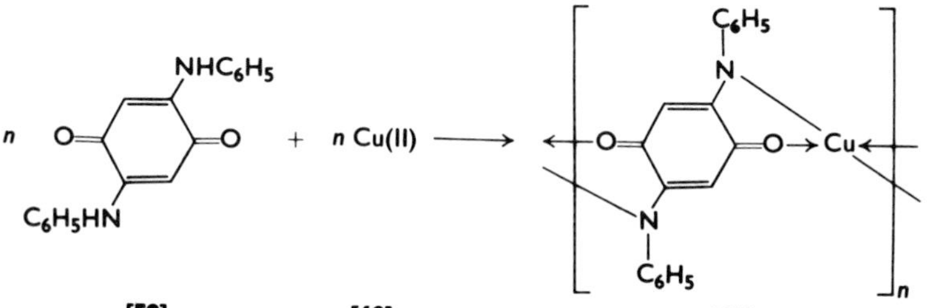

n

NHC₆H₅

O=⬡=O

C₆H₅HN

[59]

$+$ n Cu(II) $\longrightarrow$

[60]

[61] (VII-21)

METHOD 3. POLYMERIZATION OF OXIMES OF ACYLOINS AND α-DIKETONES

Oximes of acyloins and α-diketones polymerize with metals to yield ring-containing products. Poly[Cu(II) benzoin oxime] was postulated to possess structure [63] (*63*).

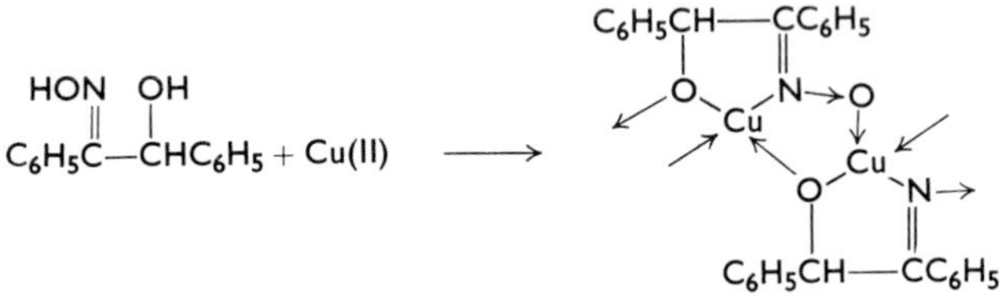

$$
\text{[62]} \qquad \text{[60]} \qquad\qquad \text{[63]} \qquad\qquad\qquad \text{(VII-22)}
$$

The bis(ligands) [64] have been polymerized with both Cu(II) and Co(II) to yield brown polymers. Dimethylformamide was used for the reaction solvent (*45*). The cobalt-containing polymers are more thermally stable than the analogous copper polymers. The structure shown for these polymers [65] is that which was reported (*45*), but a five-ring structure analogous to [63] was not ruled out. For this reason, this polymer class is included in this chapter rather than Chapter IX on oxygen chelate ligands.

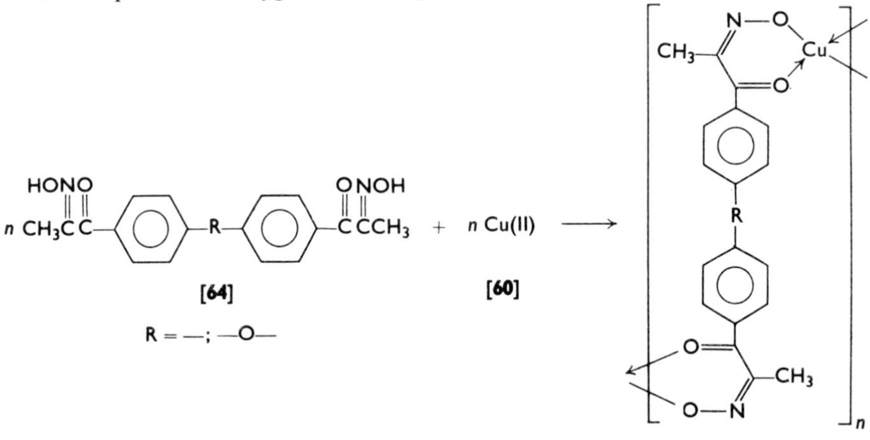

$$
\text{[64]} \qquad\qquad \text{[60]}
$$

R = —; —O—

$$
\text{[65]} \qquad\qquad \text{(VII-23)}
$$

METHOD 4. POLYMERIZATION OF BIS(PYRAZINYLMETHYL) DIKETONES WITH METAL SALTS

The polymerization of bis(pyrazinylmethyl) diketones with metal acetates proceeds via the enol form (*6*). Treating the bis(ligand) in pyridine solution at 50°–90°C with an aqueous metal salt gave intractable colored precipitates. Only elemental analyses were presented to substantiate the proposed structures for the products. They are shown in Eq. (VII-24).

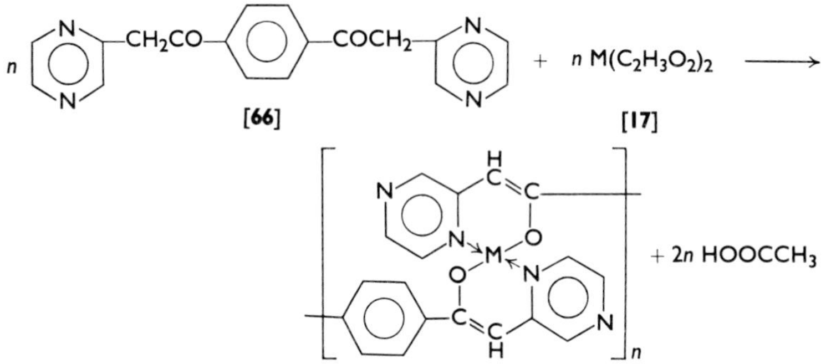

(VII-24)

METHOD 5. POLYMERIZATION OF 2,2'-PYRIDOINS

2,2'-Pyridoin [68] has been polymerized with metal acetates in alcohol containing a little acetic acid (13). The polymers from Ni(II), Cu(II), and Zn(II) possessed molecular weights of 2500–3000. From the structural evidence that was obtained in the work, the Cu(II) polymers were postulated to possess a planar-sheetlike structure, whereas the Ni(II) polymer had octahedral coordination. The Zn(II) polymer was a three-dimensional network, a fact that could account for its greater thermal stability. Substituted pyridoins have also been polymerized and are detailed in Table VII.5 (pp. 204–206).

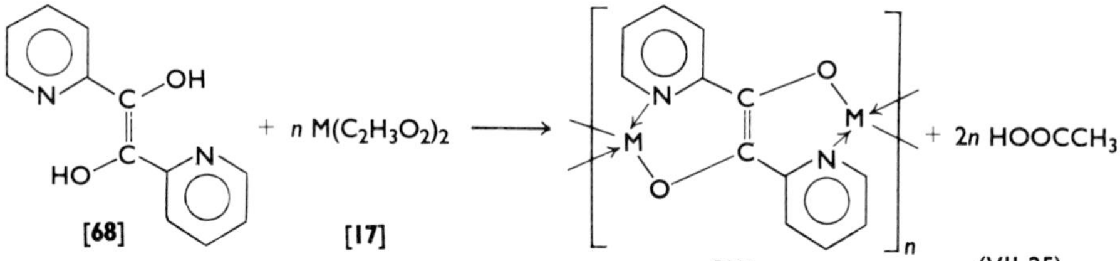

(VII-25)

METHOD 6. POLYMERIZATION OF BIS(HYDROXAMIC ACIDS) AND BIS(HYDRAZIDES) WITH METAL SALTS

A cryptic mention that bis(hydroxamic acid)–metal polymers have been studied was noted (19, p. 3). No other data were published.

(VII-26)

Polymeric nickel bis(hydrazides) have been prepared (38). Purification problems prohibited extensive work. Fiber formation was demonstrated to a degree when a limited amount of water was present in the nickel hydrazides.

TABLE VII.1

Polymers from Bis(amino acids)

No.	Structure	Metal (M)	Method	Color	Solubility	Remarks and property data	References
1	R = —(meso and racemic)	Cu(II)	A,1	Blue	Insoluble	Crystalline. Diffuse reflectance data	74
		Ni(II)	A,1	Pale blue	Sl. sol. H_2O	Amorphous. Diffuse reflectance data	74
2	R = $(CH_2)_2$	Cu(II)	A,1	Blue	Insol. H_2O	—	62
3	R = $(CH_2)_6$	Cu(II)	A,1	—	—	—	17
4	R = $(CH_2)_6$	Co(III)	A,1	Tan	H_2SO_4, HNO_3	Cross-linked. T_m = >300°C	2, 4, 17
5	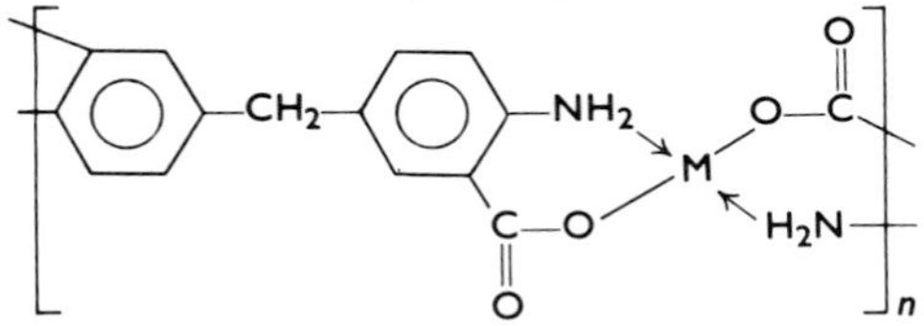	Cu(II)	A,1	—	—	—	17
6		Co(III)	A,1	—	—	—	17

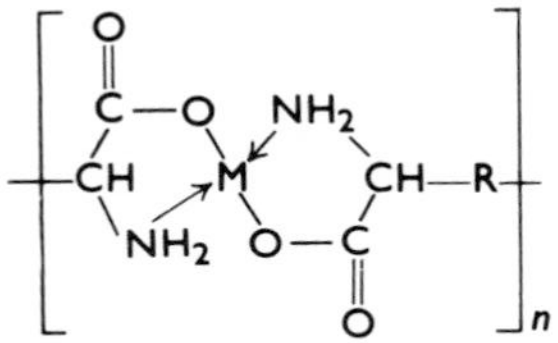

189

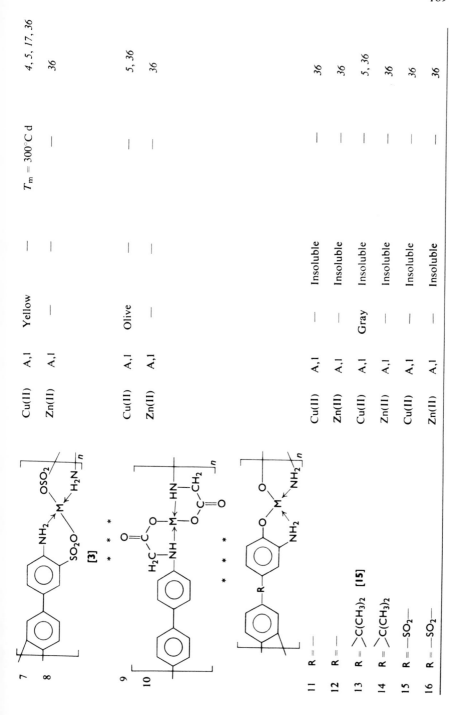

[3]

9

10

11 R = —

12 R = —

13 R = $C(CH_3)_2$ **[15]**

14 R = $C(CH_3)_2$

15 R = —SO_2—

16 R = —SO_2—

					$T_m = 300°C$ d	
7	Cu(II)	A,1	Yellow	—		4, 5, 17, 36
8	Zn(II)	A,1	—	—	—	36
9	Cu(II)	A,1	Olive	—		5, 36
10	Zn(II)	A,1	—	—	—	36
11	Cu(II)	A,1	—	Insoluble	—	36
12	Zn(II)	A,1	—	Insoluble	—	36
13	Cu(II)	A,1	Gray	Insoluble	—	5, 36
14	Zn(II)	A,1	—	Insoluble	—	36
15	Cu(II)	A,1	—	Insoluble	—	36
16	Zn(II)	A,1	—	Insoluble	—	36

TABLE VII.2
Metal Bis(8-hydroxyquinolinates) and Related Types

(5,8-dihydroxyquinoxaline)

No.	Structure	Metal (M)	Method	Color	Solubility	T_m (°C)	Molecular weight, remarks, and property data	References
1	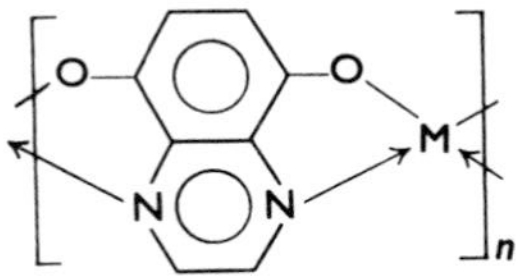	Bi(III)	B,1	Scarlet	Acetone	—	—	1
2		Cd(II)	B,1	Violet	—	—	—	1, 39
3		Co(II)	B,1	Violet	Acetone	—	—	1, 39
4		Cu(I)	B,1	Violet	—	—	—	1, 39
5		Fe(II)	B,1	Blue	—	—	—	1, 39
6		Ni(II)	B,1	Violet	Acetone	—	—	1, 39
7		Pb(II)	B,1	Red	—	—	—	1, 39
8		Zn(II)	B,1	Violet	Acetone	—	—	1, 39
9		Ga(III), In(III), MoO$_4$(II), Tl(III), V(V) WO$_4$(II)	B,1	Orange to red	—	—	—	39
10		Ag(I), Au(III)	B,1	Blue	—	—	—	39
11		Ti(IV)	B,1	Brown	—	—	—	39

191

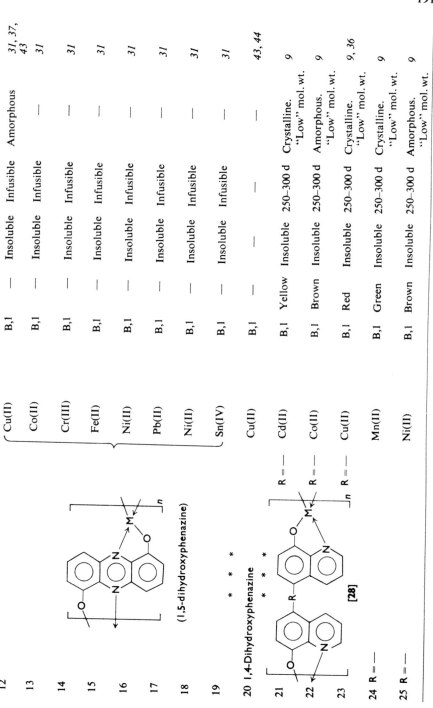

(1,5-dihydroxyphenazine)

20 1,4-Dihydroxyphenazine

[28]

No.	R	M		Color	Solubility	Thermal	Crystallinity	Ref.
12		Cu(II)	B,l	—	Insoluble	Infusible	Amorphous	31, 37, 43
13		Co(II)	B,l	—	Insoluble	Infusible	—	31
14		Cr(III)	B,l	—	Insoluble	Infusible	—	31
15		Fe(II)	B,l	—	Insoluble	Infusible	—	31
16		Ni(II)	B,l	—	Insoluble	Infusible	—	31
17		Pb(II)	B,l	—	Insoluble	Infusible	—	31
18		Ni(II)	B,l	—	Insoluble	Infusible	—	31
19		Sn(IV)	B,l	—	Insoluble	Infusible	—	31
		Cu(II)	B,l	—	—	—	—	43, 44
21	R=—	Cd(II)	B,l	Yellow	Insoluble	250–300 d	Crystalline. "Low" mol. wt.	9
22	R=—	Co(II)	B,l	Brown	Insoluble	250–300 d	Amorphous. "Low" mol. wt.	9
23	R=—	Cu(II)	B,l	Red	Insoluble	250–300 d	Crystalline. "Low" mol. wt.	9, 36
24	R=—	Mn(II)	B,l	Green	Insoluble	250–300 d	Crystalline. "Low" mol. wt.	9
25	R=—	Ni(II)	B,l	Brown	Insoluble	250–300 d	Amorphous. "Low" mol. wt.	9

TABLE VII.2—continued

Metal Bis(8-hydroxyquinolinates) and Related Types

No.	Structure	Metal (M)	Method	Color	Solubility	T_m (°C)	Molecular weight, remarks, and property data	References
26	R = —	Zn(II)	B,1	Yellow	Insoluble	250–300 d	Crystalline. "Low" mol. wt.	9, 36
27	R = —N=N—	Various	B,1	—	—	—	—	4, 5, 22, 69
28	R = —CH₂— [25]	Cd(II)	B,1	Yellow	—	280 d	Amorphous. Mol. wt. = 8370	4, 5, 8, 47, 69
29	R = —CH₂— [25]	Co(II)	B,1	Green	—	250 d	EPR and TGA data	4, 5, 27, 28, 46, 47, 61, 69
30	R = —CH₂— [25]	Cu(II)	B,1	Yellow	—	320 d	EPR and TGA data Mol. wt. = 1390	4, 5, 27, 28, 46, 47, 61, 69
31	R = —CH₂— [25]	Hg(II)	B,1	—	—	—	EPR and TGA data	4, 5, 8, 69
32	R = —CH₂— [25]	Mg(II)	B,1	—	—	—	EPR and TGA data	4, 5, 8, 46, 69
33	R = —CH₂— [25]	Mn(II)	B,1	Green	—	260 d	Amorphous. EPR & TGA data	4, 5, 27, 28, 46, 47, 61, 69
34	R = —CH₂— [25]	Ni(II)	B,1	Brown	—	240 d	Crystalline. EPR & TGA data Mol. wt. = 680	4, 5, 27, 28, 46, 47, 69

					280 d	Crystalline.EPR & TGA data Mol. wt.= 7240	
35 R = —CH₂— **[25]**	Zn(II)	B,1	Yellow-green	—	—	—	4, 5, 8, 27, 28, 46, 47, 61, 69
36 R = $>$C(CH₃)₂	—	—	—	—	—	—	2–5
37 R = —S—	Cu(II)	B,1	—	—	—	—	3–5, 36
38 R = —S—	Zn(II)	B,1	—	—	—	—	36
39 R = —SO₂—	Cu(II)	B,1	—	—	—	—	3–5, 8, 36
40 R = —SO₂—	Zn(II)	B,1	—	—	—	—	36
41 R = —SO₂—	Co(II), Mn(II), Ni(II)	B,1	—	—	—	—	8
42	Cu(II)	B,1	—	—	—	TGA data (vacuum) reported	29
43	Co(II)	B,1	—	—	—	TGA data (vacuum) reported	29
44 R = —N=CH—⟨C₆H₄⟩—CH=N—	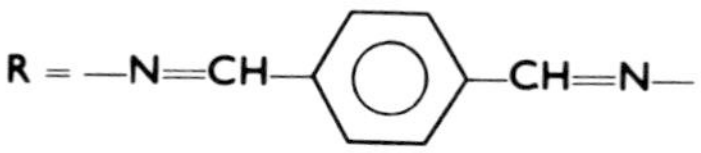 Mn(II)	B,1	—	—	—	TGA data (vacuum) reported	29
45	Ni(II)	B,1	—	—	—	TGA data (vacuum) reported	29
46	Zn(II)	B,1	—	—	—	TGA data (vacuum) reported	29

TABLE VII.2—continued

Metal Bis(8-hydroxyquinolinates) and Related Types

No.	Structure	Metal (M)	Method	Color	Solubility	T_m (°C)	Molecular weight, remarks, and property data	References
47	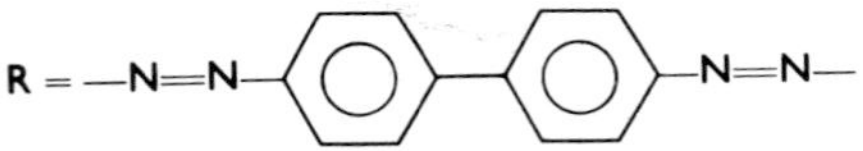 R = —N=N— (biphenyl azo)	Various	B,1	—	—	—	Color tests only	12, 60, 69
48	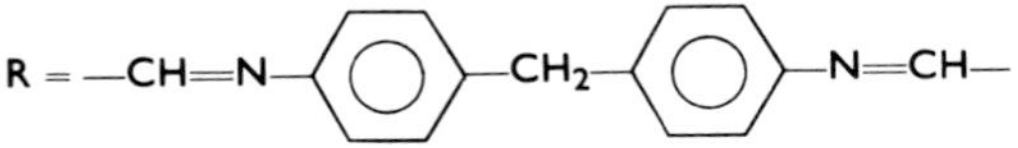	Cu(II)	B,1	—	Insoluble	350 d (TGA)	Stability studied in air and vacuum	28
49		Co(II)	B,1	—	Insoluble	415 d (TGA)	—	28
50	R = —CH=N—...—CH₂—...—N=CH—	Mn (II)	B,1	—	Insoluble	470 d (TGA)	—	28
51		Ni(II)	B,1	—	Insoluble	380 d (TGA)	—	28
52		Zn(II)	B,1	—	Insoluble	430 d (TGA)	—	28
53	* * * * (sulfur-bridged bis-quinoline sulfonic acid)	—	—	—	—	—	—	4, 5

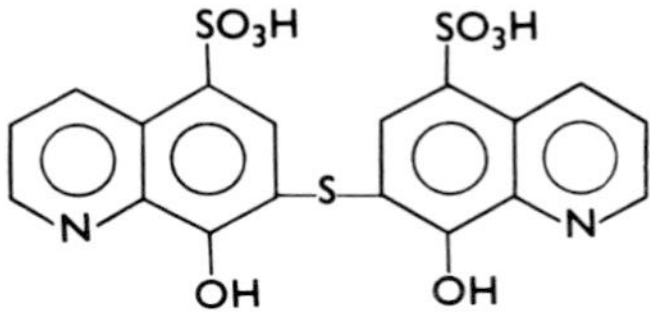

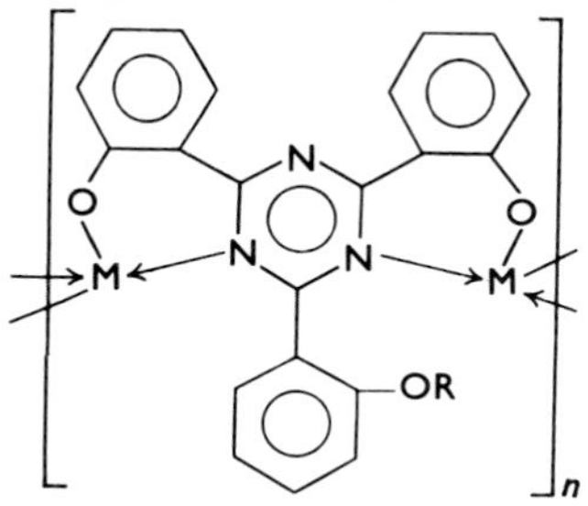

Compound	R	M	Column	Color				Ref.
54	R = H [31]	Cu(II)	B,1	Green	—	>360	—	32, 34
55	R = H	Zn(II)	B,1	Yellow	—	>500	—	32, 34
56	R = CH$_3$	Cu(II)	B,1	—	—	—	—	32
57	R = —CO—CH$_3$	Be(II)	B,1	Yellow	—	>360	—	32, 34
58	R = —CO—CH$_3$	Cu(II)	B,1	Green	—	>360	—	32, 34
59	R = —CO—CH$_3$	Co(II)	B,1	Brown	—	>360	—	34
60	R = —CO—CH$_3$	Fe(II)	B,1	Red-brown	—	>360	—	34
61	R = —CO—CH$_3$	Mg(II)	B,1	Yellow	—	>360	—	34
62	R = —CO—CH$_3$	Mn(II)	B,1	Red	—	>360	—	34
63	R = —CO—CH$_3$	Ni(II)	B,1	Yellow	—	>360	—	34
64	R = —CO—CH$_3$	Pb(II)	B,1	Yellow	—	>360	—	34

TABLE VII.3

Metal-Containing Poly(Schiff Bases)

No.	Structure	Metal (M)	Method	Color	Solubility	Molecular weight	T_m, remarks, and property data	References
1	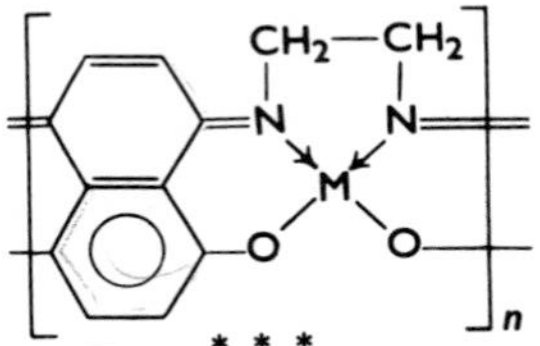	Mg(II) [35]	C,1	Violet	—	—	—	16
2		Ba, Be, Cd, Cu, Mg, Ni	C,1	—	—	—	—	16
3 R = H	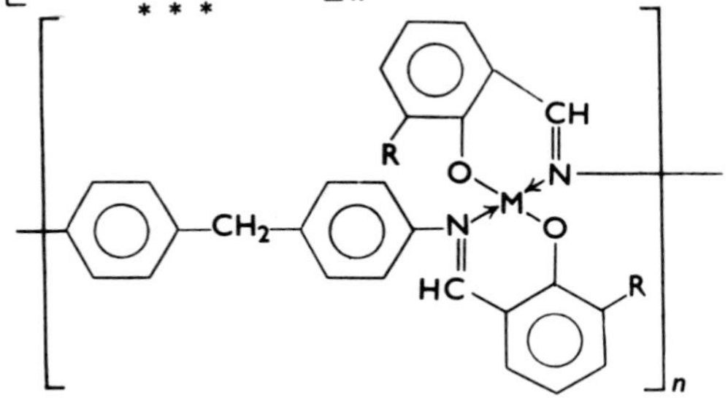	Cu(II)	C,1	—	—	—	T_m = >300°C	14, 15
4 R = H [39]		Ni(II)	C,1	Yellow	Insoluble	—	Decomposes when heated	15
5 R = —OCH₃		Cu(II)	C,2	Black	CHCl₃	—	—	18
6 R = —OCH₃		Ni(II)	C,2	—	—	—	—	18

	M		Color	Solubility	MW	Property	Ref.
7 R = —OCH₃	UO₂(II)	C,2	—	—	—	—	18
8 R = —OCH₃	Zn(II)	C,2	—	—	—	—	18

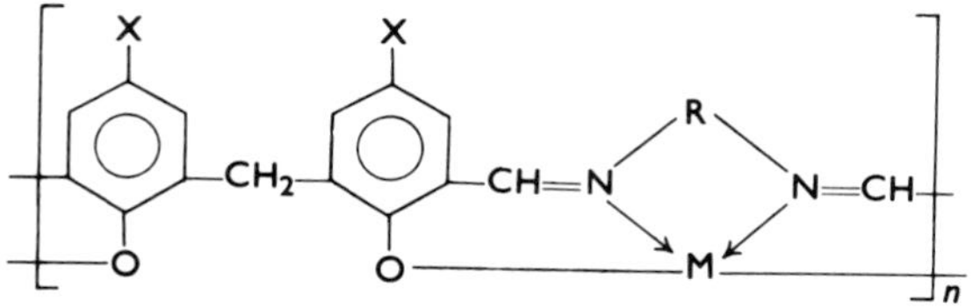

	M		Color	Solubility	MW	Property	Ref.
9 R = (CH₂)₂; X = Cl	UO₂(II)	C,1	—	—	10,514	$T_m = 270°C\ d$	75
10 R = (CH₂)₂; X = Br	UO₂(II)	C,1	—	—	9,296	$T_m = 260°C\ d$	75
11 R = 1,2-C₆H₄; X = Cl	UO₂(II)	C,1	—	—	8,631	$T_m = 300°C\ d$	75
12 R = 1,2-C₆H₄; X = Br	UO₂(II)	C,1	—	—	11,384	$T_m = 300°C\ d$	75
13 R = 1,4-C₆H₄; X = Cl	UO₂(II)	C,1	—	—	1,981	$T_m = 280°C\ d$	75
14 R = 1,4-C₆H₄; X = Br	UO₂(II)	C,1	—	—	2,336	$T_m = 270°C\ d$	75

	M		Color	Solubility	MW	Property	Ref.
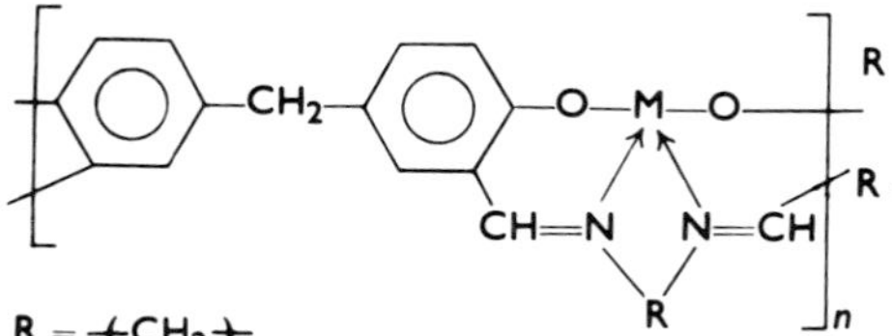 15 R = 2 H	Cu(II)	a	Green	Insoluble	53,500	Amorphous. Infusible	56, 64, 67
16 R = 2 H	Cd, Co, Fe, Ni, Zn	a	Various	Insoluble	—	Amorphous. Infusible	56, 64
17 R = (CH₂)₂	Cu(II)	a	Green	Insoluble	76,400	—	56, 64, 67
18 R = (CH₂)₂	Cd, Co, Fe, Ni, Zn	a	Various	Insoluble	—	—	56, 64

TABLE VII.3—continued

Metal-Containing Poly(Schiff Bases)

No.	Structure	Metal (M)	Method	Color	Solubility	Molecular weight	T_m, remarks, and property data	References
19	R = $-(CH_2)_6$	Cu(II)	a	Green	Insoluble	64,000	—	56, 64, 67
20	R = $-(CH_2)_6$	Cd, Co, Fe, Ni, Zn	a	Various	—	—	—	56, 64
21	R = 1,2-C_6H_4	Cu(II)	a	Brown	Insoluble	41,100	—	56, 64, 67
22	R = 1,2-C_6H_4	Cd, Co, Fe, Ni, Zn	a	Various	Insoluble	—	—	56, 64

No.	R / A	Metal	Code	Color	Solvents	—	Property	Ref.
23	R = $(CH_2)_2$; A = Cl^-	Ni(II)	C,1	Green	H_2O, CH_3OH	—	Amorphous. Infusible	65
24	R = $(CH_2)_2$; A = SO_4^{2-}	Fe(II)	C,1	Violet	H_2O	—	Amorphous. Infusible	65
25	R = $(CH_2)_2$; A = Cl^-	Co(II)	C,1	Brown	H_2O	—	Amorphous. Infusible	65
26	R = $(CH_2)_6$; A = SO_4^{2-}	Fe(II)	C,1	Violet	H_2O, C_5H_5N	—	Amorphous. Infusible	65
27	R = $(CH_2)_6$; A = Cl^-	Co(II)	C,1	Brown	H_2O, CH_3OH	—	Amorphous. Infusible	65
28	R = $1,2$-C_6H_4; A = Cl^-	Co(II)	C,1	Brown	H_2O, CH_3OH, C_5H_5N	—	Amorphous. Infusible	65
29	R = $1,2$-C_6H_4; A = SO_4^{2-}	Fe(II)	C,1	Violet	H_2O, CH_3OH, C_5H_5N	—	Amorphous. Infusible	65
30	R = $1,2$-C_6H_4; A = Cl^-	Ni(II)	C,1	Green	H_2O, CH_3OH	—	Amorphous. Infusible	65

No.	R	Metal	Code	Color			Property	Ref.
31	R = $=C(CH_3)-CH-C(C_6H_5)O-$	Ni(II)	C,2	Brown	—	—	$T_m = >310°C$	58
32	R 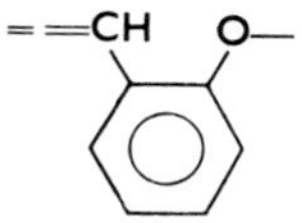 = $=CH$— (o-phenoxy)	Ni(II)	C,2	Red	—	—	—	57

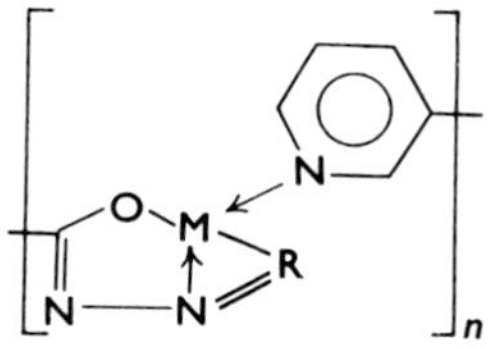

TABLE VII.3—continued

Metal-Containing Poly(Schiff Bases)

No.	Structure	Metal (M)	Method	Color	Solubility	Molecular weight	T_m, remarks, and property data	References
33	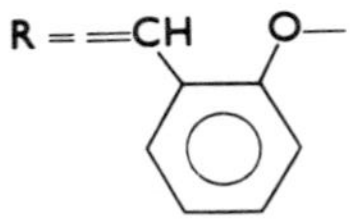 R $=$ CH	Ni(II)	C,1; C,2	Orange	—	—	—	57
34	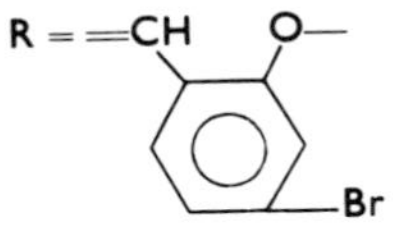 [46] R $=$ CH	Ni(II)	C,2	Orange	—	—	—	57
35	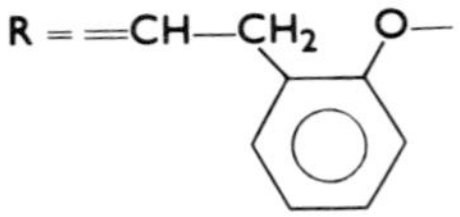 R $=$ CH—CH$_2$	Ni(II)	C,2	Orange	—	—	—	57
36	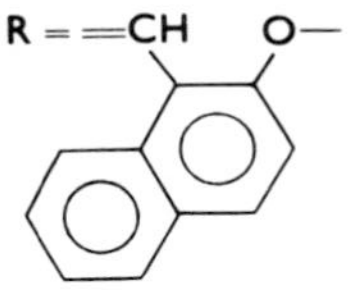 R $=$ CH	Ni(II)	C,2	Red	—	—	—	57

* * *

37

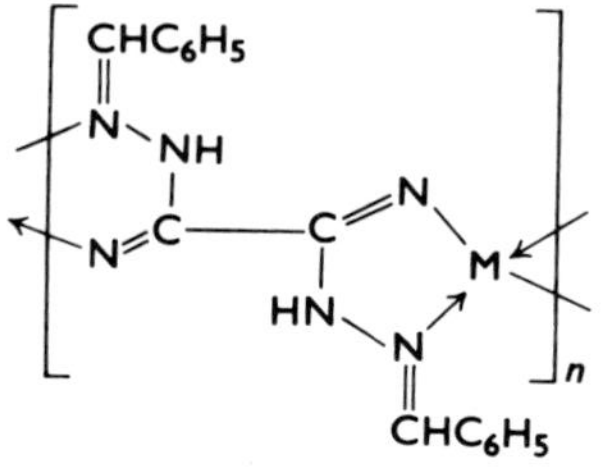

[48]

Ni(II)   C,2   Brown   Insoluble   —   —   59

---

a Prepared by postchelation on the prepolymer, but included for comparison.

TABLE VII.4

Polymers from Bis(*o*-hydroxyazo) Ligands

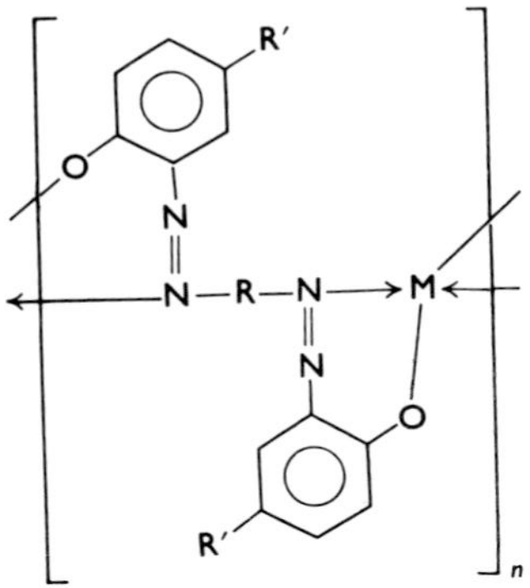

No.	Structure	Metal (M)	Method	Color	Solubility	T_m (°C)	References
		Cu(II)	D,1	Black	Insoluble	>300	*19, 20*
1	R = p-C$_6$H$_4$; R' = CH$_3$						
2	R = (biphenyl with R'' groups); R' = R'' = H	Cu(II)	D,1	Black	Insoluble	>300	*19, 20*

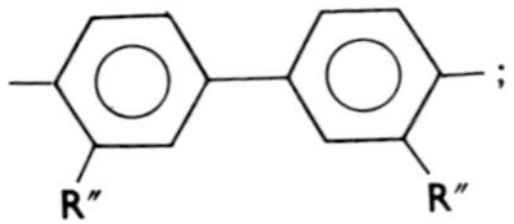

* * *

203

	R =						
3	R = (biphenyl); R′ = OCH₃; R″ = H	Cu(II)	D,1	Black	Insoluble	>300	*19, 20*
4	R 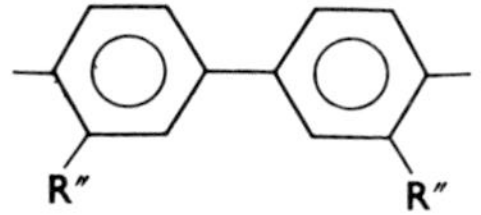 = (biphenyl); R′ = CH₃; R″ = OCH₃	Cu(II)	D,1	Black	C₆H₅Cl, DMF	>300	*19, 20*
5	R 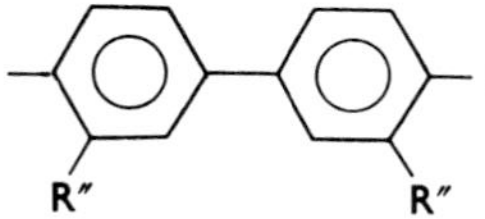 = (biphenyl); R′ = C(CH₃)₃; R″ = OCH₃	Cu(II)	D,1	Black	Insoluble	>300	*19, 20*
6	R 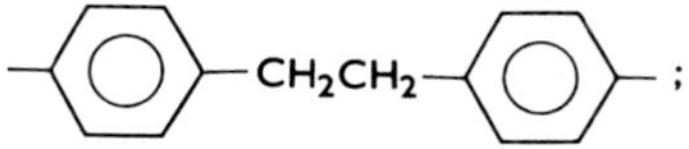 = —CH₂CH₂— (diphenyl); R′ = CH₃	Cu(II)	D,1	Black	Insoluble	>300	*19, 20*
7	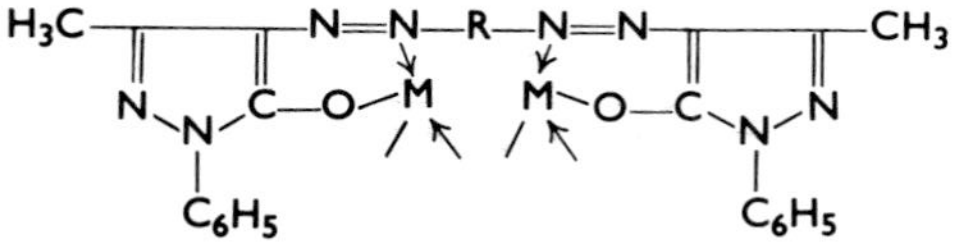 (structure)	Cu(II)	D,1	Black	Insoluble	—	*19, 20*

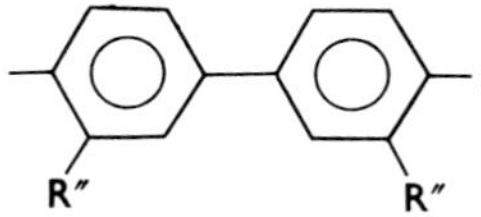

R = various radicals

TABLE VII.5

Polymers from Miscellaneous Bis(N:O) Ligands

No.	Structure	Metal (M)	Method	Color	Molecular weight	T_m (°C)	Remarks and property data	References
1	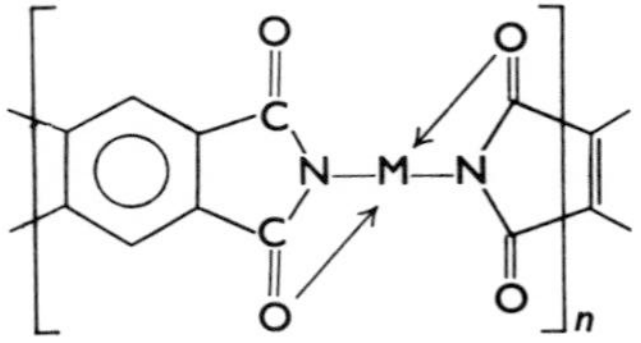 [56]	Hg(II)	E,1	—	—	510 d	—	23
2		Bi, Ca, Cd	E,1	—	—	—	—	23
		Co, Cu, Hg	E,1	—	—	—	—	23
		Mn, Ni, Zn	E,1	—	—	—	—	23
3	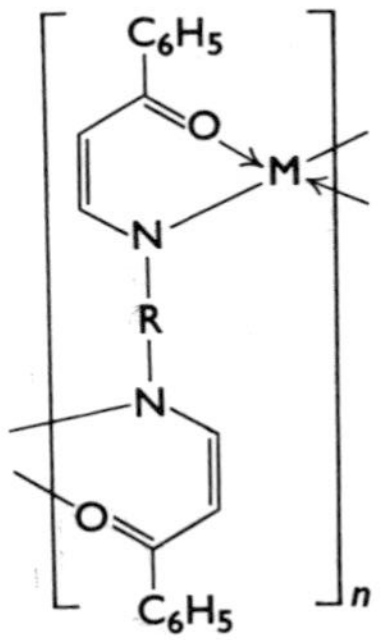 R = 1,4-C_6H_4 [58]	Cu(II)	E,2	—	—	—	Soluble in naphthalene, phenanthrene	54
4	R = 4,4'-C_6H_4—C_6H_4	Cu(II)	E,2	—	—	—	Soluble in naphthalene, phenanthrene	54

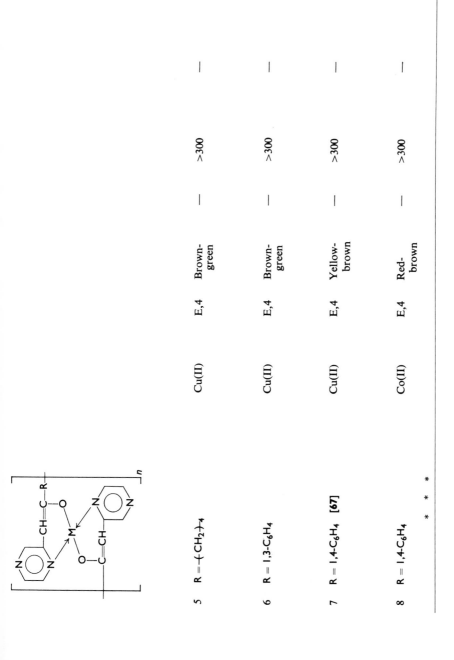

5	R = +(CH$_2$)$_4$	Cu(II)	E,4	Brown-green	—	>300	—	6
6	R = 1,3-C$_6$H$_4$	Cu(II)	E,4	Brown-green	—	>300	—	6
7	R = 1,4-C$_6$H$_4$ [67]	Cu(II)	E,4	Yellow-brown	—	>300	—	6
8	R = 1,4-C$_6$H$_4$	Co(II)	E,4	Red-brown	—	>300	—	6

* * *

TABLE VII.5—*continued*

Polymers from Miscellaneous Bis(N:O) Ligands

[69]

No.	Structure	Metal (M)	Method	Color	Molecular weight	T_m (°C)	Remarks and property data	References
9	R = H	Ni(II)	E,5	—	2,500–3,000 (elemental analysis)	330 d (TGA)	Magnetic properties measured	13
10	R = H	Cu(II)	E,5	Blue	2,500–3,000 (elemental analysis)	298 d (TGA)	Magnetic properties measured	13
11	R = H	Zn(II)	E,5	White	2,500–3,000 (elemental analysis)	310 d (TGA)	Magnetic properties measured	13
12	R = CH₃	Ni(II)	E,5	Green	2,500–3,000 (elemental analysis)	310 d (TGA)	Magnetic properties measured	13
13	R = CH₃	Cu(II)	E,5	Green	2,500–3,000 (elemental analysis)	260 d (TGA)	Magnetic properties measured	13
14	R = CH₃	Zn(II)	E,5	Yellow	2,500–3,000 (elemental analysis)	350 d (TGA)	Magnetic properties measured	13

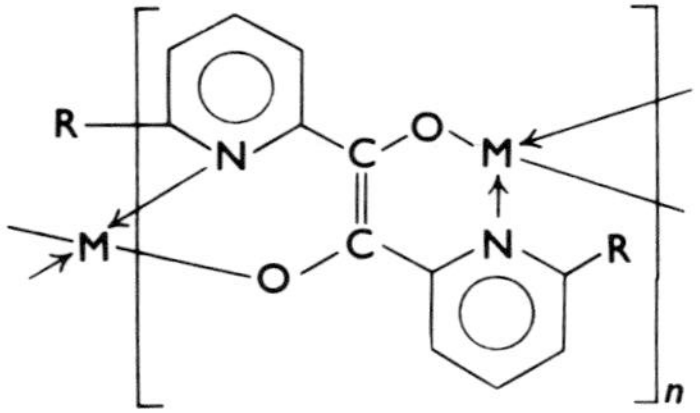

REFERENCES

1. Adachi, J., *Nippon Kagaku Zasshi* **76**, 311 (1955); *Chem. Abstr.* **51**, 17936 (1957).
2. Bailar, J. C., Jr., WADC Tech. Rept. No. 57-657, p. 35 (1958).
3. Bailar, J. C., Jr., and Judd, M., WADC Tech. Rept. No. 58-51 (1958).
4. Bailar, J. C., Jr., Martin, K. V., Judd, M. L., and McLean, J. A., Jr., WADC Tech. Rept. No. 57-391, Part I (1957).
5. Bailar, J. C., Jr., Martin, K. V., Judd, M. L., and McLean, J. A., Jr., WADC Tech. Rept. No. 57-391, Part II (1958).
6. Behun, J. D., U.S. Patent 3,190,854 (Wyandotte Chemicals Corp.) (1965); *Chem. Abstr.* **63**, 5866 (1965).
7. Belskii, N. K., and Tsikunov, V. N., *Dokl. Akad. Nauk SSSR* **142**, 380 (1962); *Chem. Abstr.* **57**, 1766 (1962).
8. Belskii, N. K., and Tsikunov, V. N., *Vysokomolekul. Soedin.* **5**, 754 (1963); *Resins, Rubbers, Plastics* p. 2675 (1963).
9. Berg, E. W., and Alam, A., *Anal. Chim. Acta* **27**, 454 (1962).
10. Berlin, A. A., Liogon'kii, B. I., and Abdulla-Zade, E. A., *Vysokomolekul. Soedin.* **A9**, 1725 (1967).
11. Boreskov, G. K., Keier, N. P., Rubtsova, L. F., and Rukhadze, E. G., *Dokl. Akad. Nauk SSSR* **144**, 1069 (1962); *Chem. Abstr.* **57**, 13959 (1962).
12. Boyd, T., Degering, E. F., and Shreve, R. N., *Ind. Eng. Chem. Anal. Ed.* **10**, 606 (1938).
13. Brierly, M., and Geary, W. J., *J. Chem. Soc., A, Inorg. Phys., Theoret.* p. 321 (1967); *Chem. Abstr.* **66**, 7181, 76345z (1967).
14. Drinkard W. C., Jr., and Chakravarty, D. N., WADC Tech. Rept. No. 59-427, p. 367 (1960).
15. Drinkard, W. C., Jr., and Chakravarty, D. N., WADC Tech. Rept. No. 59-761, p. 232 (1960).
16. Dubský J. V., Langer, A., and Wagner, E., *Mikrochemie* **22**, 108 (1937); *Chem. Abstr.* **31**, 4233 (1937).
17. Elliott, J. R., Ph.D. Thesis, University of Illinois (1943).
18. Fernelius, W. C., WADC Tech. Rept. No. 56-203 (1956).
19. Fernelius, W. C., Shamma, M., Davis, L. A., Goldberg, D. E., Martin, B. B., Martin, D. F., and Thomas, F. D., III, WADC Tech. Rept. No. 56-203, Part III (1958).
20. Fernelius, W. C., Shamma, M., Garofano, N. R., Goldberg, D. E., Martin, D. F., and Thomas, F. D., III, WADC Tech. Rept. No. 56-203, Part II (1957).
21. Goodwin, H. A., and Bailar, J. C., Jr., *J. Am. Chem. Soc.* **83**, 2467 (1961).
22. Gutzeit, G., and Monnier, R., *Helv. Chim. Acta* **16**, 478 (1933).
23. Hojo, N., Shirai, H., and Suzuki, A., *J. Chem. Soc. Japan, Ind. Chem. Sect.* **69**, 253 (1966); *Chem. Abstr.* **65**, 7282 (1966).
24. Hoover, F. W., and Miller, H. C., British Patent 791,325 (E. I. duPont de Nemours & Co.) (1958); *Chem. Abstr.* **52**, 14193 (1958).
25. Hoover, F. W., and Miller, H. C., British Patent 807,198 (E. I. duPont de Nemours & Co.) (1959); *Chem. Abstr.* **53**, 11888 (1959).
26. Hoover, F. W., and Miller, H. C., U.S. Patent 2,933,475 (E. I. duPont de Nemours & Co.) (1960); *Chem. Abstr.* **54**, 14780 (1960).
27. Horowitz, E., and Perros, T. P., *J. Inorg. & Nucl. Chem.* **26**, 139 (1964).
28. Horowitz, E., and Perros T. P., *J. Res. Natl. Bur. Std.* **A69**, 53 (1965); *Chem. Abstr.* **62**, 13252 (1965).
29. Horowitz, E., Tryon, M., Christensen, R. G., and Perros, T. P., *J. Appl. Polymer Sci.* **9**, 2321 (1965); *Chem. Abstr.* **63**, 7121 (1965).

30. Hovey, R., O'Connell, J. J., and Martell, A. E., *J. Am. Chem. Soc.* **81**, 3189 (1959).
31. Inoue, H., Hayashi, S., Takinchi, T., and Imoto, E., *Kogyo Kagaku Zasshi* **65**, 1622 (1962); *Resins, Rubbers, Plastics* p. 1487 (1963).
32. Johns, I. B., and DiPietro, H. R., *J. Org. Chem.* **27**, 592 (1962).
33. Johns, I. B., and DiPietro, H. R., U.S. Patent 3,169,943 (Monsanto Research Corp.) (1965); *Chem. Abstr.* **62**, 10620 (1965).
34. Johns, I. B., and DiPietro, H. R., U.S. Patent 3,211,698 (Monsanto Research Corp.) (1965); *Chem. Abstr.* **64**, 6845 (1966).
35. Johns, I. B., and DiPietro, H. R., U.S. Patent 3,211,699 (Monsanto Research Corp.) (1965); *Chem. Abstr.* **64**, 6845 (1966).
36. Judd, M. L., *Dissertation Abstr.* **19**, 2456 (1959).
37. Kanda, S., and Saito, Y., *Bull. Chem. Soc. Japan* **30**, 192 (1957); *Chem. Abstr.* **51**, 17562 (1957).
38. Karipides, D. G., *Dissertation Abstr.* **22**, 59 (1961).
39. Kawai, S., Hamaguchi, H., and Tatsumoto, M., *Bunseki Kagaku* **5**, 165 (1956); *Chem. Abstr.* **51**, 9401 (1957).
40. Keier, N. P., *Nauchn. Osnovy Podbora i Proizv. Katalizatorov Akad. Nauk SSSR, Sibirsk. Otd.* p. 218 (1964); *Chem. Abstr.* **63**, 7681 (1965).
41. Keier, N. P., Boreskov, G. K., Rubtsova, L. F., and Rukhadze, E. G., *Kinetika i Kataliz* **3**, 680 (1962); *Chem. Abstr.* **58**, 7412 (1963).
42. Keier, N. P., Troitskaya, M. G., and Rukhadze E. G., *Kinetika i Kataliz* **3**, 691 (1962); *Chem. Abstr.* **58**, 7413 (1963).
43. Kidani, Y., *Chem. Pharm. Bull. (Tokyo)* **6**, 563 (1958); *Chem. Abstr.* **53**, 12298 (1959).
44. Kidani, Y., *Chem. Pharm. Bull. (Tokyo)* **7**, 68 (1959); *Chem. Abstr.* **54**, 22666 (1960).
45. Korshak, V. V., Mirkamilova, M. S., and Bekasova, N. I., *Vysokomolekul. Soedin.* **B9**, 64 (1967); *Chem. Abstr.* **66**, 8961, 95420m (1967).
46. Korshak, V. V., Slinkin, A. A., Vinogradova, S. V., and Babchinitser, T. M., *Vysoko-molekul. Soedin.* **3**, 1624 (1961); *Chem. Abstr.* **56**, 14457 (1962).
47. Korshak, V. V., Vinogradova, S. V., and Babchinitser, T. M., *Vysokomolekul. Soedin.* **2**, 498 (1960); *Chem. Abstr.* **55**, 3104 (1961).
48. Martell, A. E., and Calvin, M., "Chemistry of the Metal Chelate Compounds," p. 457. Prentice-Hall, Englewood Cliffs, New Jersey, 1952.
49. Marvel, C. S., Aspey, S. A., and Dudley, E. A., *J. Am. Chem. Soc.* **78**, 4905 (1956).
50. Marvel, C. S., and Bonsignore, P. V., *J. Am. Chem. Soc.* **81**, 2668 (1959).
51. Marvel, C. S., and Tarköy, N., *J. Am. Chem. Soc.* **79**, 6000 (1957).
52. Marvel, C. S., and Tarköy, N., *J. Am. Chem. Soc.* **80**, 832 (1958).
53. Mattison, L. E., Phipps, M. S., Kazan, J., and Alfred, L., *J. Polymer Sci.* **54**, 117 (1961).
54. Nesmeyanov, A. N., Rybinskaya, M. I., and Slonimskii, G. L., *Vysokomolekul. Soedin.* **2**, 526 (1960); *Chem. Abstr.* **55**, 4408 (1961).
55. Pfeiffer, P., and Pfitzner, H., *J. Prakt. Chem.* [2] **145**, 243 (1936); *Chem. Abstr.* **30**, 5197 (1936).
56. Rode, V. V., Nekrasov, L. I., Terent'ev, A. P., and Rukhadze, E. G., *Vysokomolekul. Soedin.* **4**, 13 (1962); *Chem. Abstr.* **57**, 1055 (1962).
57. Sacconi, L., *Gazz. Chim. Ital.* **83**, 894 (1953); *Chem. Abstr.* **48**, 10471 (1954).
58. Sacconi, L., *Z. Anorg. Allgem. Chem.* **275**, 249 (1954).
59. Sacconi, L., and Caroti, G., *Z. Anorg. Allgem. Chem.* **271**, 176 (1953).
60. Shreve, R. N., and Bennett, R. B., *J. Am. Chem. Soc.* **65**, 2243 (1943).
61. Slinkin, A. A., Dulov, A. A., and Rubinshtein, A. M., *Izv. Akad. Nauk SSSR, Ser. Khim.* p. 1769 (1964); *Chem. Abstr.* **62**, 2838 (1965); *Bull. Acad. Sci. USSR, Div. Chem. Sci. (English Transl.)* p. 1679 (1964).

62. Stephen H., and Weizman, C., *J. Chem. Soc.* **103**, 269 (1913).
63. Suter, H. A., and West, P. W., *Anal. Chim. Acta* **13**, 501 (1955).
64. Terent'ev, A. P., Rode, V. V., and Rukhadze, E. G., *Vysokomolekul. Soedin.* **2**, 1557 (1960); *Chem. Abstr.* **55**, 19303 (1961).
65. Terent'ev, A. P., Rode, V. V., and Rukhadze, E. G., *Vysokomolekul. Soedin.* **5**, 1658 (1963); *Chem. Abstr.* **60**, 15992 (1964).
66. Terent'ev, A. P., Rode, V. V., and Rukhadze, E. G., *Vysokomolekul. Soedin.* **5**, 1666 (1963); *Chem. Abstr.* **60**, 15992 (1964).
67. Terent'ev, A. P., Rode, V. V., Rukhadze, E. G., and Filatov, E. S., *Proc. Acad. Sci. USSR, Chem. Sect.* (*English Transl.*) **138**, 620 (1961); *Chem. Abstr.* **56**, 10927 (1962).
68. Terent'ev, A. P., Vozzhennikov, V. M., Zvonkova, Z. V., and Badzhadze, L. I., *Proc. Acad. Sci. USSR, Chem. Sect.* (*English Transl.*) **140**, 1018 (1961); *Chem. Abstr.* **56**, 9556 (1962).
69. Tseng, H.-M., Yu, S.-W., and Hsu, J.-H., *K'o Hsueh Ch'u Pan She* p. 286 (1963); *Chem. Abstr.* **63**, 14992 (1965).
70. Uhlig, E., *Z. Anorg. Allgem. Chem.* **306**, 71 (1960); *Chem. Abstr.* **55**, 4225 (1961).
71. Uhlig, E., *Z. Anorg. Allgem. Chem.* **312**, 332 (1961); *Chem. Abstr.* **56**, 13777 (1962).
72. Vainshtein, E. E., Akopdzhanov, R. G., Kefeli, L. M., and Keier, N. P., *Vysokomolekul. Soedin.* **7**, 847 (1965); *Chem. Abstr.* **63**, 6463 (1965); *Polymer Sci.* (*USSR*) (*English Transl.*) **7**, 934 (1965).
73. Vinogradova, S. V., Vasnev, V. A., and Korshak, V. V., *Vysokomolekul. Soedin.* **B9**, No. 7, 520 (1967); *Chem. Abstr.* **67**, 6985, 73915v (1967).
74. Yoshikawa, Y., and Yamaski, K., *Bull. Chem. Soc. Japan.* **40**, 813 (1967).
75. Zelentsov, V. V., Pai, W. M., Savich, I. A., and Spitsyn, V. I., *Vysokomolekul. Soedin.* **3**, 1535 (1961); *Chem. Abstr.* **56**, 10375 (1962).

CHAPTER VIII

Metallorganic Ring Polymers from Nitrogen:Sulfur Chelate Ligands

A. Polymers from Bis(thiopicolinamides)

METHOD 1. POLYMERIZATION OF BIS(THIOPICOLINAMIDES) WITH METAL SALTS OR METAL CHELATES

Thiopicolinamides are known to form chelates with metal ions. The synthesis of suitable bis(thiopicolinamides) to serve as ligands for polymer formation was reported in 1958 (2–4, 20). Heating a metal acetylacetonate with a stoichiometric amount of a bis(thiopicolinamide) effects chelate exchange and the formation of polymer as a residue product (VIII-1). Acetylacetone is removed as a volatile by-product. Direct synthesis of these polymers from a metal acetate and the bis(thiopicolinamide) has been used more widely. Generally, methanolic solutions of the metal acetate are added to solutions of the bis(ligand) in dimethylformamide, benzene, or chloroform (8, 20, 26, 31, 32). Almost always the polymer precipitates in quantitative yield, but in some cases, other isolation techniques have been required.

The polymeric metal bis(thiopicolinamides) that have been prepared are all colored, insoluble materials. Their molecular weights have been roughly estimated to be about 15,000 (20), but actual determination by the radioactive end group technique has given higher values, i.e., 30–40,000 (28). Most of these polymers have been shown to be amorphous by X-ray diffraction analysis. The thermogravimetric behavior of poly[metal bis(thiopicolinamides)] has been investigated. The Zn(II) derivatives exhibited the greatest thermal stability (20). A great variety of physicochemical properties has been measured for some members of this polymer class (26, 27, 32, 35). Electrical conductivities (33, 34) and some chemical resistance data have also been reported (32). In a study of the changes in the EPR spectra of some of these polymers on being heated, it was concluded that a uniform polymer structure is not achieved during the actual polymerization (12). Subsequent heating of the polymer is required for complete complex formation. Diffuse reflectance spectra have also been determined in structural studies on these materials (*29*).

The catalytic activity of several metal α-thiopicolinamide polymers for chemical reactions has been determined. The decomposition of hydrazine (*12, 18*), isopropanol (*6*), formic acid (*6*), hydrogen peroxide (*19*), and the oxidation of cumene (*17, 21*) and ethylbenzene (*21*) to their hydroperoxides have been investigated. The copper(II) chelate of bis(α-thiopicolinamido)-diphenyl catalyzes a 94–96% conversion of cumene to its hydroperoxide in 5 hours at 80°–95°C (*17*).

A large number of structurally similar polymers from bis(thioquinaldin-amides) and zinc, copper, and nickel have been prepared (*8*). The methods used were similar. Some of these products which were soluble in dimethyl-formamide were thought to possess only three or four "mer" units. Insoluble products were judged to be of higher molecular weight ($n = 10$–15). The thermal stability of this series of polymers, as adjudged from the reported decomposition temperatures, was in the following order: Zn(II) > Ni(II) > Cu(II). This relative order has been noted with other polychelates. Infrared and magnetic property data are available for these materials (*8*).

B. Polymers from Bis(thiooxamides)

Method 1. Polymerization of Bis(thiooxamides) with Metal Salts

Dithiooxamide, or rubeanic acid as it is commonly referred to in the literature, has been widely used for the quantitative analysis of metals. In particular, copper, nickel, and cobalt form complexes that can be analyzed gravimetrically or photometrically (*15*, *36*). The ligand is mixed with a metal salt with or without an acid acceptor being present. Useful acid acceptors include sodium acetate, triethylamine, and ammonia (*22*). For cases where they have been reported, molecular weight data show that the products are low polymers (*14*). Interfacial polymerization techniques gave the zinc(II) polymer with a DP of approximately 20 (*25*).

$$ n\ H_2NCCNH_2 + n\ Ni(C_2H_3O_2)_2 $$

[5]   [6]

[7] + 2n HOOCCH$_3$

[9]

(VIII-2)

[8] + 2n HOOCCH$_3$

[9]

A structure containing four-membered chelate rings [7] was first proposed for these polymers (*15*), but was soon discarded by subsequent workers (*11*, *22*) who favored the five-ring structure [8]. The most recent work on the structure of copper rubeanate indicates that it possesses a three-dimensional structure (*16*, *30*). A solid–solid reaction between dithiooxamide and copper(II) bis(8-hydroxyquinolinate) yielded a product that was fractionated into several different crystalline fractions. A detailed study of the infrared, magnetic and electrical properties of these products supported structures [11] and [12]. They differ in that [11] has copper atoms in both directions, whereas, the copper atoms of [12] are all in one plane. The reaction of copper with rubeanic acid has been patented as the basis of a photocopying process (*13*).

The work that has been published on this polymerization shows it to be quite specific. Heavy metal ions such as silver and cadmium yield complexes that decompose spontaneously to the metallic sulfides (*24*). Attempted polymerization of bis(thioamides) of higher diacids led to formation of metallic sulfides in the case of adipic, pimelic, and terephthalic bis(thioamide) (*22*). However, malonic bis(thioamide) does yield polymer (*22*). Apparently, the six-membered ring that is formed can exist in this case [14], although it is less stable than the five-membered ring [8] (*5, 22, 23*). The rings that are required for polymer formation from the higher bis(thioamides) are apparently excluded, and the reaction forms metal sulfides instead.

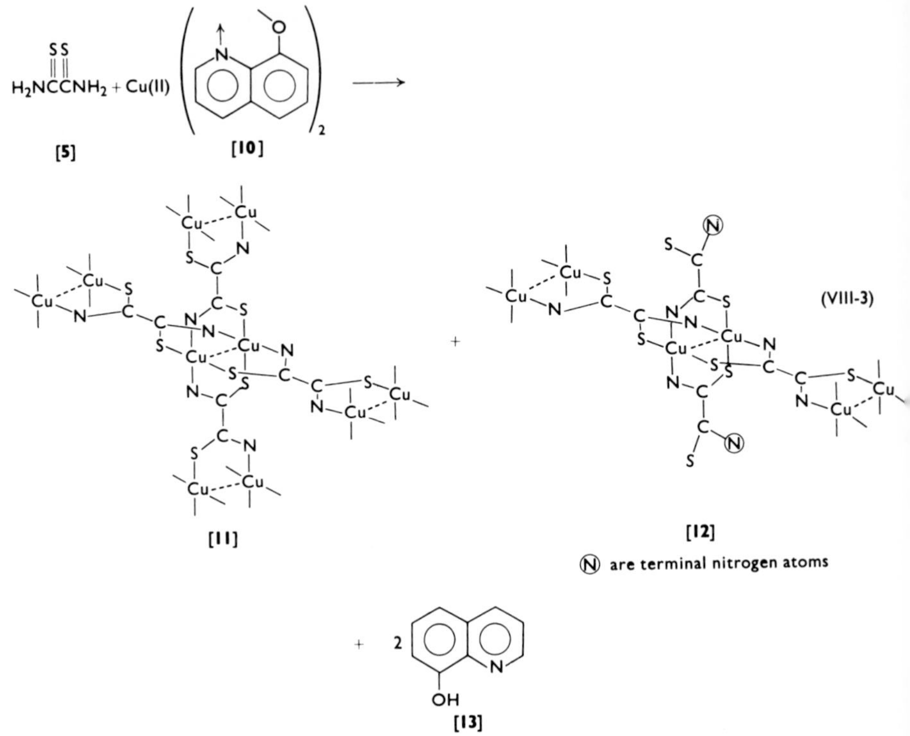

(VIII-3)

[11]

[12]

Ⓝ are terminal nitrogen atoms

[13]

N,N'-Disubstituted bis(thioamides) have been prepared and polymerized (*14, 37*). Polymer was only obtained from *N,N'*-dimethyldithiooxamide but complex formation was observed in all cases. However, *N,N,N',N'*-tetraethyldithiooxamide failed to complex with Ni(II), a fact which was interpreted to be evidence for the structure of the chelates proposed earlier [8].

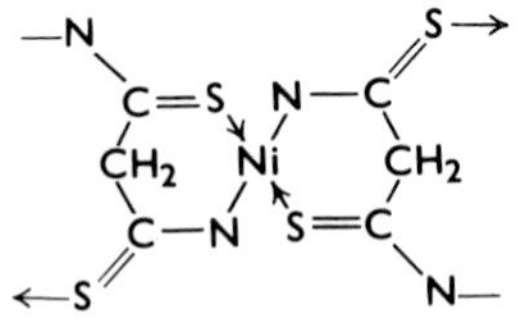

(VIII-4)

[14]

C. Polymers from Bis(thiosemicarbazones)

METHOD 1. POLYMERIZATION OF BIS(THIOSEMICARBAZONES) WITH METAL SALTS

Polymerization of bis(thiosemicarbazones) with metals has been effected in dimethylformamide at reflux. In the case of naphthazarin (7, 10) the bis-(thiosemicarbazone) was formed *in situ* during the polymerization reaction.

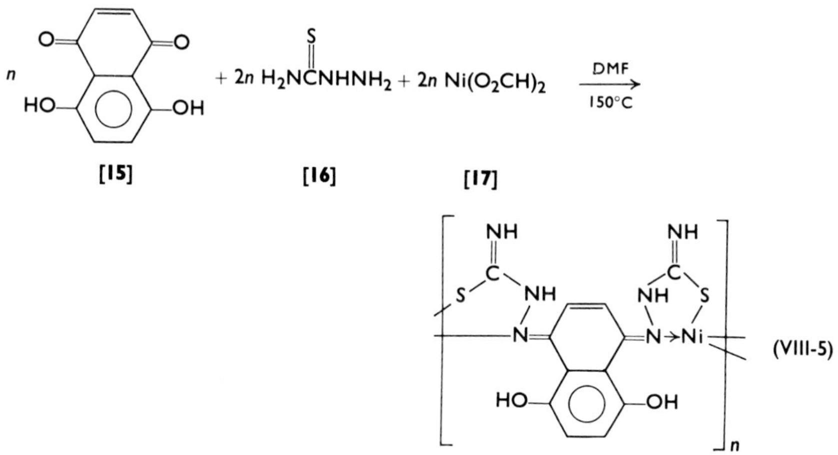

[15]   [16]   [17]

(VIII-5)

[18]

A similar polymerization was effected with terephthalaldehyde bis(thiosemi-carbazone). The bis(thiosemicarbazone) of 2,4-pentanedione was polymerized in alcohol solution (9). All of these polymers were insoluble, thus preventing determination of their molecular weights. Thermogravimetry was used to obtain some thermal stability data and, as shown in Table VIII.3 (p. 224), the naphthazarin-derived polymers possess a high order of thermal stability.

TABLE VIII.1

Polymers from Bis(thiopicolinamides)

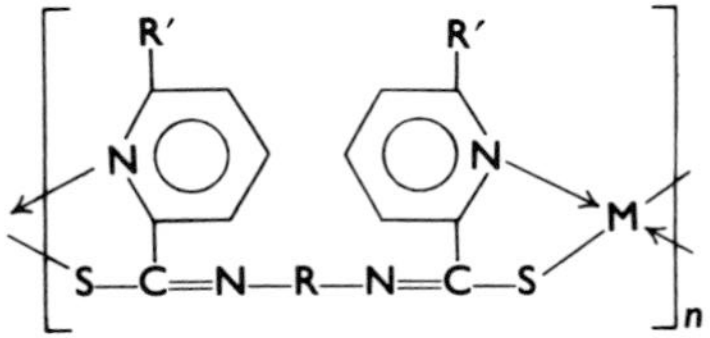

No.	Structure	Metal (M)	Method	Color	Solubility	T_m (°C)	Molecular weight, remarks, and property data	References
1	R = 1,4-C$_6$H$_4$—; R′ = H	Cu(II)	A,1	—	—	—	EPR data	12
1a	R = 4,4′-C$_6$H$_4$—C$_6$H$_4$; R′ = H	Co(II)	A,1	—	—	>350 d	Amorphous	26, 27 31, 32, 33, 34
2	R = 4,4′-C$_6$H$_4$—C$_6$H$_4$; R′ = H	Cu(II) [3]	A,1	Brown	Insoluble	>220 (TGA)	Mol. wt. = 15,000	3, 4, 12, 20, 21
		Cu(II)	A,1	—	—	>350 d	Amorphous. Mol. wt. = 42,100	12, 17, 21, 26–28, 31–34
3	R = 4,4′-C$_6$H$_4$—C$_6$H$_4$; R′ = H	Ni(II)	A,1	Brown	Insoluble	>220 (TGA)	Mol. wt. = 15,000	3, 4, 20
		Ni(II)	A,1	—	DMF, CHCl$_3$, C$_6$H$_6$	>350 d	Amorphous	26, 27, 31, 32, 34
4	R = 4,4′-C$_6$H$_4$—C$_6$H$_4$; R′ = H	Zn(II)	A,1	Yellow	Insoluble	>380 (TGA)	Mol. wt. = 15,000	2–4, 20
		Zn(II)	A,1	—	—	>350 d	Amorphous	26, 27, 31–34

No.	R / R'	Metal	Method		Solubility	m.p.	Other physical data	References
5	R = 4,4'-C$_6$H$_4$—C$_6$H$_4$; R' = CH$_3$	Co(II)	A,1	—	—	>350 d	Amorphous. Other physical data	26, 27, 31–34
6	R = 4,4'-C$_6$H$_4$—C$_6$H$_4$; R' = CH$_3$	Cu(II)	A,1	—	—	>350 d	Amorphous. Mol. wt. = 35,600	26–28, 31–34
7	R = 4,4'-C$_6$H$_4$—C$_6$H$_4$; R' = CH$_3$	Ni(II)	A,1	—	DMF, CHCl$_3$, C$_6$H$_6$	>350 d	Amorphous	26, 27, 31, 32, 34,
8	R = 4,4'-C$_6$H$_4$—C$_6$H$_4$; R' = CH$_3$	Zn(II)	A,1	—	—	>350 d	Amorphous	26, 27, 31–34
9	R = (3-CH$_3$-phenyl)(3-CH$_3$-phenyl)biphenyl; R' = H	Co(II)	A,1	—	—	—	Amorphous	26, 31, 33
10	R = (3-CH$_3$-phenyl)(3-CH$_3$-phenyl)biphenyl; R' = H	Cu(II)	A,1	—	—	—	Amorphous	12, 26, 31, 33
11	R = (3-CH$_3$-phenyl)(3-CH$_3$-phenyl)biphenyl; R' = H	Ni(II)	A,1	—	DMF, CHCl$_3$, C$_6$H$_6$	—	Amorphous	26, 31
12	R = (3-CH$_3$-phenyl)(3-CH$_3$-phenyl)biphenyl; R' = H	Zn(II)	A,1	—	—	—	Amorphous	26, 31, 33
13	R = (3-CH$_3$-phenyl)(3-CH$_3$-phenyl)biphenyl; R' = CH$_3$	Co(II)	A,1	—	—	—	Amorphous	26, 31, 33
14	R = (3-CH$_3$-phenyl)(3-CH$_3$-phenyl)biphenyl; R' = CH$_3$	Cu(II)	A,1	—	—	—	Amorphous	26, 31, 33
15	R = (3-CH$_3$-phenyl)(3-CH$_3$-phenyl)biphenyl; R' = CH$_3$	Ni(II)	A,1	—	DMF, CHCl$_3$, C$_6$H$_6$	—	Amorphous	26, 31
16	R = (3-CH$_3$-phenyl)(3-CH$_3$-phenyl)biphenyl; R' = CH$_3$	Zn(II)	A,1	—	—	—	Amorphous	26, 31, 33

TABLE VIII.1—continued

Polymers from Bis(thiopicolinamides)

No.	Structure	Metal (M)	Method	Color	Solubility	T_m (°C)	Molecular weight, remarks, and property data	References
17	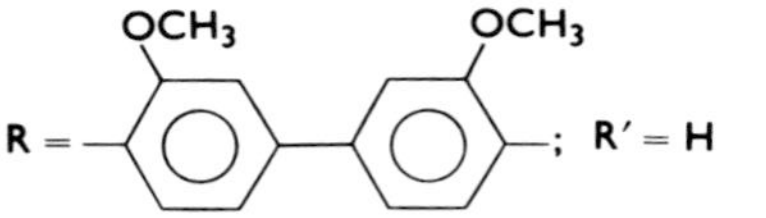 R = (OCH3, OCH3 biphenyl); R' = H	Co(II)	A,1	—	—	—	Amorphous	26, 31, 33
18		Cu(II)	A,1	—	—	—	Amorphous	12, 26, 31, 33
19		Ni(II)	A,1	—	DMF, CHCl₃, C₆H₆	—	Amorphous	26, 31
20		Zn(II)	A,1	—	—	—	Amorphous	26, 31, 33
21	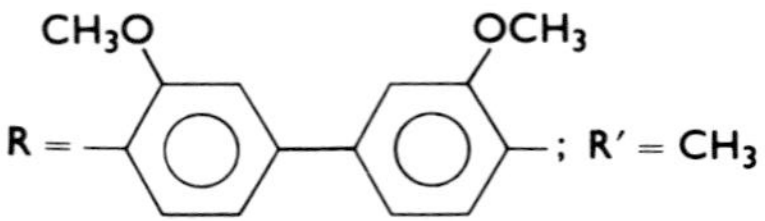 R = (OCH3, CH3O biphenyl); R' = CH₃	Co(II)	A,1	—	—	—	Amorphous	26, 31, 33
22		Cu(II)	A,1	—!	—	—	Amorphous	26, 31, 33
23		Ni(II)	A,1	—	DMF, CHCl₃, C₆H₆	—	Amorphous	26, 31
24		Zn(II)	A,1	—	—	—	Amorphous	26, 31, 33
24a	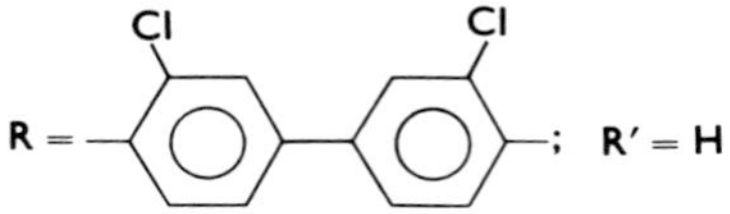 R = (Cl, Cl biphenyl); R' = H	Cu(II)	A,1	—	—	—	EPR data	12
25	R = 4,4'-C₆H₄OC₆H₄; R' = H	Cu(II)	A,1	Brown	Insoluble	>300	TGA, >270°C d	20

No.	R, R'	M		Color	Solubility	Temp.	TGA	Refs.
26	R = 4,4'-$C_6H_4OC_6H_4$; R' = H	Ni(II)	A,1	Brown	Insoluble	>300	TGA, >340°C d	20
27	R = 4,4'-$C_6H_4OC_6H_4$; R' = H	Zn(II)	A,1	Yellow	Insoluble	>300	TGA, >370°C d	2, 20
28	R = 4,4'-$C_6H_4COC_6H_4$; R' = H	Cu(II)	A,1	Red	Insoluble	>310 d (TGA)	—	3, 4, 20
29	R = 4,4'-$C_6H_4COC_6H_4$; R' = H	Ni(II)	A,1	Brown	Insoluble	>310 d (TGA)	—	3, 4, 20
30	R = 4,4'-$C_6H_4COC_6H_4$; R' = H	Zn(II)	A,1	Yellow	Insoluble	>390 d (TGA)	—	2-4, 20
31	R = 4,4'-$C_6H_4SO_2C_6H_4$; R' = H	Cu(II)	A,1	Brown	Insoluble	>290 d (TGA)	—	3, 4, 20
32	R = 4,4'-$C_6H_4SO_2C_6H_4$; R' = H	Ni(II)	A,1	Brown	Insoluble	>290 d (TGA)	—	3, 4, 20
33	R = 4,4'-$C_6H_4SO_2C_6H_4$; R' = H	Zn(II)	A,1	Yellow	Insoluble	>340 d (TGA)	—	2-4, 20

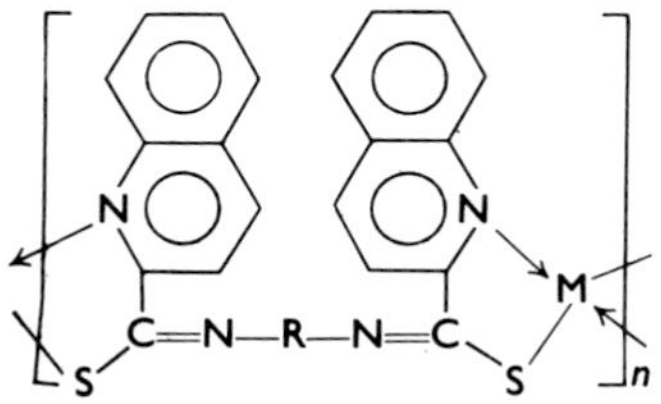

No.	R	M		Color	Solubility	Temp.	TGA	Refs.
34	R = 1,4-C_6H_4	Cu(II)	A,1	Red-brown	—	320 d	—	8
35	R = 1,4-C_6H_4	Ni(II)	A,1	Black	—	360 d	—	8
36	R = 1,4-C_6H_4	Zn(II)	A,1	Red	—	440 d	—	8

TABLE VIII.1—*continued*

Polymers from Bis(thiopicolinamides)

No.	Structure	Metal (M)	Method	Color	Solubility	T_m (°C)	Molecular weight, remarks, and property data	References
37	R' = H	Cu(II)	A,1	Brown	—	280 d	—	8
38	R' = H	Ni(II)	A,1	Violet	—	380 d	—	8
39	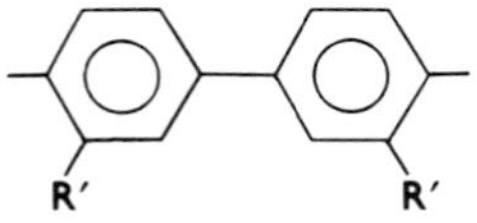 R' = H	Zn(II)	A,1	Orange	—	475 d	—	8
40	R' = CH_3	Cu(II)	A,1	Yellow-green	—	320 d	—	8
41	R' = CH_3	Ni(II)	A,1	Violet	—	445 d	—	8
42	R' = CH_3	Zn(II)	A,1	Orange	—	475 d	—	8
43	R = $4,4'\text{-}C_6H_4CH_2C_6H_4$	Cu(II)	A,1	Brown	—	360 d	—	8
44	R = $4,4'\text{-}C_6H_4CH_2C_6H_4$	Ni(II)	A,1	Black	DMF	380 d	—	8
45	R = $4,4'\text{-}C_6H_4CH_2C_6H_4$	Zn(II)	A,1	Orange	DMF	410 d	—	8
46	R =	Cu(II)	A,1	Red-brown	—	420 d	—	8
47	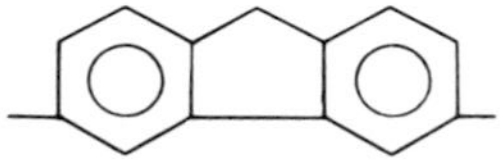	Ni(II)	A,1	Violet	—	400 d	—	8
48		Zn(II)	A,1	Yellow	—	420 d	—	8

No.	R	Metal	Method	Color	Solvent	Temp		
49	R = 4,4'-C$_6$H$_4$COC$_6$H$_4$	Cu(II)	A,1	Black	—	390 d	—	∞
50		Ni(II)	A,1	Black	DMF	410 d	—	∞
51		Zn(II)	A,1	Yellow	DMF	460 d	—	∞
52	R 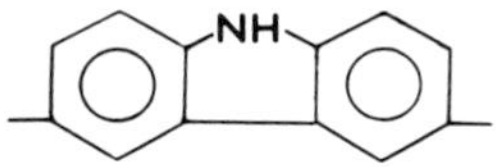 =	Cu(II)	A,1	Red	—	400 d	—	∞
53	R = 4,4'-C$_6$H$_4$—O—C$_6$H$_4$	Cu(II)	A,1	Red-brown	—	340 d	—	∞
54	R = 4,4'-C$_6$H$_4$—O—C$_6$H$_4$	Ni(II)	A,1	Black	—	400 d	—	∞
55	R = 4,4'-C$_6$H$_4$—O—C$_6$H$_4$	Zn(II)	A,1	Yellow	—	460 d	—	∞
56	R = 4,4'-C$_6$H$_4$—S—C$_6$H$_4$	Cu(II)	A,1	Brown	—	360 d	—	∞
57	R = 4,4'-C$_6$H$_4$—S—C$_6$H$_4$	Ni(II)	A,1	Brown	DMF	370 d	—	∞
58	R = 4,4'-C$_6$H$_4$—S—C$_6$H$_4$	Zn(II)	A,1	Yellow	DMF	380 d	—	∞
59	R = 4,4'-C$_6$H$_4$SO$_2$C$_6$H$_4$	Cu(II)	A,1	Green	—	380 d	—	∞
60	R = 4,4'-C$_6$H$_4$SO$_2$C$_6$H$_4$	Ni(II)	A,1	Brown	—	410 d	—	∞
61	R = 4,4'-C$_6$H$_4$SO$_2$C$_6$H$_4$	Zn(II)	A,1	Yellow	—	500 d	—	∞

TABLE VIII.2

Polymers from Bis(thiooxamides)

No.	Structure	Metal (M)	Method	Color	Solubility	Remarks and property data	References
1	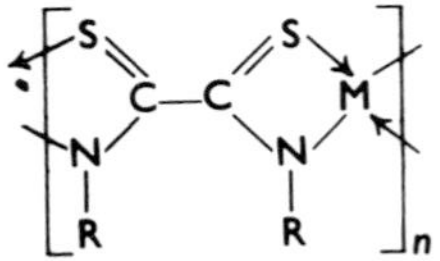 R = H	Ag(I)	B,l	Black	—	—	5, 24
2	R = H	Au(II)	B,l	Brown	—	—	24
3	R = H see pp. 213–214	Cd(II)	B,l	Yellow	—	—	24
4	R = H	Co(II)	B,l	—	—	—	5, 22, 24, 36
5	R = H	Cu(II)	B,l	Green	—	Amorphous	1, 5, 11, 13, 15, 16, 22, 24, 30
6	R = H	Hg(II)	B,l	White	—	—	5
7	R = H	Ni(II) [7]	B,l	Blue	—	Amorphous	1, 5, 22, 24, 36
8	R = H	Pt(II)	B,l	Brown	—	—	24
9	R = H	Zn(II)	B,l	Yellow	Insoluble	DP = 20 (IR)	22, 24, 25
10	R = CH$_3$	Ni(II)	B,l	—	Sl. sol. hot solvents	Crystalline. $T_m = >400°C$	14, 37
11	R = C$_2$H$_5$	Ni(II)	B,l	—	—	—	37

Structure (applies to rows above, R = H):

223

	R	Metal		Color	Solvent	T_m	Ref
12	R = $C_6H_5CH_2$	Ni(II)	B,1	Purple	—	—	14
13	R = $n\text{-}C_{18}H_{37}$	Ni(II)	B,1	Purple	Hot $C_6H_5NO_2$	$T_m = >200°C$	14
14	R = $HOCH_2CH_2$	Ni(II)	B,1	Brown	—	—	14
15	R = $CH_3COOCH_2CH_2$	Ni(II)	B,1	Blue	—	—	14
16	R = $(CH_3)_2NCH_2CH_2CH_2$	Ni(II)	B,1	Red	—	—	14
17	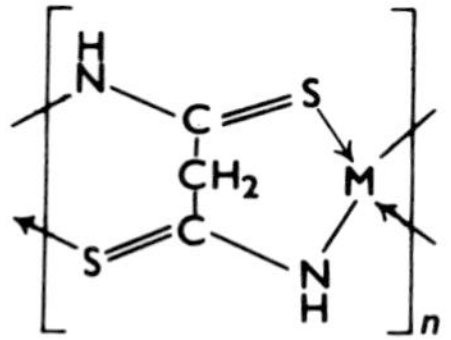	Co(II)	B,1	—	—	—	22
18		Cu(II)	B,1	—	—	—	22

TABLE VIII.3

Polymers from Bis(thiosemicarbazones)

No.	Structure	Metal (M)	Method	Color	Solubility	T_m (°C)	Remarks and property data	References
1	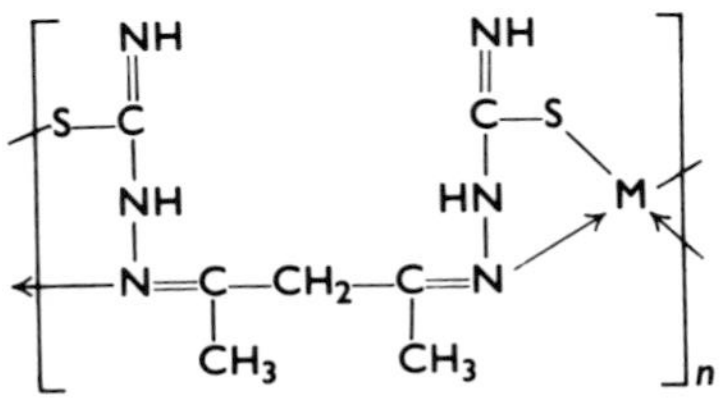	Ni(II)	C,1	—	—	180 d	—	9
2		Zn(II)	C,1	—	—	>180 d	—	9
3	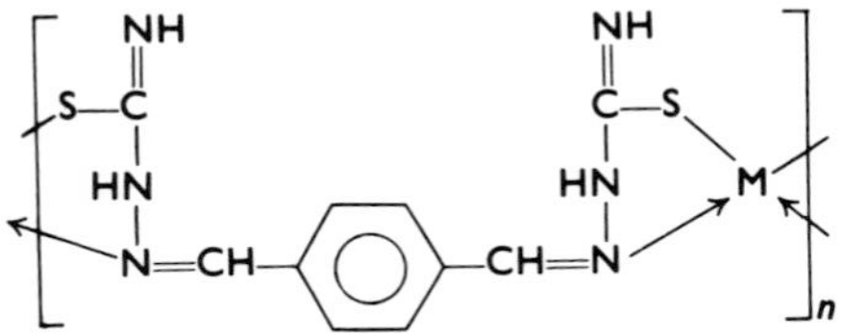	Cd(II)	C,1	—	—	—	—	10
4		Ni(II)	C,1	Yellow	Insoluble	Infusible	>250°C d by DTA	10
5		Zn(II)	C,1	Yellow	Insoluble	Infusible	>250°C d by DTA	10
6	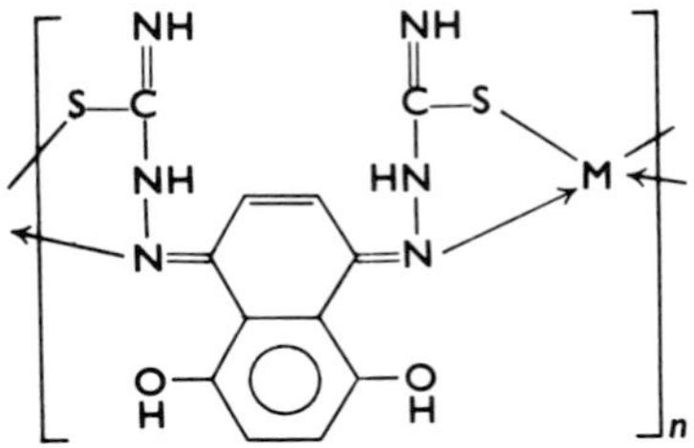	Ni(II) [18]	C,1	Black	Insoluble	400 d (DTA)	—	7,10
7		Zn(II)	C,1	Black	Insoluble	Infusible	>400°C d by DTA	7,10

REFERENCES

1. Amon, W. F., and Kane, M. W., U.S. Patent 2,505,085 (Polaroid Corp.) (1950); *Chem. Abstr.* **44**, 7091 (1950).
2. Bailar, J. C., Jr., WADC Tech. Rept. No. 57-657, p. 35 (1958).
3. Bailar, J. C., Jr., Martin, K. V., Judd, M. L., and McLean, J. A., Jr., WADC Tech. Rept. No. 57-391, Part I (1957).
4. Bailar, J. C., Jr., Martin, K. V., Judd, M. L., and McLean, J. A., Jr., WADC Tech. Rept. No. 57-391, Part II (1958).
5. Barceló, J. R., *Spectrochim. Acta* **10**, 245 (1958); *Chem. Abstr.* **52**, 9765 (1958).
6. Boreskov, G. K., Keier, N. P., Rubtsova, L. F., and Rukhadze, E. G., *Dokl. Akad. Nauk SSSR* **144**, 1069 (1962); *Chem. Abstr.* **57**, 13959 (1962).
7. Chakravarty, D. N., and Drinkard, W. C., Jr., *J. Indian Chem. Soc.* **37**, 517 (1960); *Chem. Abstr.* **55**, 20752 (1961).
8. Chupakhin, O. N., Pushkareva, Z. V., and Krylov, E. I., *Vestn. Akad. Nauk Kaz. SSR* **19**, 85 (1963); *Chem. Abstr.* **61**, 1953 (1964).
9. Drinkard, W. C., Jr., and Chakravarty, D. N., WADC Tech. Rept. No. 59-427, p. 367 (1960).
10. Drinkard, W. C., Jr., and Chakravarty, D. N., WADC Tech. Rept. No. 59-761, p. 232 (1960).
11. Evans, R. V. G., and Gibson, C. S., *J. Chem. Soc.* p. 431 (1949).
12. Gerasimova, G. F., Anufrienko, V. F., and Keier, N. P., *Kinetika i Kataliz* **7**, 1078 (1966); *Chem. Abstr.* **66**, 9865, 105317z (1967).
13. Haas, H. C., U.S. Patent 3,306,744 (Polaroid Corp.) (1967).
14. Hurd, R. N., DeLaMater, G., McElheny, G. C., and Pfeiffer, L. V., *J. Am. Chem. Soc.* **82**, 4454 (1960).
15. Jensen, K. A., *Z. Anorg. Chem.* **252**, 227 (1944).
16. Kanda, S., Ito, K., and Nogaito, T., *J. Polymer. Sci.*, C, No. 17, 151 (1967).
17. Keier, N. P., *Nauchn. Osnovy Podbora i Proizv. Katalizatorov Akad. Nauk SSSR, Sibirsk. Otd.* p. 218 (1964); *Chem. Abstr.* **63**, 7681 (1965).
18. Keier, N. P., Boreskov, G. K., Rubtsova, L. F., and Rukhadze, E. G., *Kinetika i Kataliz* **3**, 680 (1962); *Chem. Abstr.* **58**, 7412 (1963).
19. Keier, N. P., Troitskaya, M. G., and Rukhadze, E. G., *Kinetika i Kataliz* **3**, 691 (1962); *Chem. Abstr.* **58**, 7413 (1963).
20. Martin, K. V., *J. Am. Chem. Soc.* **80**, 233 (1958).
21. Min'kov, A. I., Alikina, G. M., Gridnev, Yu. M., and Keier, N. P., *Kinetika i Kataliz* **7**, 632 (1966); *Chem. Abstr.* **65**, 18453f (1966).
22. Odnoralova, V. N., and Kudryavtsev, G. I., *Vysokomolekul. Soedin.* **4**, 1314 (1962); *Chem. Abstr.* **58**, 14113 (1963).
23. Piper, T. S., *J. Am. Chem. Soc.* **80**, 30 (1958).
24. Răy, P., and Răy, R. M., *Quart. J. Indian Chem. Soc.* **3**, 118 (1926); *Chem. Abstr.* **20**, 3690 (1926).
25. Rose, S. H., Block, B. P., and Davis, J. E., *Inorg. Chem.* **3**, 1258 (1964).
26. Terent'ev, A. P., Mochalina, I. G., Rukhadze, E. G., and Povolotskaya, E. M., *Vysokomolekul. Soedin.* **6**, 1267 (1964); *Chem. Abstr.* **61**, 14794 (1964).
27. Terent'ev, A. P., Rode, V. V., and Rukhadze, E. G., *Vysokomolekul. Soedin.* **5**, 1666 (1963); *Chem. Abstr.* **60**, 15992 (1964).
28. Terent'ev, A. P., Rode, V. V., Rukhadze, E. G., and Filatov, E. S., *Proc. Acad. Sci. USSR, Chem. Sect. (English Transl.)* **138**, 620 (1961); *Chem. Abstr.* **56**, 10927 (1962).

29. Terent'ev, A. P., Rukhadze, E. G., Kharakhorin, F. F., and Petrov, V. M., *Proc. Acad. Sci. USSR, Chem. Sect. (English Transl.)* **168**, 606 (1966); *Dokl. Akad. Nauk SSSR* **168**, 1082 (1966); *Chem. Abstr.* **65**, 18710c (1966).

30. Terent'ev, A. P., Rukhadze, E. G., Kharakhorin, F. F., and Petrov, V. M., *Vysokomolekul. Soedin.* **B9**, 100 (1967); *Chem. Abstr.* **66**, 8972, 95538f (1967).

31. Terent'ev, A. P., Rukhadze, E. G., Mochalina, I. G., and Panova, G. V., *Vysokomolekul. Soedin., Geterotsepnye Vysokomolekul. Soedin.* p. 123 (1964); *Chem. Abstr.* **62**, 2830 (1965).

32. Terent'ev, A. P., Rukhadze, E. G., Rode, V. V., and Panova, G. V., *Vysokomolekul. Soedin.* **4**, 566 (1962); *Chem. Abstr.* **57**, 16851 (1962); *Resins, Rubbers, Plastics* p. 2227 (1962).

33. Terent'ev, A. P., Rukhadze, E. G., Vozzhennikov, V. M., Zvonkova, Z. V., Oboladze, N. S., and Mochalina, I. G., *Dokl. Akad. Nauk SSSR* **147**, 1094 (1962); *Chem. Abstr.* **58**, 10317 (1963).

34. Terent'ev, A. P., Vozzhennikov, V. M., Zvonkova, Z. V., and Badzhadze, L. I., *Proc. Acad. Sci. USSR, Chem. Sect. (English Transl.)* **140**, 1018 (1961); *Chem. Abstr.* **56**, 9556 (1962).

35. Vainshtein, E. E., Akopdzhanov, R. G., Kefeli, L. M., and Keier, N. P., *Vysokomolekul. Soedin.* **7**, 847 (1965); *Chem. Abstr.* **63**, 6463 (1965); *Polymer Sci. (USSR) (English Transl.)* **7**, 934 (1965).

36. Xavier, J., and Răy, P., *J. Indian Chem. Soc.* **35**, 432 (1958); *Chem. Abstr.* **53**, 16815 (1959).

37. Xavier, J., and Răy, P., *J. Indian Chem. Soc.* **35**, 589 (1958); *Chem. Abstr.* **53**, 16815 (1959).

CHAPTER IX

Metallorganic Ring Polymers from Oxygen Chelate Ligands

A. Poly[metal bis(β-diketonates)]

If one simply considers the number of bis(ligands) that have been synthesized and polymerized with metals, poly[metal bis(β-diketonates)] are the most widely investigated class of chelate polymers. Perhaps, as we shall see below, this contributed to the fact that the greatest success in synthesizing truly high molecular weight chelate polymers has been achieved with this ligand class.

METHOD 1. POLYMERIZATION OF METAL β-DIKETONATES

Recent structural investigations of "monomeric" metal acetylacetonates show that they can associate to low polymers. X-Ray studies have shown that zinc acetylacetonate is trimeric ([Zn(AcAc)$_2$]$_3$) (8). Other examples are [Ni(AcAc)$_2$]$_3$ and [Co(AcAc)$_2$]$_4$. The tendency of these molecules to form polymers is stated to result from a preference of the metal atoms for a coordination number greater than four, but not necessarily six. Ferrous acetylacetonate is a monomer in dilute benzene solution, but is a hexamer at 5°C in concentrated solution. Similar associative tendencies were found for Fe(II) (trifluoroacetylacetonato)$_2$, Fe(II) (hexafluoroacetylacetonato)$_2$, and Fe(II) (2,2,6,6-tetramethylheptane-3,5-dionato)$_2$ (23).

Homopolymers of metal acetylacetonates have been prepared by heating monomeric chelates in solvents containing oxygen or nitrogen atoms that possess free electron pairs. Dioxane, tetrahydrofuran, acetylacetone, trimethylamine, or carbon tetrachloride solutions of the chelates were heated at 50°–80°C and then cast on solid surfaces (121). Hard, glassy films were obtained that were subsequently fired to give thin metal and metal oxide films for electronic uses. The initially formed chelate films were thought to be polymeric because of their low vapor pressure, lack of crystallinity, and because the monomeric chelate could be recovered unchanged after identical time/temperature heating cycles in certain other solvents. For example, after heating nickel acetylacetonate in benzene the starting monomer was recovered; in acetylacetone, polymer was formed. No other properties of the polymeric films were reported.

[1]   [2]

METHOD 2. POLYMERIZATION OF BIS(β-DIKETONES) WITH METAL SALTS OR METAL CHELATES

Polymerization of metal salts such as acetates, chlorides, sulfates, and acetylacetonates with bis(ligands) (95, 96) has been reported many times (IX-2). Added bases have been used. In one case, prior formation of the dipotassium salt in methanol allowed the preparation of some polymers that were unobtainable without this step (25, 26). Although water-miscible solvents like ethanol, dioxane, dimethylformamide, and tetrahydrofuran are used most frequently, decalin, Dowtherm, and toluene are also useful. This was especially true when metal acetylacetonates were used as the metal donor. Interfacial polymerization with chloroform as the organic solvent has been described (45, 133). Added organic base was used as the acid acceptor in this case.

$$n\ CH_3COCH_2CORCOCH_2COCH_3 + n\ MSO_4 \longrightarrow$$

[3]   [4]

$+ n\ H_2SO_4$ (IX-2)

[5]   [6]

Bulk polymerization of bis(β-diketones) with metal acetylacetonates has been reported frequently (IX-3). Although metal acetylacetonates are preferred, the basic acetate of beryllium, $Be_4O\ (C_2H_3O_2)_6$, was also useful (140).

Reported temperatures for this polymerization vary somewhat depending on the metal cation. With Cu(II), a maximum temperature of 105°–110°C was employed (*35*). Temperatures as high as 260°C were used in other cases (*76*). With Be(II), this method has yielded very high molecular weight, soluble polymer. Fractionation of the product obtained from Be(II) and 4,4′-di(acetoacetyl)diphenyl ether yielded a fraction with an osmometric molecular weight of 126,000 (*76*). A product with an intrinsic viscosity of 1.2 was obtained from sebacoyl diacetone and Be(II) using a melt, bulk procedure (*85*).

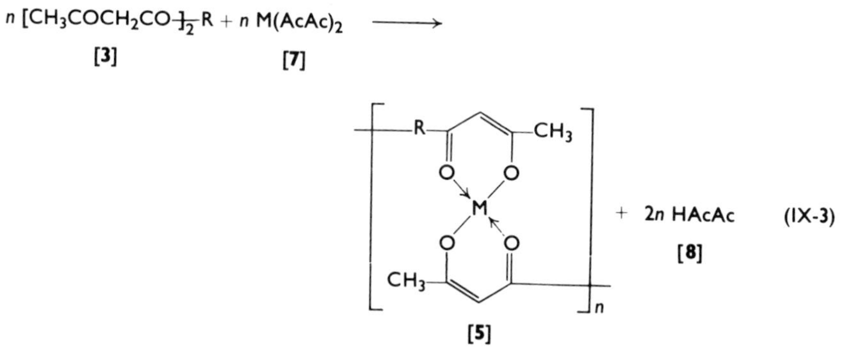

n [CH3COCH2CO]2 R + n M(AcAc)2
[3]
[7]
R
CH3
M
CH3
n
+ 2n HAcAc
[8]
(IX-3)
[5]

Korshak and his co-workers have studied the mechanism of polycoordination reactions. They have studied reaction (IX-3) both in solution and in the melt using 4,4′-bis(acetoacetyl)diphenyl ether as the ligand. Most of the work was done with beryllium as the cation, but cupric (*78*) and zinc (*66*) cations were also studied. Dimethylformamide and a mixture of diphenyl ether and diphenyl (73% and 27%, respectively) were used as the solvents in most of the work. Detailed kinetic study of the reaction in Eq. (IX-4) showed it to be bimolecular

n CH3COCH2CO
O + n Be(AcAc)2
k1
k2
[9]
[10]
CH3
Be
CH3
n
+ 2n HAcAc
(IX-4)
[11]

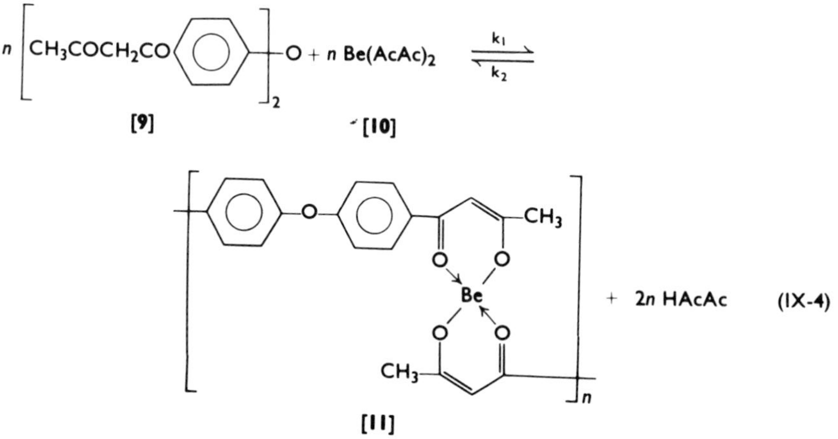

and reversible with an activation energy of 25 kcal/mole (137). Over the temperature range investigated (55°–85°C), the equilibrium constant was independent of temperature. Additional work on the process and polymer shown in Eq. (IX-4) has been reported ($82, 83$).

A novel ligand incorporating a β-diketone system is exemplified by [12], p-(1,3-butanedione)-N-phenylglycine (98). Polymerization of this ligand with the metal ions shown in Eq. (IX-5) gave the variety of products, [13], [14], and [15], shown. The polymers were all insoluble and hence molecular weight data were not obtainable. They were thermally stable, decomposing at 300°–450°C, with the beryllium and zinc polymers possessing the highest degree of thermal stability.

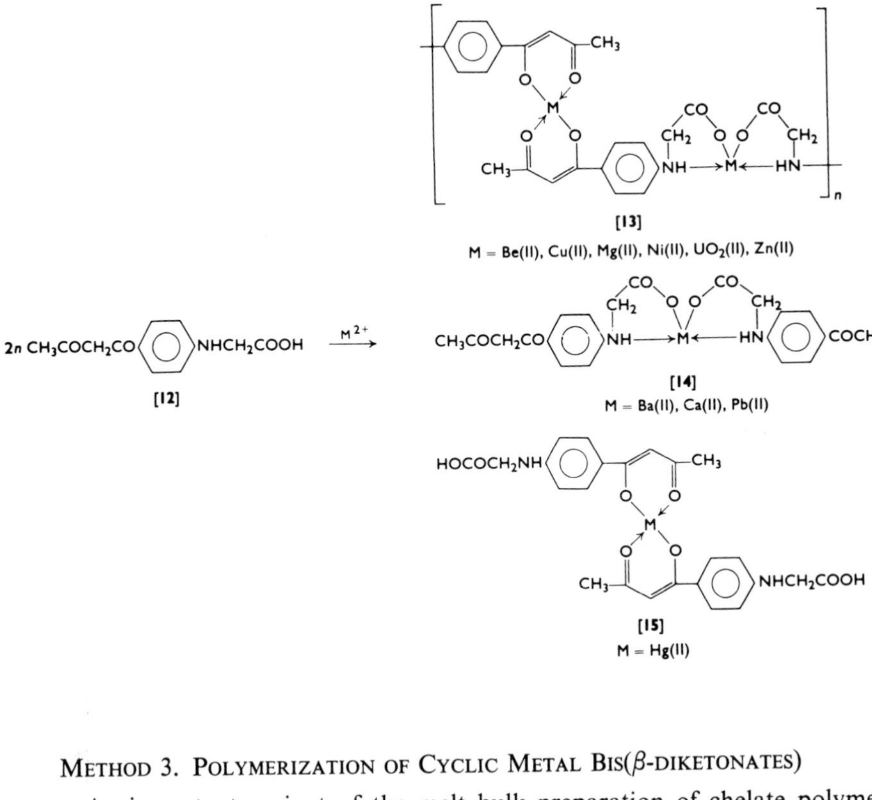

[13]

M = Be(II), Cu(II), Mg(II), Ni(II), UO₂(II), Zn(II)

$2n$ CH₃COCH₂CO⟨○⟩NHCH₂COOH $\xrightarrow{M^{2+}}$

[12]

[14]

M = Ba(II), Ca(II), Pb(II)

(IX-5)

[15]

M = Hg(II)

METHOD 3. POLYMERIZATION OF CYCLIC METAL BIS(β-DIKETONATES)

An important variant of the melt, bulk preparation of chelate polymers consists of isolating an intermediate cyclic chelate monomer, followed by its ring-opening polymerization. This technique was discovered in the bis(β-diketonate) series of polymers and resulted in the preparation of the first truly high molecular weight, linear, soluble chelate polymers (62). An example is shown in Eq. (IX-6). Heating the low polymer obtainable from a bis(β-diketone) and beryllium sulfate under vacuum yielded cyclic monomers as sublimates. The cyclic products were of permissible ring sizes, otherwise cyclic dimers and higher cycles were obtained. Heating the initial low polymers obtained from 4,4'-bis(acetoacetyl)diphenyl ether and 4,4'-bis(acetoacetyl)-diphenylethane under vacuum gave cyclic dimers and trimers (84–86). Preparation of polymeric bis(β-diketonates) from these macrocyclic chelates is effected by heating them above their melting points in bulk (62). Linear, high molecular weight products are obtained with intrinsic viscosities in the range of 0.1–2.7.

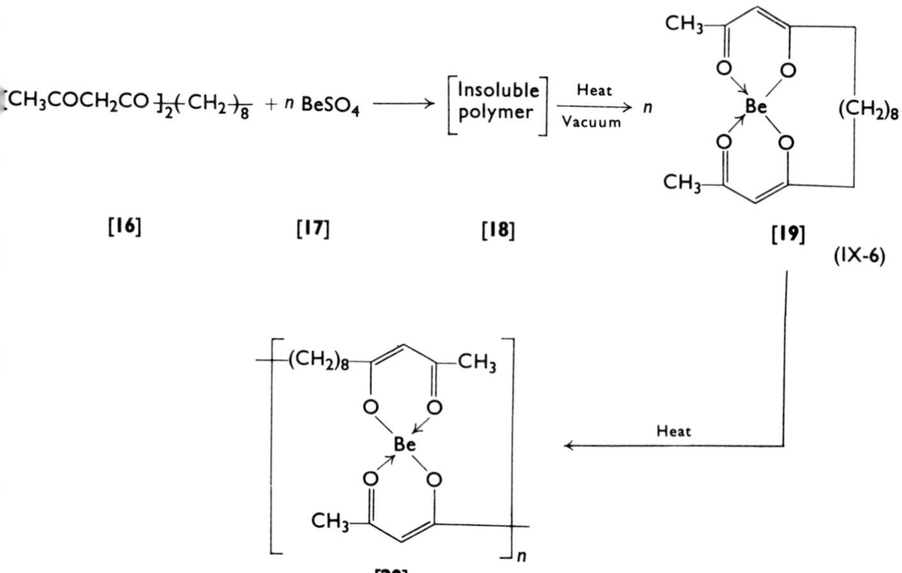

(IX-6)

The reversible nature of this polymerization was demonstrated by heating the polymers under vacuum to regenerate the cyclic monomer. The rates of degradation were found to be as shown in (IX-7). The relative order found is that which is expected from considering the increasing strain incorporated into the macrocycles with decreasing chain length. This order was corroborated by the reverse of the polymerization reaction. Polymerization of the monomer with $R = +CH_2+_6$ occurred instantly at 110°C on melting; whereas when $R = +CH_2+_{10}$ the monomer could be partially recovered after being heated for 1 minute in the melt at 140°C. Examples of cyclic monomers with R containing hetero atoms were also studied in this pioneering work (62).

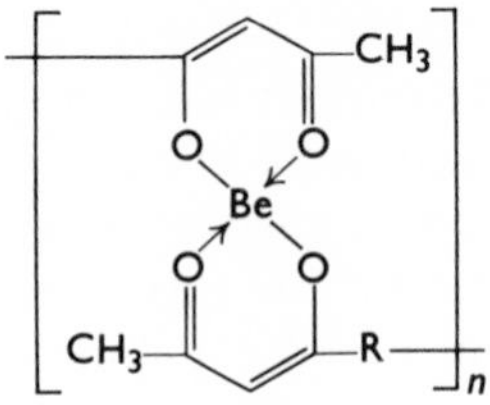

(IX-7)

[21]

$$R = +CH_2\mathbf{\overline{)}_{10}} \sim +CH_2\mathbf{\overline{)}_{12}} > +CH_2\mathbf{\overline{)}_{8}} > +CH_2\mathbf{\overline{)}_{7}} \gg +CH_2\mathbf{\overline{)}_{6}}$$

METHOD 4. POLYMERIZATION OF BIS(β-DIKETONES) WITH METAL CARBONYLS OR METAL ALKYLS

An attempt was made to use metal carbonyls and metal alkyls as reactants in bis(β-diketone) polymerizations (37). It was unsuccessful. Both nickel carbonyl and bis(triphenylphosphine)nickel dicarbonyl were unreactive towards bis(β-diketones). Diethylberyllium and tri(isobutyl)aluminum were also considered as reactants for this type of polymerization, but no positive results were obtained either.

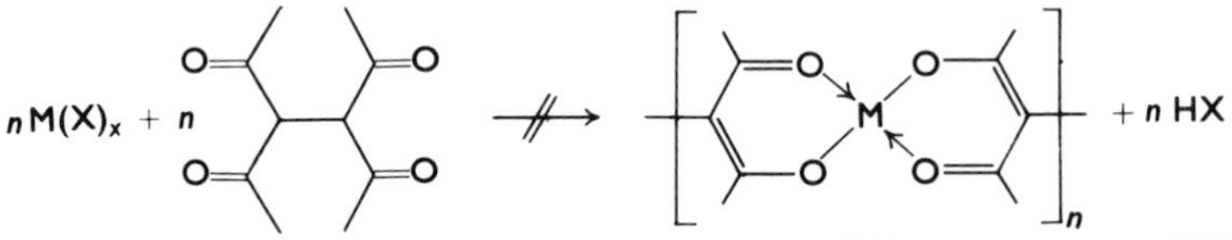

(IX-8)

[22]　　　[23]　　　　　　　　[24]　　　　[25]

X = alkyl or CO

METHOD 5. POLYMERIZATION OF BIS(β-DIKETONES) WITH HEXACOORDINATING METALS

Hexacoordinating metal atoms have been incorporated into bis(β-diketone) polymers by exchanging a tetraalkyl titanate with a bis(ligand) (74).

[26]　　　　　　　　　　　[27]

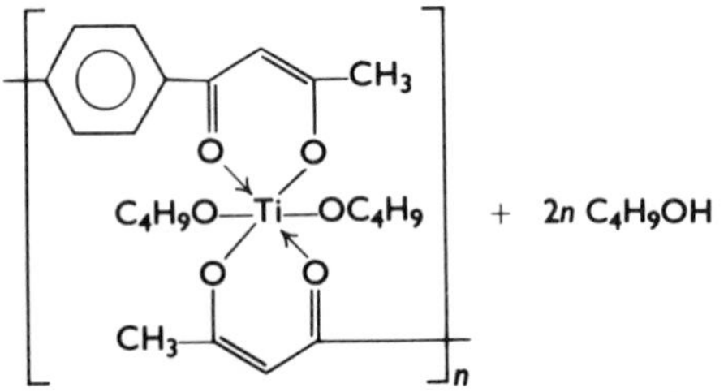

(IX-9)

[28]　　　　　　　　　　[29]

Precoordinated metal derivatives have also been used (105).

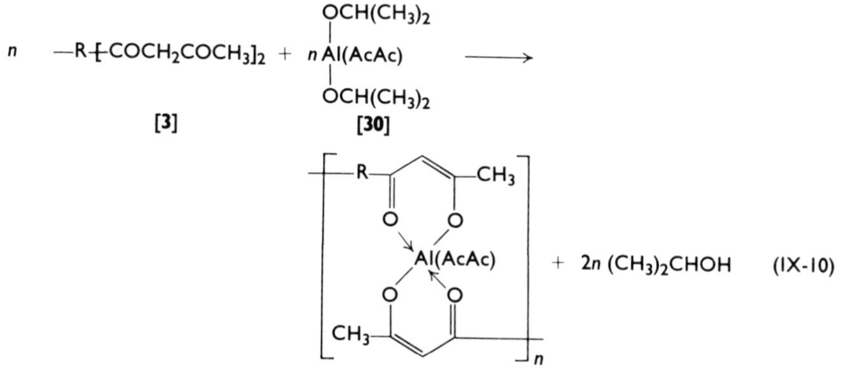

$$n \quad -R\text{-}[COCH_2COCH_3]_2 \; + \; n\,Al(AcAc) \xrightarrow{\quad}$$

with $OCH(CH_3)_2$ groups above and below Al in [30]

[3]   [30]

$$+ \; 2n \; (CH_3)_2CHOH \quad (IX\text{-}10)$$

[31]   [32]

Molecular weights of 1000–2000 are obtained by the above techniques.

Polymers containing structural features similar to that shown in Eq. (IX-10) have also been prepared by an alcoholysis reaction. Heating glycols in bulk with chelates containing two ester groups at 200°–250°C effects polymer formation (105). An example is shown in Eq. (IX-11). No structural data were presented to prove structure [35]. Since some decomposition occurred during the polymerization, other possibilities exist for the structure of the product.

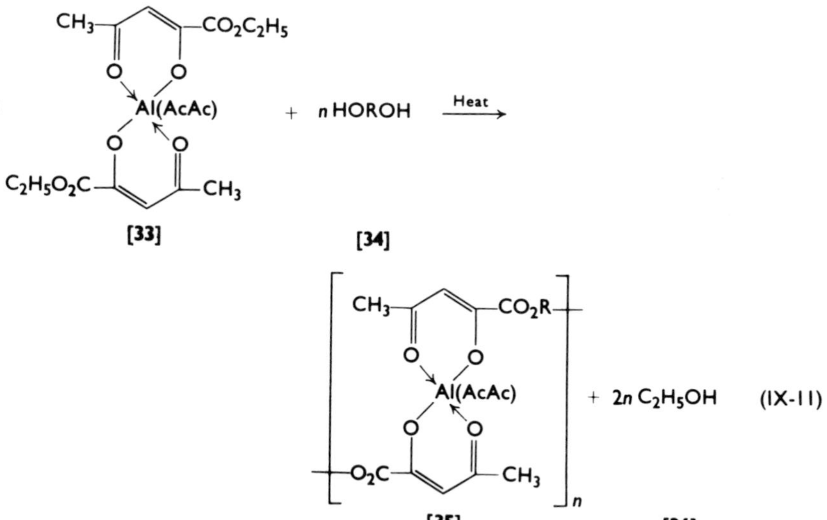

$$n \quad \cdots \; + \; n\,HOROH \xrightarrow{\text{Heat}}$$

[33]   [34]

$$+ \; 2n \; C_2H_5OH \quad (IX\text{-}11)$$

[35]   [36]

With few exceptions, most of the polymers prepared from bis(β-diketones) possess a high degree of "organic character" in their repeat unit. Stated another way, the metal atom constitutes a minor part of the total weight of the repeat unit. Perhaps it is for this reason that many polymeric metal bis(β-diketonates) are soluble in organic solvents. Although the more powerful solvents like dimethylformamide are frequently cited as being useful, benzene and dioxane are also effective. Benzene has been particularly useful for beryllium-containing polymers. Many examples of insoluble polymers are also cited in the literature. Melt processes at too vigorous reaction conditions can lead to insolubilization. A correlation between solubility and ionic radius of the metal in the chain has been described (65).

Only beryllium-containing bis(β-diketonates) possess high molecular weights. Viscometry and osmometry have been used to prove this fact (62, 76, 85, 86). In other cases where molecular weights have been determined by ebullioscopy or elemental analyses, the values that were found were well below the level at which plastic properties appear. Crystallinity data on this class of polymeric metal chelates are too scattered to attempt to draw any correlations. Polymeric chelates with aliphatic repeat units tend to be amorphous, whereas those with aromatic (particularly p-disubstituted) links have been crystalline in most cases. Beryllium-containing poly[bis(β-diketonates)] prepared by polymerization of their cyclic monomers possessed relatively low glass transition temperatures (62). The glass transition temperatures of the polymers [21] probably reflect the overwhelmingly hydrocarbonlike nature of the repeat units. The higher value (55°C) for the oxygen-containing connecting link was thought to be indicative of a lack of free rotation for the oxygens adjacent to the chelate ring. The physical properties shown in (IX-12) are reminiscent of polyethylene.

$R = —(CH_2)_8—$; $T_g = 35°C$

Tensile modulus (25°C) = 122,000 psi

Tensile strength = 2710 psi   (IX-12)

Melt index (190°C) = 0.1–2.0 dg/min

$R = —O(CH_2)_6O—$; $T_g = 55°C$

[21]

The reported melting points for metal bis(β-diketonate) polymers are intimately connected with their thermal stability. The data reported in Table IX.1 (pp. 258–273) on melting points are an accumulation of various types. Fortunately, some very excellent studies on the thermal stability of metal bis(β-diketonate) polymers have been described (25–28, 35, 138). Most importantly, these studies have also addressed themselves to the question of how much thermal stability chelation imparts to polymers and monomers.

Keep in mind that the original impetus for military support of polymeric chelate research had the development of thermally stable materials as its goal. Acetylacetone was found to be more stable at 266°C *in vacuo* than its chelates containing Cu(II), Ni(II), Co(II), Co(III), Al(III), Cr(III), Fe(III), and Mn(III) (*27, 28, 138*). Thus, the introduction of these metals into the acetylacetone molecule results in a decrease in its thermal stability. The thermal stability of polymeric chelates [37] prepared from tetraacetylethane have been studied by thermogravimetry in argon at atmospheric pressure (*25, 26*).

(IX-13)

[37]

The following order of decreasing heat stability was observed:

Mg > Ni > Co > Cu > Zn > Cd

The free ligand tetraacetylethane itself, was more heat-stable than its Cu, Zn, and Cd polymers, whereas its Mg, Ni, and Co polymers possessed greater thermal stability. This result, in contrast to the result obtained with acetylacetone, indicates that chelation can confer added heat stability. However, the relative order of decreasing heat stability that was found for divalent metal acetylacetonates was similar to that observed for metal–tetraacetylethane polymers:

Ni > Cu > Co and Mg > Zn, Cd

The temperature range at which decomposition became appreciable was from 225° to 350°C in all of the above cases; hence, outstanding thermal stability was not apparent.

The volatile decomposition products obtained from the thermolysis of the metal–tetraacetylethane polymers were analyzed by mass spectrometry and the nonvolatile residue by elemental and X-ray analysis (*26*). A postulated decomposition mechanism involved an initial dehydrogenation step to form a more highly conjugated polymeric species with the chelate ring intact. The hydrogen formed during this process is either released or reacts to reduce part of the metal to the metallic form, with attendant formation of tetraacetylethane. X-Ray powder patterns of pyrolysis residues showed that the Cu, Ni, and Co polymers yielded free metals, while the Zn and Mg polymers gave metal oxides. The cadmium polymer gave a mixture of the metal and oxide at lower temperature. Liberated tetraacetylethane can dehydrate to yield 3,4-diacetyl-

2,5-dimethylfuran, which could then be pyrolyzed to give the other observed products [see Eq. (IX-14)]. Formation of oxides from the less easily reducible metals could involve attack of the chelate ring by hydrogen with formation of metal oxide, tetraacetylethane, and unidentified organic products from tetraacetylethane by loss of oxygen atoms. Pyrolysis of the Mg(II)–tetraacetylethane polymer must proceed by a different mechanism since the furan derivative [39] was not observed among the products.

$$(CH_3CO)_2CHCH(COCH_3)_2 \xrightarrow{\text{Heat}} \quad + \quad H_2O \qquad (\text{IX-14})$$

[38]

[39]

Heat

$\longrightarrow H_2 + CH_4 + CO + CO_2 + CH_3COCH_3$

[40]

Another study aimed at uncovering unusual properties that chelation sites impart to polymers involved differential thermal analysis of the copper(II) chelates of a series of bis(β-diketones) (IX-15) (35). A linear decrease in thermal stability with an increase in the methylene chain length was found. This is similar to purely organic chain compounds. If the chelate site alone were the decomposition mode, the decomposition temperature might be expected to be constant. It was concluded that the bis(β-diketonate) site did not confer any unusual thermal properties. The interpretations drawn from these results could be clouded because aluminum oxide was mixed with the chelate as a standard during the DTA analysis. Its effect on the results was not discussed.

(IX-15)

[41]

x = 2, 3, 4, 5, 7, 8

Several other orders of decreasing thermal stability for metal chelate polymers derived from a variety of bis(β-diketone) ligands have been published.

Be > Cu > Ni > Zn > Co	(103)
Cu > Be > Ni > Co > Zn > Mn > Cd	(67)
Hg > Be > Cu > Ni > Co > Zn > Mn > Cd	(69)

They correlate quite well considering differences in measuring techniques. A correlation between thermal stability and instability constants has also been reported (69). A limited amount of magnetic data is available for metal bis(β-diketonate) polymers (26, 75).

Several patents have described some coatings applications based on chelated poly(β-dicarbonyl) compounds. Poly(allyl acetoacetate) was cross-linked by chelate exchange with bis(methyl salicylate)beryllium (21) to yield clear, hard films upon air-drying or baking at 120°C. Another system that was investigated was ethylene–vinyl salicylate copolymers and copper bis(butyl acetoacetate). Exchange at 125°C yielded tough films with a tensile strength of 4040 psi, elongation at break of 425%, and a modulus of 11,600 psi. The films were reported to be unaffected by exposure to ultraviolet light for 500 hours (52, 53). Polymeric metal β-diketonates are catalysts for the decomposition of hydrogen peroxide and ascorbic acid (101).

B. Polymers from Bis(1,2-hydroxyketo) Ligands

Monomeric chelates derived from 1,2-hydroxyketo ligands comprise one of the oldest known classes. The use of this type of ligand in analytical and dye chemistry contributed to the early interest. Certain polymerizable bis(1,2-hydroxyketo) compounds are well characterized and readily accessible. Monocyclic bis(ligands) of this class include 2,5-dihydroxybenzoquinone [42] (41, 42, 55–57, 113, 114), 2,5-dihydroxyterephthalaldehyde [43] (6), and 2,4-diacetylresorcinol [44] (54).

Five- and six-membered chelate rings are formed from the 1,2- and 1,3-dioxy ligand systems, respectively. The 1,3-dioxy ligands resemble enols of 1,3-dicarbonyl compounds and, hence, give products that are structurally similar to those obtained from the polymerization of bis(β-diketones).

METHOD 1. POLYMERIZATION OF BIS(LIGANDS) WITH METAL SALTS OR METAL CHELATES

Solution polymerization of the bis(ligand) with a metal salt has been used almost exclusively with this class.

$$n \quad [45] \quad + \quad n\,MX_2 \quad \longrightarrow$$

[45]   [46]

$$[47] \quad + \quad 2n\,HX \qquad (IX\text{-}17)$$

Solvents that have been used include ethanol, water, dimethylformamide, dimethyl sulfoxide, and triethylamine (24). Polymerization temperatures have ranged from room temperature to the boiling point of the solvent. Interfacial procedures using benzene (54) and methylene chloride (63, 64) as the organic phase have been described. Early precipitation of the polymeric chelates was a universal occurrence in the systems described above. This could cause formation of low molecular weight product. Some very interesting methods for slowly mixing the monomers were investigated in the system of Cu(II) and alizarin but without avail (36, 115). Metal acetates are used most frequently, but the use of sulfates, chlorides, nitrates, and acetylacetonates has been described. Diethylzinc has been used (113). In many instances, particularly where analytical separations are being attempted, acids are added (55). Hydrochloric (55), sulfuric (39), and acetic acids (40) are useful. The amine complex of the metal has been used in the interfacial polymerization attempts (54, 63, 64). The free bis(hydroxyketo) ligand has been used most frequently. Apparently to increase its water solubility, the diammonium (41) and disodium salts (57) of 2,5-dihydroxybenzoquinone have been used. Copolymers from two different bis(ligands) and/or two different metals have been studied (80, 81).

Bulk polymerization of the metal bis(acetylacetonate) with the bis(ligand) has been studied less often (63, 77). No advantages were reported.

The polymers that have been prepared from this class of bis(ligand) were generally insoluble and infusible. Many form hydrates quite readily. Slight solubility has been reported in several instances in solvents such as cresol, pyridine, and water. The insolubility of the products, along with consideration of the structural possibilities derivable from the ligand, has led to the conclusion that the products are (must be) polymeric (55). However, in the case of some 2,5-dihydroxybenzoquinone complexes (41), a monomeric structure was suggested based on metal-to-carbon ratios and changes in them based on starting monomer ratios. Three polymer samples prepared from 2,5-dihydroxybenzoquinone and lead nitrate using 1:2, 1:1, and 2:1 molar ratios possessed identical compositions (one metal to one quinone). This result supported structure [48]. If the products were polymeric, their compositions should have varied because of end-group differences.

(IX-18)

[48]

M = divalent metal
X = OH or other

Molecular weights of 1000–7000 have been reported (77) for some similar polymers from 1,4-dihydroxyanthraquinone. The zinc–1,4-dihydroxyanthraquinone polymer was found to possess molecular weights of 1460–2220, determined by a sophisticated ultracentrifugation study (88). Differences in the preparative procedure that were used were slight, but could conceivably explain the variations. Insolubility of these products is the major reason that the molecular weight question cannot be answered by more conventional polymer techniques.

An interesting question regarding the structures of these polymers can be raised because of their insolubility. Namely, are they simple linear [50] polymers or are more complex features present? For example, a two-dimensional lattice structure [51] could form if each metal atom were coordinated by three different ligand molecules. Coordination of each atom with four different ligand molecules can lead to three-dimensional lattice structures [52]. These structures probably represent idealized cases, with an actual polymer possessing a mixed structure. In the case of polymers derived from methylene bis(5-salicylaldehyde), study of many physicochemical properties (electron paramagnetic resonance, infrared, and reflectance spectra) has led to the conclusion that two- and three-dimensional lattice structures predominate (128). The specific ligand structure and coordinating characteristics of the metal ion plays a major role in determining the polymer structure in this and other cases.

The thermal stability of members of this class of polymers has been investigated. Since they are not fusible to clear, stable melts, most of the melting point data reported in Table IX.2 (pp. 274–279) represent decomposition points observed in capillaries or by thermogravimetric techniques. Similar trends in

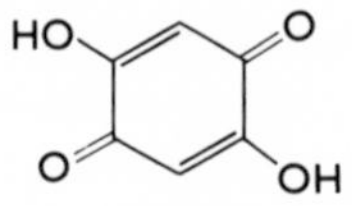

[42]   represented by   [49]

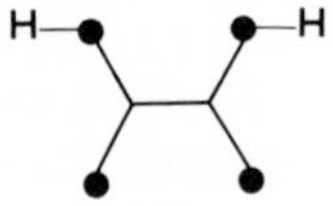

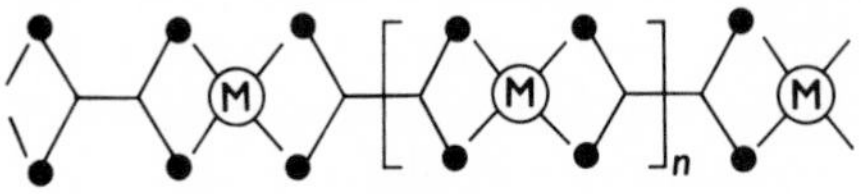

[50]

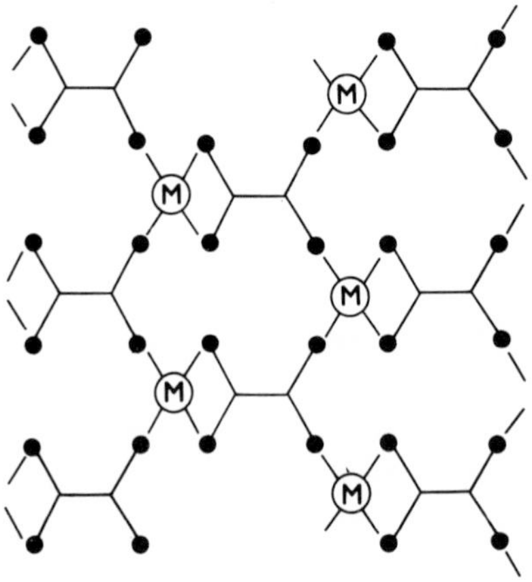

[51]   (IX-19)

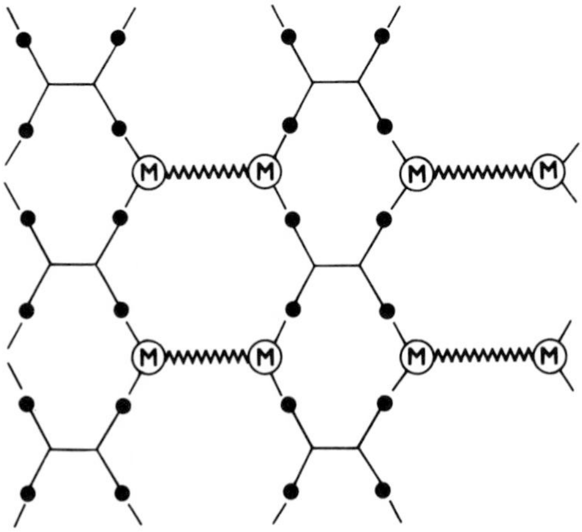

MMMM denotes ligand molecules perpendicular to page

[52]

thermal stability have been found by different workers (see the following tabulation). The majority of the polymeric chelates of bis(hydroxyketo) compounds decompose in the 300°–400°C range. Thermal stability in excess of 450°C was reported for the copper(II)–naphthazarin polymer by one group (34), but this result is not in accord with the trend shown below.

Relative Thermal Stability of the Polymers Prepared from Bis(1,2-hydroxyketo) Ligands

Ligand	Relative stability	Ref.
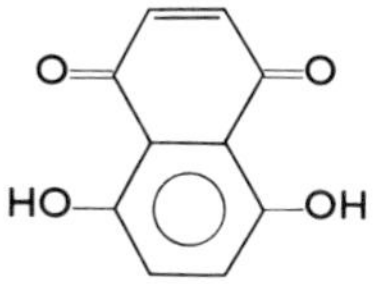 **[53]**	Be(II) > Ni(II) > Zn(II) > Co(II) > Cu(II)	20
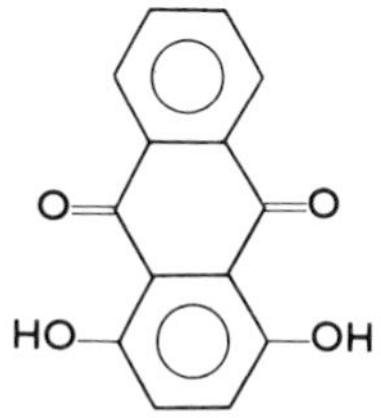 **[45]**	Be(II) > Ni(II) > Mg(II) > Zn(II) > Mn(II) > Cd(II) > Cu(II) > Ca(II) > Co(II)	81
and 1,5-dihydroxyanthraquinone	Zn(II) and Ni(II) > various other	54
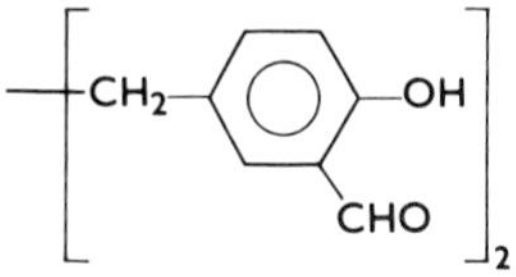 **[54]**	Ni(II) > Cu(II) > Co(II) > Fe(II)	127

Thermomechanical curves have been reported for metal–1,4-dihydroxy-anthraquinone polymers. The temperature at which a maximum deflection occurs is usually an approximation to the glass transition temperature. In this case, the meaning of the reported temperatures is not clear because in some instances they are higher than the reported decomposition temperatures. To the extent that they are reliable guides to T_g's, these polymers have some of the highest T_g's known. The reported ranges (350°–400°C) are consistent with the rigid polycyclic backbones of these polymers.

Magnetic properties of this class of coordination polymer have been studied (7, 75, 123, 127, 128). The magnetic moments of a series of quinizarin–metal polymers have been interpreted to yield information about the hybridization that is present in their structure (75).

EPR signals have also been detected and described (7, 123, 127, 128). Electrical conductivity data have been obtained for the 1,4- and 1,5-dihydroxyanthraquinone polymers (54, 123). They are typical organic semiconductors. An increase in the electrical conductivity of the polymers correlates with an increase in the ionization tendency of the metal ions; less of a change was found with changes in the ligand (54). These changes were small. Hence, the structure (degree of order) of the polymer and the character of the electronic interactions within the whole solid are thought to be determining. Charge-transfer complexes were postulated to take part in the mechanism of conduction (123).

The catalytic activity of some of these polymers for the decomposition of hydrazine (19, 59), isopropanol (19), formic acid (19), hydrogen peroxide (60) and for the oxidation of cumene to its hydroperoxide has been studied (58). 2,5-Dihydroxybenzoquinone selectively precipitates thorium and zirconium in the presence of other rare earths (55). Analysis of beryllium by spectrophotometric studies of its complexes with naphthazarin and/or alkannin has been developed into a rapid, sensitive, and accurate method (134). The synthesis of many of the polymers in Table IX.2 (pp. 274–279) for use as dyes was performed in 1912 (48).

C. Polymeric Metal Carboxylates

METHOD 1. POLYMERIC BASIC BERYLLIUM CARBOXYLATES

Incorporation of the basic beryllium carboxylate structure into a polymeric repeat unit has been investigated in a search for thermally stable polymers (97). Replacement of two of the acid groups in basic beryllium acetate by the carboxyl groups of a dibasic acid was studied. The structure of the monomeric acetate consists of a beryllium atom at each of the vertices of a tetrahedron bonded to an oxygen atom at the center. Acetate groups occupy the six edges of the tetrahedron. Polymers of this type were apparently prepared, but not recognized as such, during earlier attempts at preparing the basic succinates (100, 126) and malonates. The products were described as being "slimes" and "glasses." More recent work (97) utilized the reaction of basic beryllium acetate with diacid chlorides for polymer preparation. Equimolar amounts were condensed in solvents such as benzene and xylene at 80°–110°C. All of the products were low molecular weight powders.

$$n\ Be_4O(O_2CR)_6 + n\ ClOCR'COCl \longrightarrow$$

[55] [56]

$$\left[\left(\begin{array}{c}Be_4O\\(RCO_2)_4\end{array}\right)\left(\begin{array}{c}O\\O\end{array}CR'C\begin{array}{c}O\\O\end{array}\right)\right]_n + 2n\ RCOCl \qquad \text{(IX-20)}$$

[57] [58]

Various combinations of basic beryllium acetate, propionate, and benzoate were reacted with the acid chlorides of adipic, sebacic, β-ethyladipic, terephthalic, and isophthalic acids. Solution viscosities of the products (in toluene) were very low. Elemental analytical data tended to confirm this fact by showing the presence of inordinate amounts of end groups.

The above polymers, though soluble when initially prepared, disproportionate at room temperature to basic beryllium carboxylates and a cross-linked polymer.

$$\left[\left(\begin{array}{c}Be_4O\\(RCO_2)_4\end{array}\right)\left(\begin{array}{c}O\\O\end{array}CR'C\begin{array}{c}O\\O\end{array}\right)\right]_n \longrightarrow$$

[57]

$$Be_4O(RCO_2)_6 + \left[(Be_4O)\left(\begin{array}{c}O\\O\end{array}C-R'-C\begin{array}{c}O\\O\end{array}\right)_3\right]_n \qquad \text{(IX-21)}$$

[59] [60]

Those containing aromatic dibasic acid groups were more stable, but could also be converted to the insoluble form by heating. Attempts to prepare the soluble polymers by melt polymerization or in more concentrated solutions gave cross-linked materials directly.

Basic beryllium acetate, when heated with alcohols, forms polymer and acetic anhydride (46, 49). The polymer that is formed generally contains some coordinated alcohol. Pyridine effects a similar reaction. Apparently, linear or sheetlike polymers of variable composition are formed.

$$Be_4O(OCOCH_3)_6 \xrightarrow[\text{[62]}]{\text{ROH}} Be_4O_m(OCOCH_3)_{8-2m} + m(CH_3CO)_2O \qquad \text{(IX-22)}$$

[61] [63] [64]

A proposed propagation step is shown in Eq. (IX-23). Thermolysis of the product that was prepared in refluxing ethanol [65] gave ethanol at 100°C, ethanol and acetic anhydride at 130°–140°C, basic beryllium acetate at 200°C, and ultimately formed pure BeO at temperatures greater than 300°C.

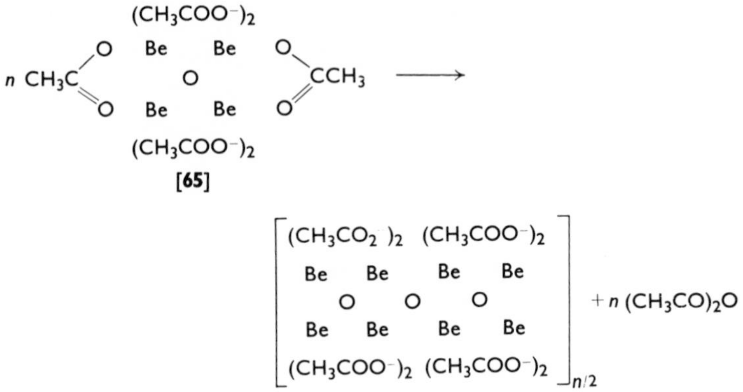

$$+ n (CH_3CO)_2O \qquad (IX-23)$$

[66]

METHOD 2. POLYMERIZATION OF BIS(α-HYDROXY ACIDS)

Polymerization of bis(α-hydroxy acids) has been studied. Titration of the acid with aqueous or alcoholic alkali, followed by addition of a metal salt, has been used to prepare a series of insoluble salts from divalent metals (73).

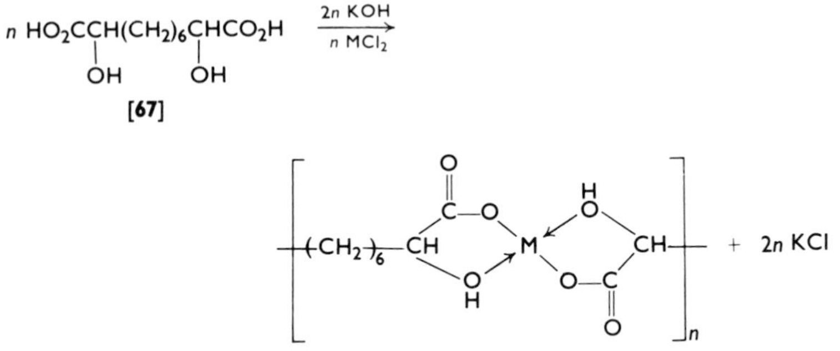

$$+ 2n \, KCl \qquad (IX-24)$$

[68]   [69]

Their insolubility prevented molecular weight determinations. The thermal stability of the products obtained from α,α'-dihydroxysebacic acid, decreased in the order: Ni > Co > Cu > Zn > Cd. α,α'-Dihydroxysebacic and α,α'-dimethoxysebacic acids have been converted to tin-containing (71) and thallium-containing (70) polymers. A variety of dialkyl- and diaryltin compounds was employed for these syntheses. The reduced viscosities that were measured were all very low (0.02–0.04).

Phenylthallium diisobutyrate (70) polymerizes with dibasic acids to yield polymeric phenylthallium carboxylates (IX-25) (70). These products, which are soluble in a variety of solvents, also possessed very low reduced viscosities. The polymerization was conducted in ethanol or chloroform at 40°C for 1 hour. The products were white powders. Their increased solubility is attributed to the presence of the phenyl group on the metal atom.

$$n \text{ HO}_2\text{CCH(CH}_2)_6\text{CHCO}_2\text{H} + n \text{ (RCOO)}_2\text{TlC}_6\text{H}_5 \longrightarrow$$

with OH, OH groups below

[67]   [70]

$$\left[(\text{CH}_2)_6\text{CHCOOTlOOCCH} \right]_n + 2n \text{ RCOOH} \quad \text{(IX-25)}$$

with C_6H_5 group and O–H groups

[71]   [72]

Bis(salicylic acids) have been polymerized with metal salts to yield the chelate polymers (IX-26). Metal acetylacetonates (72), and metal chlorides and acetates have been used. Aqueous (9, 99, 131) or organic (72) media are suitable. Data indicating that high molecular weight products were obtained have not been presented. The insolubility of the products is the main reason. A comparative study of the polymerization of a free bis(salicylic acid), the corresponding bis(methyl salicylate), and the corresponding bis(methyl ether salicylic acid) has been reported (72).

$$n \text{ HO} \cdots \text{HO}_2\text{C} \cdots \text{CH}_3 \cdots \text{CO}_2\text{H} \cdots \text{OH} + n \text{ MX}_2 \longrightarrow$$

[73]   [46]

$$\left[\cdots \text{C(CH}_3)_2 \cdots \text{M} \cdots \right]_n + 2n \text{ HX} \quad \text{(IX-26)}$$

[74]

Products with ferromagnetic properties were obtained by heating the polymeric chelated salicylates shown in Eq. (IX-27) at 120°–150°C (9).

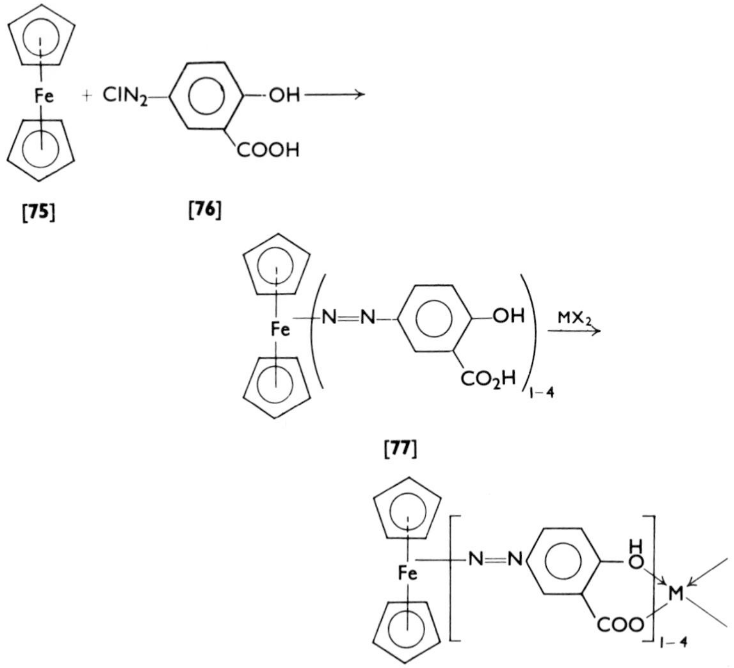

[75]   [76]

[77]

(IX-27)

[78]

METHOD 3. MISCELLANEOUS POLYMERIC CARBOXYLATES

A study of the magnetic properties of the copper salts of dibasic acids has produced evidence for a polymeric structure (87). For the series [79] the copper salts all possessed magnetic moments that were less than the theoretical spin-only moment for a single unpaired electron, except for $x = 3$. This suggested the existence of polymeric molecules involving coordinate links.

$$n \, HOOC\text{--}(CH_2)_{x-2}\text{--}COOH + n \, Cu(II) \longrightarrow$$

[79]   [80]

$x = 2, 4\text{--}10$

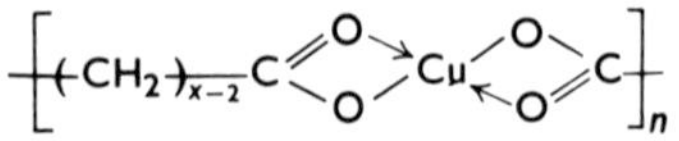

(IX-28)

[81]

Chromium complexes of carboxylic acids appear to be coordination polymers. Chromic oxide or chromyl chloride is reduced in the presence of a carboxylic acid by an alcohol to yield complexes of varying structure (50, 104). Further reaction of these complexes with water results in polymerization by bridging with hydroxide ions.

$$RCO_2H + CrO_2Cl_2 + R'OH \longrightarrow$$

[82]

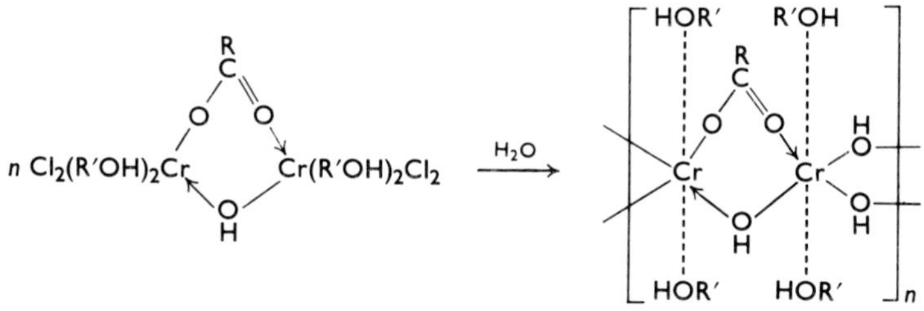

(IX-29)

[83]　　　　　　　　　　　　　[84]

The structures of the products from reactions of this type have not been rigorously defined in all cases. They do possess commercial utility as coatings for various types of substrates when applied with heating to effect further polymerization. If the substrate possesses a functional group with active hydrogens, bond formation can occur (50, 104, 109). Products that might possess structures similar to these materials have been prepared from carboxylic acids and titanium salts (91, 92).

The ability of aluminum soaps to gel hydrocarbons has long been suggestive of a polymeric structure. A study of the infrared absorption changes accompanying peptization of cyclohexane gels of these aluminum salts substantiated a polymeric structure (93).

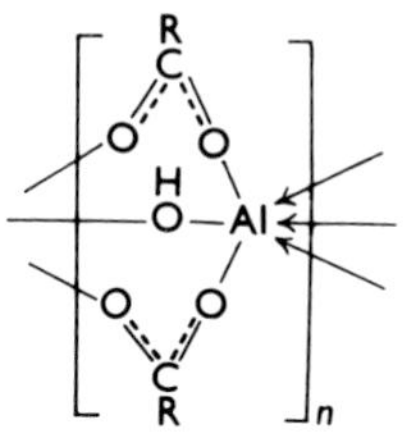

(IX-30)

[85]

Polychelates of chlorendic acid [86] are prepared by bubbling oxygen through a mixture of the acid and metal in acetone (130). Copper-, manganese-, and lead-containing polymers were reported. Molecular weights of 1700 to 1900 were determined by vapor-phase osmometry on the polymers. Elemental analyses supported a cyclic structure for the oligomer.

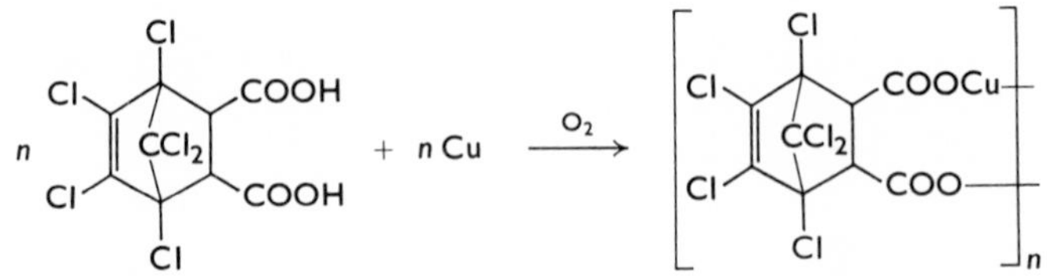

(IX-31)

[86]   [87]   [88]

Aliphatic (42) and aromatic (131, 132) tetracarboxylic acids have been polymerized with tetravalent metal and metalloidal salts. Low molecular weight products that decomposed at less than 200°C were obtained by reaction of silicon tetrachloride with aliphatic tetraacids. Pyromellitic acid and 2,3,6,7-naphthalenetetracarboxylic acid are converted to polymers by reaction with metal salts in water at 100°C (IX-32). The thermal stabilities of thorium-containing products were compared. The naphthalene-derived polymer was found to be less stable (360°C d) than the pyromellitic polymer. This result was attributed to the possibility that in thorium pyromellitate the thorium coordination shell is completed exclusively by carbonyl groups of neighboring chains, whereas in the naphthalene salt, water occupies two of the coordination sites of thorium. Uranium salts were less stable thermally than the thorium analogs (131).

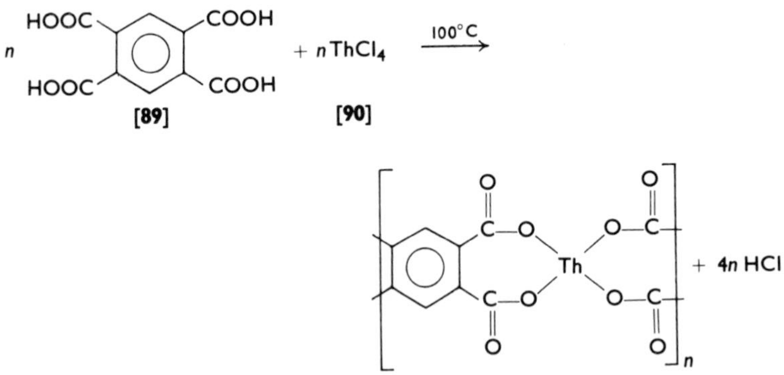

[89]   [90]

+ 4n HCl   (IX-32)

[91]   [92]

Poly(amic acids) prepared from diamines and pyromellitic anhydride react with metal acetylacetonates to yield polymers with chelated metal ions (3). These products form tough films, which indicated that the initially high molecular weight of the poly(amic acid) was retained on chelation. Heating these products gave electrically conductive materials containing free metal (3).

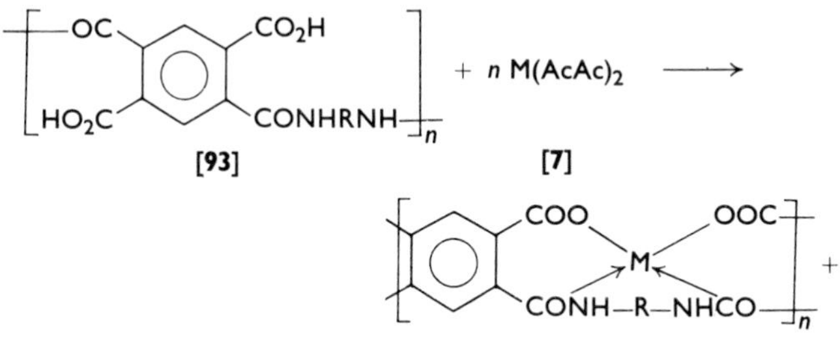

$$2n\ R_2P(O)OH + n\ M(AcAc)_2 \longrightarrow \quad\quad + 2n\ HAcAc \quad (IX\text{-}33)$$

(Structure [93] + [7] → [94])

D. Polymeric Metal Phosphinates

METHOD 1. POLYPHOSPHINATES OF TRIVALENT AND TETRAVALENT, CHELATED METAL ATOMS

Several different types of poly(metal phosphinates) have been described over the past few years (12, 13). One that contains a trivalent octahedral metal atom was synthesized by reaction (IX-34) and some subsequent variations of it (10, 11, 17, 22, 110). Reaction of a monomeric chelate with substituted phosphinic acids in bulk or in solution in an inert atmosphere gave polymer (11, 22). Temperatures of 170°–250°C and solvents such as biphenyl and chlorinated biphenyls were used. Other monomeric ligands such as 2-picolinic acid could be used in place of acetylacetone, but polymer formation was more difficult (119).

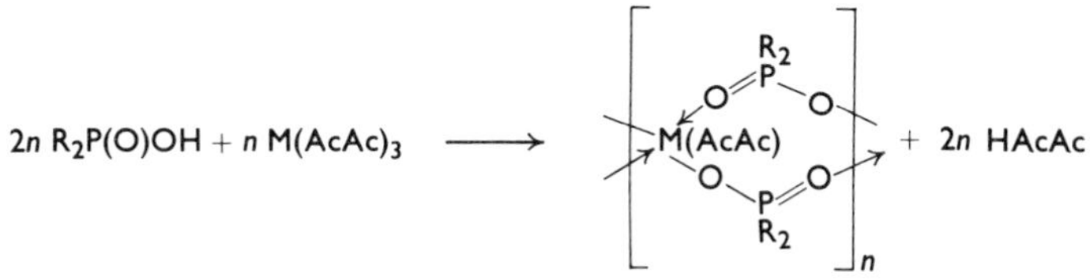

$$2n\ R_2P(O)OH + n\ M(AcAc)_3 \longrightarrow \quad\quad + 2n\ HAcAc \quad (IX\text{-}34)$$

[95]   [96]   [97]

More recently, polymers have been prepared where the coordinated ligand is the same phosphinic acid that is present in the backbone (125). Additional examples are shown in Table IX.4 (pp. 288–295).

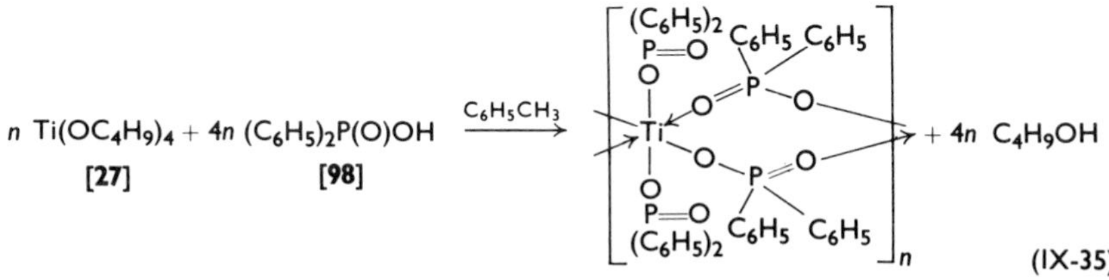

$$n\ Ti(OC_4H_9)_4 + 4n\ (C_6H_5)_2P(O)OH \xrightarrow{C_6H_5CH_3} \quad\quad + 4n\ C_4H_9OH$$

[27]   [98]

(IX-35)

[99]

Poly(metal arsinates) are also obtained by this method. The products were always partially soluble in various solvents. Increasing insolubility was thought to be due to increasing molecular weight. One Cr(III), chloroform-soluble fraction possessed a molecular weight of 10,870 (ebullioscopy). The molecular weights of the insoluble fractions were not reported.

In several instances, the lowest molecular weight fractions obtained were shown to be cyclic dimers [100] and [101] (15).

$$\overline{\;Be(AcAc)OP(C_6H_5)_2OBe(AcAc)OP(C_6H_5)_2O\;}\qquad and$$

[100]

$$\overline{\;Cr(AcAc)_2OP(C_6H_5)_2OCr(AcAc)_2OP(C_6H_5)_2O\;}\qquad (IX\text{-}36)$$

[101]

AcAc = acetylacetonate

Dimers of this type were purported to be convertible to polymer (11). Reactions (IX-37) and (IX-38) depict two routes.

$$2n\;[Cr(AcAc)_2(OP(C_6H_5)_2O)]_2 + 4n\;(C_6H_5)_2P(O)OH \xrightarrow{\;Heat\;}$$
[102]   [98]

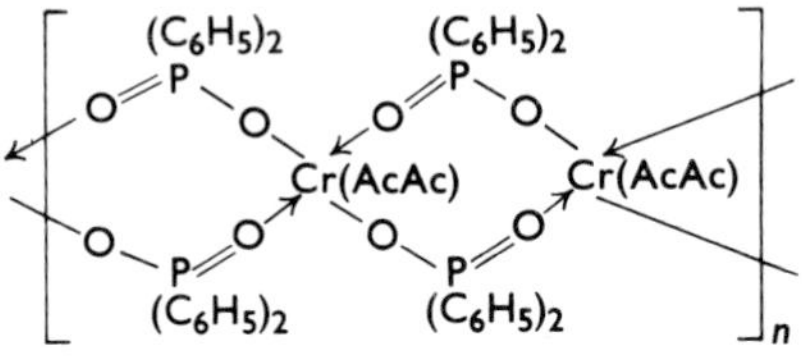

[103]

$$+ 2n\;HAcAc \qquad (IX\text{-}37)$$

$$2n[Cr(AcAc)_2(OP(C_6H_5)_2O)]_2 \xrightarrow{\;Heat\;}$$
[102]

[103]

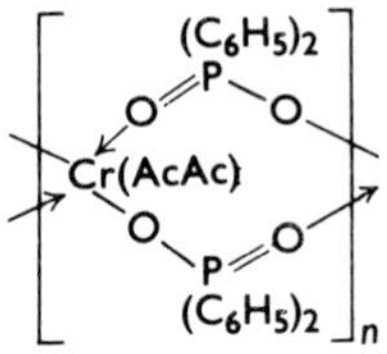

$$+ n\;Cr(AcAc)_3 \quad (IX\text{-}38)$$

[104]

Heating a preformed polymeric metal phosphinate of this type with another bidentate ligand can result in replacement of the ligand that is already present in the polymer [Eq. (IX-39)] (11).

$$\left[M(AcAc)(OP(C_6H_5)_2O)_2 \right]_n + n \quad \text{(structure [106])} \xrightarrow{\text{Heat}}$$

[105]   [106]

$$\left[\text{(structure [107])} \right]_n + n\,HAcAc \quad (IX\text{-}39)$$

[107]

Titanyl phosphinate polymers are prepared by hydrolysis of either dialkoxy or dichlorotitanium phosphinates (31). The dialkoxytitanium phosphinates were prepared from reaction of tetraalkyl titanates and phosphinic acids in bulk or refluxing toluene.

$$\left[\text{(structure [108])} \right]_n \xrightarrow{H_2O} \left[\text{(structure [109])} \right]_n \quad (IX\text{-}40)$$

[108]   [109]

R″ = alkoxy or chloro

The dichlorotitanium phosphinates are obtained from [110] by pyrolysis [Eq. (IX-41)]. The molecular weights of the titanyl polymers [111] were very high in some cases.

$$n\,TiCl_4[OP(C_6H_5)_2OC_2H_5]_2 \longrightarrow [TiCl_2[OP(C_6H_5)_2O]_2]_n + 2n\,C_2H_5Cl \quad (IX\text{-}41)$$

[110]   [111]   [112]

The polymers prepared by the method under discussion possess structures that are composed of only inorganic atoms in the backbone. Organic groups are present, but only are pendant to the main chain. Polymers incorporating Cr(III), Al(III), In(III), and Fe(III) as the central metal atoms have been reported. Only a few ligands and substituents on the phosphorus (or arsenic) atom have been investigated. Unfortunately, the insolubility of the high molecular weight products has discouraged any attempts to assemble mechanical property data. The polymer [103] shown in Eq. (IX-37) was reported to undergo weight loss at 290°–330°C by thermogravimetry (17). The titanyl phosphinate polymers were very stable thermally, undergoing weight loss at 450°C (31).

METHOD 2. POLYARSINATES OF TRIVALENT, CHELATED METAL ATOMS

Although certain arsenic-containing polymers were obtainable by Method D, 1 (see Table IX-4), others were not. Polymers derived from dimethylarsinic acid had to be prepared by addition of the sodium salt of the acid to chromic nitrate in ethanol [Eq. (IX-42)] (11) followed by reaction with sodium acetylacetonate.

$$Cr(NO_3)_3 + 3\,(CH_3)_2As(O)\bar{O}\,Na^+ \xrightarrow{\text{EtOH}} Cr[OAs(O)(CH_3)_2]_3 + 3NaNO_3$$

$$[113]\qquad\qquad [114]\qquad\qquad\qquad\qquad [115]\qquad\qquad [116]$$

$$n\,Cr[OAs(O)(CH_3)_2]_3 + n\,[CH_3COCHCOCH_3]^- \longrightarrow \hspace{2cm} \text{(IX-42)}$$
$$\hspace{6.5cm} Na^+$$
$$[115]\qquad\qquad\qquad\qquad [117]$$

$$\left[Cr(AcAc)[OAs(CH_3)_2O]_2\right]_n$$

$$[118]$$

METHOD 3. POLYPHOSPHINATES OF TRIVALENT METAL ATOMS COORDINATING HYDROXYL AND WATER

Another class of doubly bridged metal phosphinate polymers are those possessing coordinated water and hydroxide ion in place of the organic bidentate ligand ($12, 13, 116, 118, 120$). The synthesis of this class of polymer is shown in Eq. (IX-43).

$$Cr(C_2H_3O_2)_2 + 2\,KOP(O)R_2 \xrightarrow{H_2O} Cr(OP(O)R_2)_2 \cdot H_2O + 2\,KC_2H_3O_2$$

$$[119]\qquad\quad [120]\qquad\qquad\qquad\quad [121]\qquad\qquad\qquad [122]$$

$$n\,Cr(OP(O)R_2)_2 \cdot H_2O + 1/2n\,O_2 \xrightarrow{H_2O} \qquad\qquad\qquad \text{(IX-43)}$$

$$[121]\qquad\qquad\quad [123]\qquad\qquad\qquad\qquad [124]$$

The first step of this synthesis is conducted at reflux in a nitrogen atmosphere ($116, 118, 120$). A closer look at the mechanism of the polymer-forming second step has resulted in a novel postulate (13). Evidence supporting the propagation reaction in Eq. (IX-44) was uncovered.

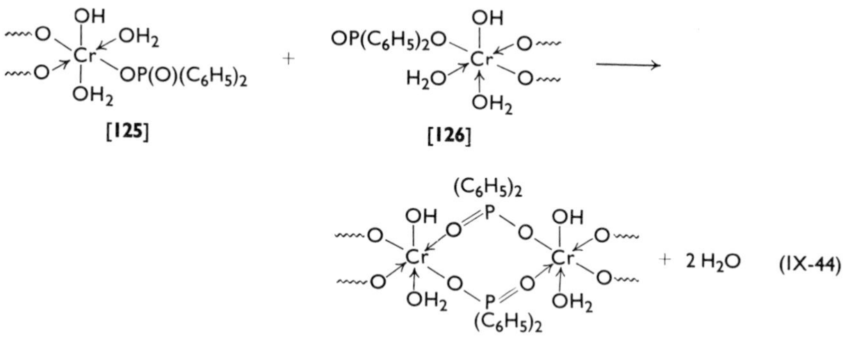

$$[125] \quad + \quad [126] \quad \longrightarrow$$

$$[127] \quad + \quad 2\,H_2O \qquad (IX\text{-}44)$$

Molecular weight distribution data fit the calculated distribution for a condensation polymerization. A novel feature of this condensation polymerization is that the displaced water molecule comes from only one of the reactants. Physical methods of structural analysis confirm the above structures for this type of polymer. Carrying out the oxidation step with other oxidizing agents can lead to the introduction of nitro or nitroso ligands instead of hydroxyl ion. Oxidation with nitrogen dioxide led to a nitro group on the metal, whereas a mixture of nitric oxide and oxygen yielded a nitroso group (*116*). Polymers of this type with arsenic and iron as the central atom also have been reported (*116*).

High molecular weight products are obtained from this polymerization. Intrinsic viscosities as high as 0.88 have been reported. Aliphatic groups such as butyl and octyl on the phosphorus atom gave polymers that could be converted to flexible films (*12, 13*). Phenyl, or methyl and phenyl groups on the phosphorus atom yield polymers that form brittle films. Crystallinity was not detectable in any of the polymers, nor did they flow at temperatures greater than 300°C. An extensive evaluation of some of the properties of poly(aqua-hydroxychromium diphenylphosphinate) has been published recently (*33*). Properties of the polymer that were studied include molecular weight distribution by gel permeation chromatography, viscometry, infrared absorption, and electrical conductivity. The Cr(III) polymer of di-*n*-octylphosphinic acid was stable in refluxing 50% sodium hydroxide for 1 hour. Thermogravimetry showed that the diphenyl Cr(III) polymer began to lose weight at 375°C (*120*). Termination of the polymer prepared from methylphenylphosphinic acid with various chelate ligands provided products that were useful viscosity stabilizers for phosphate ester lubricants and hydraulic fluids (*117*).

METHOD 4. POLYPHOSPHINATES OF DIVALENT METAL ATOMS

The most accessible doubly bridged phosphinate polymers are prepared from divalent metals salts and phosphinic acids. This polymerization has yielded high molecular weight products in many instances. An example is shown in Eq. (IX-45).

$$n \, M(C_2H_3O_2)_2 + 2n \, (C_4H_9)_2P(O)OH \longrightarrow$$

[128]   [129]

$+ \, 2n \, CH_3CO_2H$ (IX-45)

[130]   [131]

Conditions that have been reported for effecting this polymerization have included (1) reaction of the phosphinic acid with a metal acetylacetonate with or without a basic catalyst in a refluxing solvent (benzene); (2) in refluxing ethanol or acetone using the metal acetate; (3) in homogeneous solution using high-speed agitation; (4) interfacially using a water: benzene system; and (5) by heating the reactants in bulk (*12, 13, 18, 111*). Reaction of diethylzinc with phosphinic acids has also been described (*111*).

The polymers containing zinc(II) are waxy, crystalline, and soluble (*12, 13, 30*). They possess moderately high molecular weights with their melting points varying with structure. Rapid quenching of the Zn(II)–dibutylphosphinic acid polymer allows the preparation of a metastable, amorphous form that crystallizes slowly at room temperature. This fact, in addition to the fact that the polymer became brittle at −40°C, indicates that its glass transition temperatures are below room temperature. Torsional creep and recovery behavior studies were made on the zinc–phenylmethylphosphinic acid polymer within the range of 100°–200°C and unusual rheological behavior was found (*106*). Copolymers were prepared from Zn(II) and two different phosphinic acids in a 1:1 ratio and their properties are shown in the accompanying table (*18, 112*). These copolymers are interesting because in addition to the repeat units of the homopolymers, there can also be units with two different bridging phosphinate groups [132].

(IX-46)

[132]

Properties of $1:1$ $Zn[OP(R)_2O]_2-Zn[(OP(R')_2O)]_2$ Copolymers

R	R'	T_m (°C)	Cryst. tend.	Brittle point (°C)	Intrinsic viscosity (CHCl₃)
C_4H_9	C_6H_{13}	235° d	Rapid	—	0.7
C_4H_9	C_8H_{17}	150°–160°	None	−100	0.6
C_4H_9	$C_{10}H_{21}$	125°	None	−75	0.4
C_4H_9	$C_{14}H_{29}$	105°–115°	Gradual	−65	0.4
C_8H_{17}	$C_{14}H_{29}$	110°	Gradual	−80	0.4

In fact, this latter type of bridging group is favored statistically. The non-crystallizable copolymers could be pressed into amorphous, flexible films by using slight pressure at about 160°C. The crystallizable copolymers possessed good elongation and exhibited rubbery recovery when freshly prepared (and amorphous), but gradually developed crystallinity at room temperature. Cobalt(II)-containing polymers and copolymers possessed properties similar to their Zn(II) analogs (12, 13, 112).

Many different techniques have been used to gather evidence to support the doubly bridged structure for these metal phosphinate polymers. Moreover, the properties of these polymers were rationalized to fit this structure along the following lines. The low-temperature flexibility observed for amorphous poly(metal phosphinates) is consistent with what models show about this type of backbone. A high order of flexibility exists in the backbone because the alkyl side chains cause little steric hindrance and the eight-membered ring spiro structure is inherently flexible. The alkyl groups tend to shield the polymer from polar interchain attractions and reduce the resistance of the surrounding medium to movement by the polymer molecule (110). Nevertheless, the most recent evidence on the structure of these polymers does not support the doubly bridged structure (43, 44). An X-ray study on a single crystal of zinc(II) di-n-butyl phosphinate [133], supports a structure for the main chain composed of alternate single and triple phosphinate bridges between tetrahedral metal atoms. This structure [133], these authors state, is more compatible with the flexibility of this polymer class.

(IX-47)

[133]

Cobalt- and zinc-containing phosphinate polymers have been investigated by thermogravimetry in a nitrogen atmosphere. Temperatures of over 400°C were required to initiate weight loss (112). Cobalt diphenyl phosphinate was the most thermally stable of those investigated with an initial weight loss occurring at 485°C. Benzene was identified as a decomposition product from the zinc diphenyl phosphinate polymer at 500°C. This fact led to the suggestion that decomposition occurs, at least initially, without rupture of the backbone. It was also noted that the backbone is of the double chain or "ladder" type and would require cleavage of two bonds for chain scission. This fact, in addition to the possibility of additional stabilization due to chelation, was suggested as contributing to the high thermal stability of these polymers.

METHOD 5. POLYMERIZATION OF METAL CARBONYLS WITH PHOSPHINIC ACIDS

One of the few condensation polymerizations reported to be catalyzed by light results in the preparation of doubly bridged metal phosphinate polymers (107). A 250-watt sunlamp was employed to effect reaction (IX-48). Only a few examples of these products have been reported to date. They are high-melting and possess only moderately high molecular weights when soluble.

$$n\,M(CO)_x + 2n\,(C_6H_5)_2P(O)OH \longrightarrow \left[\begin{array}{c} (C_6H_5)_2 \\ CO \diagdown P \diagdown O \\ O \\ M \\ O \\ (CO)_{x-4} \diagdown P \diagdown O \\ (C_6H_5)_2 \end{array} \right]_n + 3n\,CO + n\,H_2 \qquad (IX\text{-}48)$$

[134]   [98]   [135]   [136]   [137]

METHOD 6. POLY(DIHALOPHOSPHORIC ACIDS)

A double-chain structure possessing a marked similarity to the above poly-(metal phosphinates) has been proposed for some salts of dihalophosphoric acids (47). Their structure is shown [138].

$$M(PO_2X_2)_2 \cdot 2\,C_2H_5OOCCH_3 \equiv \left[\begin{array}{c} X \diagdown P \diagdown X \\ R \\ O \\ M \\ O \\ R \\ X \diagdown P \diagdown X \end{array} \right]_n \qquad (IX\text{-}49)$$

[138]

$R = CH_3COOC_2H_5$; $X = Cl, Br$
$M = Ca, Mg, Mn$

An X-ray structure study on [139] established the existence of the doubly bridged phosphinate linkage (32). Another structure study on a monomeric compound is available that also established the existence of a doubly bridged diphenyl phosphinate structure (139). These examples are to be weighed against the recent structural evidence discussed above for metal phosphinate polymers.

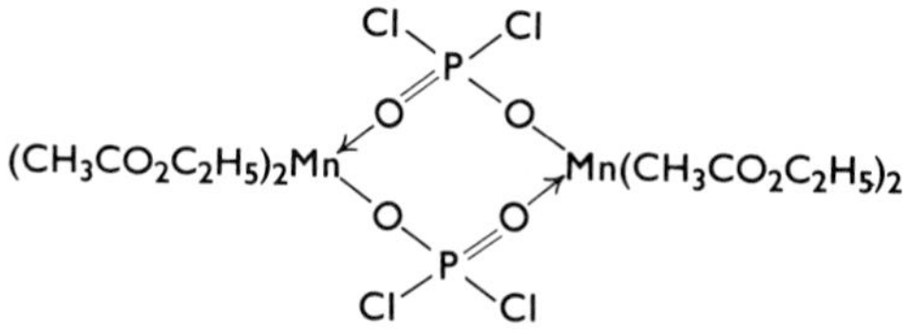

$(CH_3CO_2C_2H_5)_2Mn$ ⟶ $Mn(CH_3CO_2C_2H_5)_2$ (IX-50)

[139]

TABLE IX.1

Poly[metal bis(β-diketonates)]

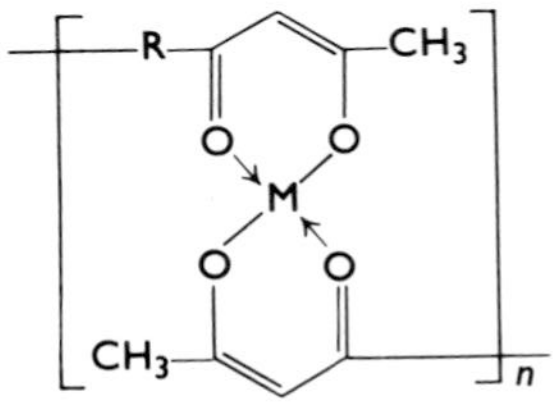

[5]

No.	Structure	Metal (M)	Method	Color	Solubility	Molecular weight	T_m (°C)	Remarks and property data	References
1	R = —	Cu(II)	A,2	Green	—	—	>250	—	36
2	R = +(CH₂)₆-	Be(II)	A,3	—	C_6H_6	[η] 2.7	—	—	62
3	R = —NH(CH₂)₆NH—	Be(II)	A,3	—	C_6H_6	[η] 2.7	—	—	62
4	R = —O+(CH₂)₆O—	Be(II)	A,3	—	C_6H_6	[η] 2.7	—	Tg = 55°C	62
5	R = +(OCH₂CH₂O)₃	Be(II)	A,3	—	C_6H_6	[η] 2.7	—	—	62
6	R = +(CH₂)₇-	Be(II)	A,3	—	C_6H_6	[η] 2.7	—	—	62
7	R = +(CH₂)₈- [20]	Be(II)	A,2	Yellow	—	[η] 1.2	60-100	—	36, 84, 85

No.	R	Metal	A,n	Color	Solubility	[η]/MW	Decomp.	Properties	Ref.
		Be(II)	A,3	—	C_6H_6	[η] 0.9	—	Amorphous. $T_g = 35°C$; Tensile modulus = 122,000 psi; Tensile strength = 2710 psi	62
8	R = $-(CH_2)_{10}-$	Be(II)	A,3	—	C_6H_6	[η] 2.7	—	—	62
9	R = $-NH(CH_2)_{10}NH-$	Be(II)	A,3	—	C_6H_6	[η] 2.7	—	—	62
10	R = $-O(CH_2)_{10}O-$	Be(II)	A,3	—	C_6H_6	[η] 2.7	—	—	62
11	R = $-(CH_2)_{12}-$	Be(II)	A,3	—	C_6H_6	[η] 2.7	—	—	62
12	R = $1,4-C_6H_4-$	Be(II)	A,2	Yellow	—	—	220 d, >295	—	36, 140
13	R = $1,4-C_6H_4-$	Co(II)	A,2	Yellow	—	—	>200	—	36
14	R = $1,4-C_6H_4-$	Cu(II)	A,2	Green	Insoluble	—	>255	—	36
15	R = $1,4-C_6H_4-$	Ni(II)	A,2	Yellow	—	—	>200	—	36
16	R = $1,4-C_6H_4-$	$-Ti-(OC_4H_9)_2$ [28]	A,5	Yellow	DMF, C_6H_6, xylene	800	—	—	74
17	R = $1,4-CH_2C_6H_4CH_2-$	Be(II)	A,2	Yellow	Insoluble	—	400 d	—	65, 69
18	R = $1,4-CH_2C_6H_4CH_2-$	Cu(II)	A,2	Green	Insoluble	—	340–350 d	—	65, 69

TABLE IX.1—*continued*

Poly[metal bis(β-diketonates)]

No.	Structure	Metal (M)	Method	Color	Solubility	Molecular weight	T_m (°C)	Remarks and property data	References
19	R = 1,4-$OCH_2C_6H_4CH_2O$—	Be(II)	A,2	—	—	—	—	—	*79*
20	R = 1,4-$OCH_2C_6H_4CH_2O$—	Ni(II)	A,2	—	—	—	—	—	*79*
21	R = 1,4-$OCH_2C_6H_4CH_2O$—	Zn(II)	A,2	—	—	—	—	—	*79*
22	R = 1,4-$OCH_2CH_2OC_6H_4OCH_2CH_2O$—	Be(II)	A,2	—	C_6H_6	[η] 2.7	—	—	*62*
23	R = 4,4′-C_6H_4—C_6H_4—	Be(II)	A,2	Yellow	DMF, $CHCl_3$, C_6H_5Br	—	>330 d	—	*67*
24	R = 4,4′-C_6H_4—C_6H_4—	Co(II)	A,2	Red	Insoluble	DP = 23 (ebullioscopy)	>330 d	—	*67*
25	R = 4,4′-C_6H_4—C_6H_4—	Cu(II)	A,2	Green	Insoluble	DP = 52 (ebullioscopy)	350 d	—	*65, 67*
26	R = 4,4′-C_6H_4—C_6H_4—	Ni(II)	A,2	Yellow	Insoluble	DP = 20 (ebullioscopy)	>330 d	—	*67*
27	R = 4,4′-C_6H_4—C_6H_4—	Zn(II)	A,2	Cream	Insoluble	DP = 7 (ebullioscopy)	260 d	—	*67*

No.	R	Metal		Color	Solubility in DMF, CHCl₃, C₆H₅Br	η_{red} 0.44 126,000 (osmometry)	m.p. (°C)		Refs.
28	R = 4,4'-C₆H₄—O—C₆H₄— [II]	Be(II)	A,2	Yellow	DMF, CHCl₃, C₆H₅Br	η_{red} 0.44 126,000 (osmometry)	280–290	Amorphous	45, 67, 76, 78, 79, 82–84, 86, 136, 137, 140
29	R = 4,4'-C₆H₄—O—C₆H₄—	Co(II)	A,2	Red	DMF	DP = 13	260–300 d	Partly crystalline	45, 67
30	R = 4,4'-C₆H₄—O—C₆H₄—	Cu(II)	A,2	Gray	Insoluble	DP = 14	300 d	Partly crystalline	45, 67, 75, 78
31	R = 4,4'-C₆H₄—O—C₆H₄—	Hg(II)	A,2	White	Insoluble	—	200–205	—	67
32	R = 4,4'-C₆H₄—O—C₆H₄—	Mg(II)	A,2	—	—	—	266	Crystalline	45
33	R = 4,4'-C₆H₄—O—C₆H₄—	Mn(II)	A,2	Yellow	DMF	DP = 11	230 d	—	67
34	R = 4,4'-C₆H₄—O—C₆H₄—	Ni(II)	A,2	Green	DMF	DP = 4	300–350 d	—	45, 67
35	R = 4,4'-C₆H₄—O—C₆H₄—	Zn(II)	A,2	White	DMF	DP = 10	230 d	Crystalline	45, 66, 67, 76
36	R = 4,4'-C₆H₄—O—C₆H₄—	Al(III), Ba(II)	A,2	—	—	—	—	—	45
		Ca(II), Cd(II)	A,2	—	—	—	—	—	45
		Fe(II)	A,2	—	—	—	—	—	45

TABLE IX.1—*continued*

Poly[metal bis(β-diketonates)]

No.	Structure	Metal (M)	Method	Color	Solubility	Molecular weight	T_m (°C)	Remarks and property data	References
37	R = 4,4'-$C_6H_4CH_2C_6H_4$	Be(II)	A,2	Yellow	DMF	DP = 3	280	—	45, 67
38	R = 4,4'-$C_6H_4CH_2C_6H_4$	Cd(II)	A,2	Yellow	DMF	—	120	—	45, 67, 69
39	R = 4,4'-$C_6H_4CH_2C_6H_4$	Co(II)	A,2	Yellow	Insoluble	—	260–270	—	45, 67, 69
40	R = 4,4'-$C_6H_4CH_2C_6H_4$	Cu(II)	A,2	Green	Insoluble	—	300 d	—	45, 67, 69
41	R = 4,4'-$C_6H_4CH_2C_6H_4$	Mn(II)	A,2	Rose	DMF	—	240–250	—	67, 69
42	R = 4,4'-$C_6H_4CH_2C_6H_4$	Ni(II)	A,2	Green	Insoluble	1500	240–250	—	45, 67, 69
43	R = 4,4'-$C_6H_4CH_2C_6H_4$	Zn(II)	A,2	Yellow	Insoluble	4300	200–210	—	45, 67, 69
44	R = 4,4'-$C_6H_4CH_2C_6H_4$	Al(III), Ba(II), Ca(II)	A,2	—	—	—	—	—	45
		Fe(II), Mg(II)	A,2	—	—	—	—	—	45

No.	R	Metal	Method	Color	Solubility	$[\eta]$	Temp	Form	Ref.
45	R = 4,4'-C₆H₄CH₂CH₂C₆H₄	Be(II)	A,2	Yellow	C₆H₆, CHCl₃, C₆H₅Br	0.42	235	Crystalline	65, 84, 86
46	R = 4,4'-C₆H₄CH₂CH₂C₆H₄	Cd(II)	A,2	White	Dioxane, DMF	—	230 d	—	65
47	R = 4,4'-C₆H₄CH₂CH₂C₆H₄	Co(II)	A,2	Orange	DMF, tricresol	—	220 d	—	65
48	R = 4,4'-C₆H₄CH₂CH₂C₆H₄	Cu(II)	A,2	Green	Insoluble	—	380 d	—	65
49	R = 4,4'-C₆H₄CH₂CH₂C₆H₄	Mn(II)	A,2	Yellow	DMF, dioxane	—	200 d	—	65
50	R = 4,4'-C₆H₄CH₂CH₂C₆H₄	Ni(II)	A,2	Blue	DMF, tricresol	—	310 d	—	65
51	R = 4,4'-C₆H₄CH₂CH₂C₆H₄	Zn(II)	A,2	White	Tetrachlorethane, tricresol	—	270 d	Crystalline	65
52	R = 4,4'-C₆H₄OCH₂CH₂OC₆H₄	Be(II)	A,2	Yellow	DMF, C₆H₆, CHCl₃	—	275	Crystalline	65
53	R = 4,4'-C₆H₄OCH₂CH₂OC₆H₄	Cd(II)	A,2	Tan	DMF, tricresol	—	250 d	—	65
54	R = 4,4'-C₆H₄OCH₂CH₂OC₆H₄	Co(II)	A,2	Orange	DMF	—	210 d	—	65
55	R = 4,4'-C₆H₄OCH₂CH₂OC₆H₄	Cu(II)	A,2	Gray	Insoluble	—	300 d	—	65
56	R = 4,4'-C₆H₄OCH₂CH₂OC₆H₄	Mn(II)	A,2	Yellow	DMF, dioxane	—	230 d	—	65

TABLE IX.1—*continued*

Poly[metal bis(β-diketonates)]

No.	Structure	Metal (M)	Method	Color	Solubility	Molecular weight	T_m (°C)	Remarks and property data	References
57	R = 4,4'-C$_6$H$_4$OCH$_2$CH$_2$OC$_6$H$_4$—	Ni(II)	A,2	Blue	Insoluble	—	260 d	—	65
58	R = 4,4'-C$_6$H$_4$OCH$_2$CH$_2$OC$_6$H$_4$—	Zn(II)	A,2	White	Tetrachlorethane, tricresol	—	240 d	—	65
59	R = 4,4'-C$_6$H$_4$O(CH$_2$)$_2$O(CH$_2$)$_2$OC$_6$H$_4$	Be(II)	A,2	Yellow	DMF, CHCl$_3$ C$_6$H$_5$Br	—	187–201	Crystalline	65
60	R = 4,4'-C$_6$H$_4$O(CH$_2$)$_2$O(CH$_2$)$_2$OC$_6$H$_4$	Co(II)	A,2	Tan	DMF, dioxane	—	180 d	—	65
61	R = 4,4'-C$_6$H$_4$O(CH$_2$)$_2$O(CH$_2$)$_2$OC$_6$H$_4$	Cu(II)	A,2	Green	Tetrachlorethane, tricresol	—	280 d	—	65
62	R = 4,4'-C$_6$H$_4$O(CH$_2$)$_2$O(CH$_2$)$_2$OC$_6$H$_4$	Mn(II)	A,2	Green	Tetrachlorethane, dioxane, cresol	—	188–220	—	65
63	R = 4,4'-C$_6$H$_4$O(CH$_2$)$_2$O(CH$_2$)$_2$OC$_6$H$_4$	Ni(II)	A,2	Green	Tetrachlorethane	—	280 d	—	65
64	R = 4,4'-C$_6$H$_4$O(CH$_2$)$_2$O(CH$_2$)$_2$OC$_6$H$_4$	Zn(II)	A,2	Yellow	DMF, tricresol	—	164–170	Crystalline	65

* * *

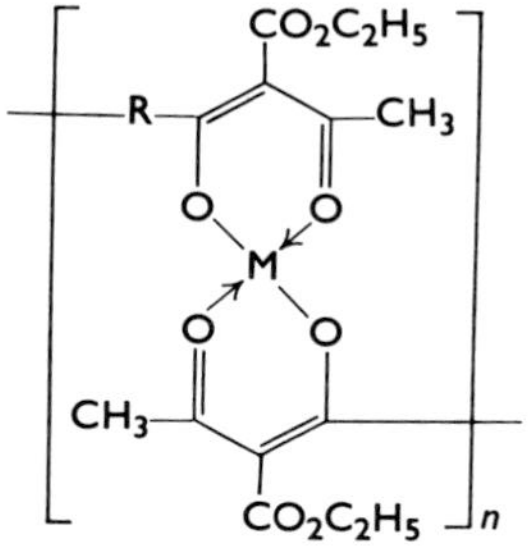

65 R = 1,4-C_6H_4

66 R = 1,4-C_6H_4

Cu(II)	A,2	Blue, green	DMF	—	>220	—	36, 74
Co(II), Hg(II), Mg(II), Ni(II), Zn(II)	A,2	—	—	—	—	—	74

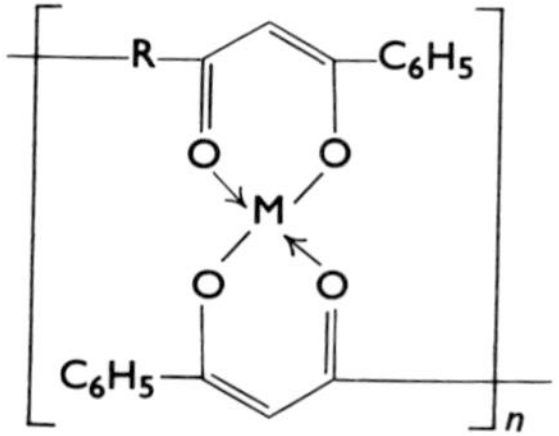

67 R = —

68 R = —

Be(II)	A,2	Yellow	—	—	>220 d	—	36
Cu(II)	A,2	Green	—	—	300 d	—	36

TABLE IX.1—*continued*

Poly[metal bis(β-diketonates)]

No.	Structure	Metal (M)	Method	Color	Solubility	Molecular weight	T_m (°C)	Remarks and property data	References
69	R = —	Fe(III)	A,2	Red	DMF	—	>250	—	36
70	R = —	Ni(II)	A,2	Yellow	—	—	>300	—	36
71	R = —	Th(III)	A,2	Brown	—	—	—	—	36
72	R = —	Zr(IV)	A,2	Brown	—	—	—	—	36
73	R = $-(CH_2)_2-$	Be(II)	A,2	Brown	C_6H_6	2160	210–220	—	36
74	R = $-(CH_2)_2-$	Cu(II) [41]	A,2	Green	—	—	300 d	—	35, 36
75	R = $-(CH_2)_3-$	Cu(II) [41]	A,2	Green	—	—	273 d	—	35
76	R = $-(CH_2)_4-$	Be(II)	A,2	Orange	DMF, CHCl₃, dioxane	—	210	—	68
77	R = $-(CH_2)_4-$	Cd(II)	A,2	White	DMF, CHCl₃, dioxane	811	140	—	68, 69
78	R = $-(CH_2)_4-$	Co(II)	A,2	Brown	DMF	—	280–330 d	—	68, 69

No.	R	Metal	Method	Color	Solvent	Value	M.p. (°C)		Ref.
79	R = $-(CH_2)_4-$	Cu(II) [41]	A,2	Green	Tetrachlorethane	—	279 d	—	35, 68, 69
80	R = $-(CH_2)_4-$	Mn(II)	A,2	Yellow	Tetrachlorethane, dioxane	4000	170 d	—	68, 69
81	R = $-(CH_2)_4-$	Ni(II)	A,2	Yellow	DMF, dioxane	—	260–280 d	—	68
82	R = $-(CH_2)_4-$	Zn(II)	A,2	Yellow	DMF, CHCl$_3$, dioxane	—	260–300 d	—	68
83	R = $-(CH_2)_5-$	Cu(II) [41]	A,2	Green	—	—	272 d	—	35
84	R = $-(CH_2)_7-$	Cu(II) [41]	A,2	Green	—	—	262 d	—	35
85	R = $-(CH_2)_8-$	Al(III)	A,2	Yellow	Insoluble	—	150–160	—	36–38
86	R = $-(CH_2)_8-$	Be(II)	A,2	Cream	C$_6$H$_6$, CHCl$_3$, DMF, o-Cresol	η_{sp} 0.1; 1520–6000	95–135; 230	—	36–38, 68, 140
87	R = $-(CH_2)_8-$	Co(II)	A,2	Tan	C$_6$H$_6$, DMF	—	110–150; 175–180	—	36, 68
88	R = $-(CH_2)_8-$	Cu(II) [41]	A,2	Green	Pyridine, dioxane	—	231 d	—	35, 36, 68
89	R = $-(CH_2)_8-$	Mg(II)	A,2	Orange	Insoluble	—	130–140	—	36
90	R = $-(CH_2)_8-$	Mn(II)	A,2	Black	CHCl$_3$, DMF, dioxane	—	180–190	—	68
91	R = $-(CH_2)_8-$	Ni(II)	A,2	Green	Dioxane	2640	190–220	—	36–38, 68

268

TABLE IX.1—*continued*

Poly[metal bis(β-diketonates)]

No.	Structure	Metal (M)	Method	Color	Solubility	Molecular weight	T_m (°C)	Remarks and property data	References
92	R = $-(CH_2)_8-$	UO$_2$(II)	A,2	Orange	C$_6$H$_5$Br, C$_6$H$_6$	3300	110–120	—	*36*
93	R = $-(CH_2)_8-$	VO(II)	A,2	Black	C$_6$H$_5$Br	—	75–100	—	*36*
94	R = $-(CH_2)_8-$	Zn(II)	A,2	Yellow	CHCl$_3$, DMF, dioxane	—	80–110	Amorphous	*36, 68*
95	R = $-(CH_2)_8-$	Zr(IV)	A,2	Orange	—	—	—	—	*36*
96	R = 1,3-C$_6$H$_4-$	Be(II)	—	Yellow	—	—	350 d	—	*67*
97	R = 1,3-C$_6$H$_4-$	Co(II)	—	Orange	—	—	330 d	—	*67*
98	R = 1,3-C$_6$H$_4-$	Cu(II)	—	Green	—	—	380 d	—	*67*
99	R = 1,3-C$_6$H$_4-$	Ni(II)	—	Yellow	—	—	350 d	—	*67*
100	R = 1,4-C$_6$H$_4-$	Cd(II)	A,2	Yellow	Insoluble	—	295–300 d	—	*67, 69, 101*
101	R = 1,4-C$_6$H$_4-$	Co(II)	A,2	Orange	Insoluble	—	350 d	—	*67, 69*

No.	R	M		Color	Solubility	Temp		Ref.
102	R = 1,4-C$_6$H$_4$—	Cu(II)	A,2	Yellow	Insoluble	400 d	—	67, 69
103	R = 1,4-C$_6$H$_4$—	Hg(II)	A,2	White	Insoluble	400 d	—	67, 69
104	R = 1,4-C$_6$H$_4$—	Mn(II)	A,2	Rose	Insoluble	240–250 d	—	67, 69
105	R = 1,4-C$_6$H$_4$—	Zn(II)	A,2	Yellow	Insoluble	300–310 d	—	67, 69

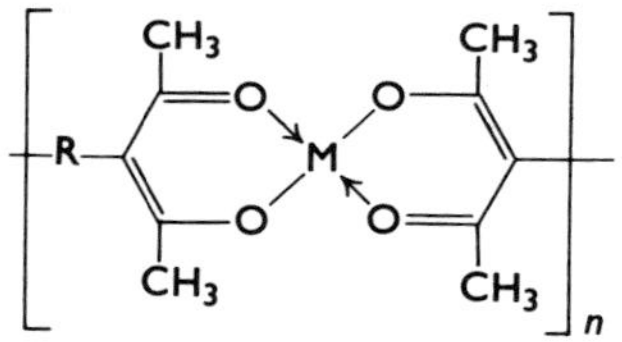

$$\left[\begin{array}{c} \text{CH}_3 \\ | \\ \text{*} \quad \text{*} \quad \text{*} \\ \end{array} \begin{array}{c} \text{CH}_3 \quad\quad \text{CH}_3 \\ \diagdown\;\diagup \\ \text{O} \quad \text{O} \\ \diagdown \text{M} \diagup \\ \text{O} \quad\quad \text{O} \\ \diagup\;\diagdown \\ \text{CH}_3 \quad\quad \text{CH}_3 \\ \text{R} \end{array} \right]_n$$

No.	R	M		Color	Solubility	Temp		Ref.
106	R = —	Be(II)	A,2	White	Insoluble	220; 350	—	36, 68
107	R = —	Cd(II)	A,2	—	Insoluble	270 d	—	26
108	R = —	Co(II)	A,2	Brown	DMF	315 d	—	26, 68
109	R = —	Cu(II)	A,2	Green	Insoluble	290 d DP = 5 (analysis)	Crystalline, paramagnetic	4, 5, 25, 26, 36, 68, 129, 133
110	R = —	Fe(III)	A,2	Red	—	230–240 d	—	36
111	R = —	Mg(II)	A.2	—	Insoluble	350 d	—	26

270

TABLE IX.1—*continued*
Poly[metal bis(β-diketonates)]

No.	Structure	Metal (M)	Method	Color	Solubility	Molecular weight	T_m (°C)	Remarks and property data	References
112	R = —|—	Ni(II)	A,2	Green	H_2O	—	340 d	—	4, 5, 26, 68
113	R = —|—	Zn(II)	A,2	Brown	Insoluble	—	320–350 d	—	26, 68
114	R = —|—	Zr(IV)	A,2	Brown	—	—	—	—	36
115	R = —CH₂—	Be(II)	A,2	—	CHCl₃, DMF	—	—	—	68
116	R = —CH₂—	Co(II)	A,2	Green	CHCl₃, DMF	2200	230–240 d	—	68, 69
117	R = —CH₂—	Cu(II)	A,2	Green	CHCl₃, DMF	3200	240–250 d	—	68, 69
118	R = —CH₂—	Zn(II)	A,2	—	CHCl₃, DMF	—	—	—	68
119	R = —CH₂—	Zr(IV)	A,2	Yellow	CHCl₃, CH₃OH, DMF	—	195–200 d	—	36, 69
120	R = —(CH₂)₃Si(CH₃)₂—O—Si(CH₃)₂—(CH₂)₃	Be(II)	A,2	—	C_6H_6	η_{red} 0.14	220	365° d (TGA)	51
121	R = —(CH₂)₃—[Si(CH₃)₂—O—]₂Si(CH₃)₂(CH₂)₃	Be(II)	A,2	—	C_6H_6	η_{red} 0.18	200	328° d (TGA)	51
122	R = —(CH₂)₃—[Si(CH₃)₂O]₃Si(CH₃)₂(CH₂)₃	Be(II)	A,2	—	C_6H_6	η_{red} 0.27	—	317° d (TGA)	51

123 R = 1,4-CH$_2$C$_6$H$_4$CH$_2$—	Be(II)	A,2	Yellow	DMF, CHCl$_3$	DP = 10	210–217	—	45, 67, 140
124 R = 1,4-CH$_2$C$_6$H$_4$CH$_2$—	Co(II)	A,2	Red	DMF	—	220	—	45, 67
125 R = 1,4-CH$_2$C$_6$H$_4$CH$_2$—	Cu(II)	A,2	Brown	DMF	DP = 7	300 d	—	45, 67
126 R = 1,4-CH$_2$C$_6$H$_4$CH$_2$—	Ni(II)	A,2	Green	DMF	—	210–217	—	45, 67
127 R = 1,4-CH$_2$C$_6$H$_4$CH$_2$—	Al(III), Ba(II), Ca(II), Cd(II), Fe(II), Mg(II), Zn(II)	A,2	—	—	—	—	—	45
127a R = 1,4-C$_6$H$_4$—	Cu(II)	A,2	Green	—	—	—	—	133

* * *

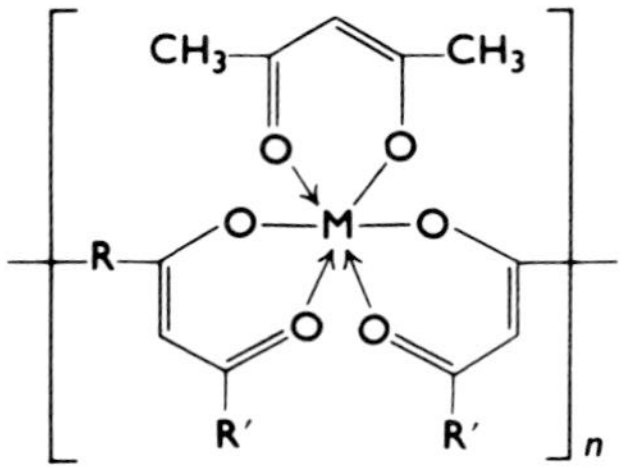

* * * *

128 R = —O(CH$_2$)$_2$O—; R' = CH$_3$	Al(III)	A,5	—	—	2020	105–120	—	105
R = —O(CH$_2$)$_2$O—; R' = CH$_3$	Al(III)	A,5	Yellow	—	770	130–150	—	105

TABLE IX.1—continued

Poly[metal bis(β-diketonates)]

No.	Structure	Metal (M)	Method	Color	Solubility	Molecular weight	T_m (°C)	Remarks and property data	References
129	R = —O$(CH_2)_2$O$(CH_2)_2$O—; R' = CH_3	Al(III)	A,5	—	—	980	105–110	—	105
	R = —O$(CH_2)_2$O$(CH_2)_2$O—; R' = CH_3	Al(III)	A,5	Yellow	—	930	80–150	—	105
130	R = —O$(CH_2)_2$O$(CH_2)_4$O—; R' = CH_3	Al(III)	A,5	—	—	1100	75–130	—	105
131	R = —OCH(CH_3)CH_2CH_2O—; R' = CH_3	Al(III)	A,5	—	—	2620	100–110	—	105
132	R = —O$(CH_2)_4$O—; R' = CH_3	Al(III)	A,5	—	—	940	95–150	—	105
	R = —O$(CH_2)_4$O—; R' = CH_3	Al(III)	A,5	Yellow	—	1160	75–95	—	105

* * *

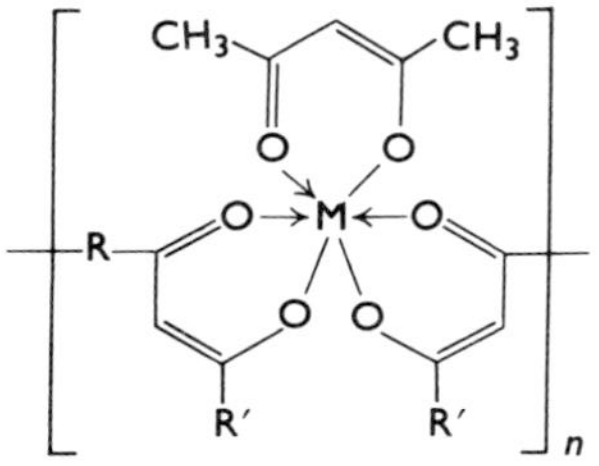

No.	R; R'	M		Color					Ref.
133	R = —O$\left(CH_2\right)_5$O—; R' = CH$_3$	Al(III)	A,5	—	—	1570	80–110	—	105
	R = —O$\left(CH_2\right)_5$O—; R' = CH$_3$	Al(III)	A,5	Yellow	—	450	40–55	—	105
134	R = —; R' = CH$_3$	Al(III)	A,5	White	—	—	>360°	—	105
135	R = —; R' = —CH$_3$, —CO$_2$C$_2$H$_5$	Al(III)	A,5	Tan	—	1860	>360	—	105
136	R = —; R' = —C$_6$H$_5$	Al(III)	A,5	—	—	—	—	—	105
137	R = —CH$_2$—; R' = —CH$_3$	Al(III)	A,5	Red	—	1070	90–150	—	105
138	R = —CH$_2$—; R' = CH$_3$, —CO$_2$C$_2$H$_5$	Al(III)	A,5	Brown	—	1275	110–130	—	105
139	R = —CH$_2$—; R' = —C$_6$H$_5$	Al(III)	A,5	Yellow	—	920	130–145	—	105

TABLE IX.2

Polymers from Bis(1,2-hydroxyketo) Ligands

No.	Structure	Metal (M)	Method	Color	Solubility	T_m (°C)	Molecular weight, remarks, and property data	References
1		Co(II)	B,1	Yellow	—	—	Forms a dihydrate	6
2		Cu(II), Co(II), Ni(II), Zn(II)	B,1	—	—	—	—	108
3		Co(II)	B,1	—	—	285–310 d	Amorphous. $\mu = 1.72$	58, 127, 128
4		Cu(II)	B,1	—	—	286–306 d	Amorphous. $\mu = 2.80$	58, 127, 128
5		Fe(II)	B,1	—	—	260–286 d	Amorphous. $\mu = 4.79$	58, 127, 128
6		Ni(II)	B,1	—	—	304–324 d	Amorphous. $\mu = 3.84$	58, 127, 128

275

	Structure	Metal	Method	Color	Solubility		Ref.
7	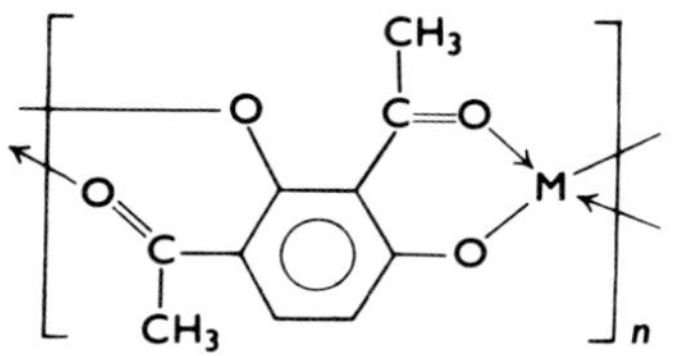	Co(II), Cr(III), Cu(II), Fe(II), Ni(II), Pb(II), Sn(II) & Sn(IV), Zn(II)	B,1	—	All were insoluble and infusible	—	54
8	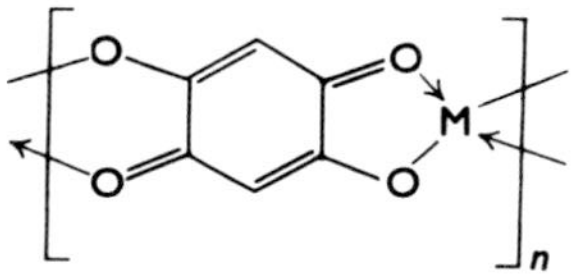	Ag(I)	B,1	Orange	Pyridine	—	41
9		Al(III)	B,1	—	<300 d	—	42
10		Ba(II)	B,1	Tan	H_2O	—	41
11		Ca(II)	B,1	Brown	H_2O	—	41
12		Cd(II)	B,1	Purple	Insoluble	—	41
13		Cu(II)	B,1	Green	Insoluble	—	41, 55–57, 114
14		Fe(III)	B,1	Black	Insoluble	—	41

TABLE IX.2—continued

Polymers from Bis(1,2-hydroxyketo) Ligands

No.	Structure	Metal (M)	Method	Color	Solubility	T_m (°C)	Molecular weight, remarks, and property data	References
15	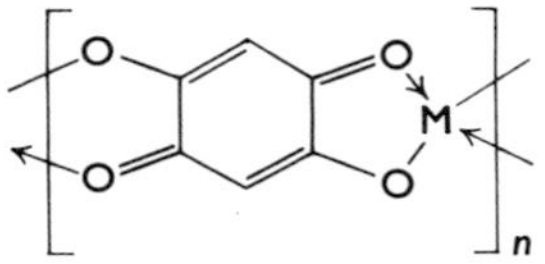	Hg(II)	B,1	Brown	Insoluble	—	—	41
16		Mg(II)	B,1	Pink	H_2O	—	—	41
17		Pb(II)	B,1	Brown	Insoluble	—	—	41
18		Sr(II)	B,1	Red	H_2O	—	—	41
19		Th(IV)	B,1	Purple	H_2O	—	—	41, 55
20		Ti(IV)	B,1	—	—	—	—	55
21		UO_2(II)	B,1	—	—	—	—	55
22		Zr(IV)	B,1	—	—	—	—	55
23		Zn(II)	B,1	Purple	H_2O	—	DP ≅ 27	41, 113
24	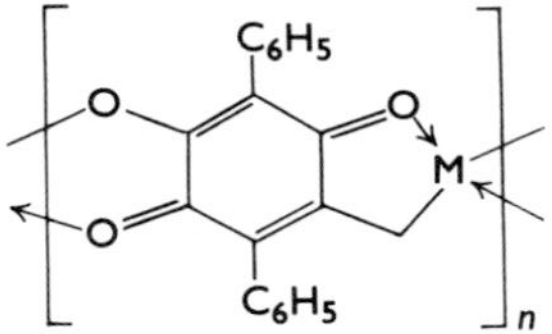	Ag(I)	B,1	Brown	Insoluble	—	—	41
25		Fe(II)	B,1	Black	Insoluble	—	—	41
26		Th(IV)	B,1	Black	Insoluble	—	—	41

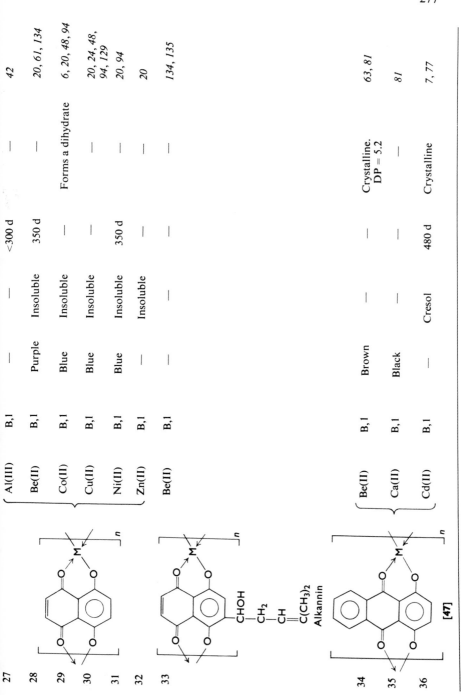

27	Al(III)	B,1	—	—	<300 d	—	42
28	Be(II)	B,1	Purple	Insoluble	350 d	—	20, 61, 134
29	Co(II)	B,1	Blue	Insoluble	—	Forms a dihydrate	6, 20, 48, 94
30	Cu(II)	B,1	Blue	Insoluble	—	—	20, 24, 48, 94, 129
31	Ni(II)	B,1	Blue	Insoluble	350 d	—	20, 94
32	Zn(II)	B,1	—	Insoluble	—	—	20
33	Be(II)	B,1	—	—	—	—	134, 135
34	Be(II)	B,1	Brown	—	—	Crystalline. DP = 5.2	63, 81
35	Ca(II)	B,1	Black	—	—	—	81
36	Cd(II)	B,1	—	Cresol	480 d	Crystalline	7, 77

Alkannin

[47]

TABLE IX.2—*continued*

Polymers from Bis(1,2-hydroxyketo) Ligands

[47]

No.	Structure	Metal (M)	Method	Color	Solubility	T_m (°C)	Molecular weight, remarks, and property data	References
37	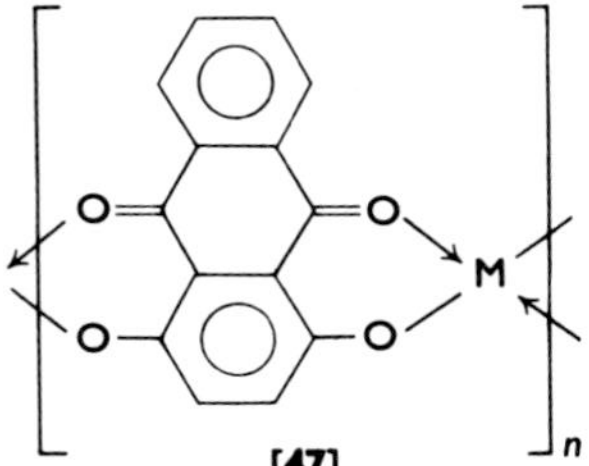	Co(II)	B,1	—	Cresol	480 d	Amorphous. $\mu = 5.4$. Mol. wt. = 6900	7, 48, 54, 75, 77, 102, 122
38		Cu(II)	B,1	Brown	Cresol	300 d	Crystalline. $\mu = 1.9$. Mol. wt. = 2000	7, 39, 40, 48, 63, 64, 75, 77, 102, 122
39		Fe(II)	B,1	—	Insoluble	Infusible	—	54
40		Hg(II)	B,1	—	—	—	—	7
41		Mg(II)	B,1	Brown	—	—	Crystalline	7, 81
42		Mn(II)	B,1	—	Cresol	480 d	Crystalline	7, 75, 77, 122
43		Ni(II)	B,1	—	Insoluble	480 d	Crystalline. $\mu = 2.0$. Mol. wt. = 3320	7, 54, 75, 77, 102, 122
44		UO$_2$(II)	B,1	—	—	—	—	48
45		Zn(II)	B,1	Brown	—	340 d	Crystalline. Mol. wt. = 3100	7, 54, 77, 88, 102, 122

46	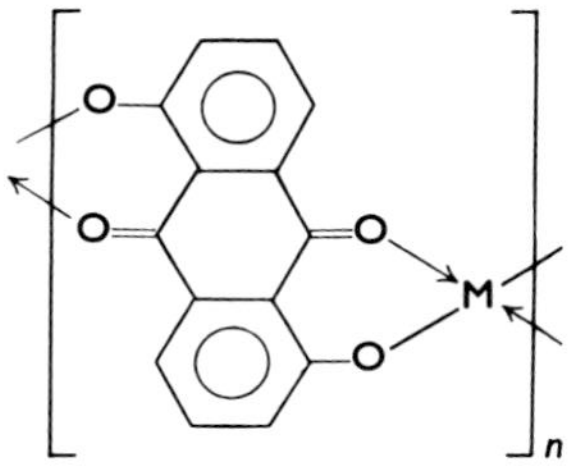 Co(II)	B,1	—	Insoluble	Infusible	—	*54*
47	Cr(III)	B,1	—	—	Infusible	—	*54*
48	Cu(II)	B,1	Violet	—	365 d	—	*39, 40, 54, 102*
49	Fe(II)	B,1	—	—	Infusible	—	*54*
50	Ni(II)	B,1	—	—	370 d	—	*54, 102*
51	Pb(II)	B,1	—	—	Infusible	—	*54*
52	Sn(II), Sn(IV)	B,1	—	—	Infusible	—	*54*
53	Zn(II)	B,1	—	—	Infusible	—	*54*

TABLE IX.3

Polymeric Metal Carboxylates

No.	Structure	Metal (M)	Method	Color	Solubility	T_m (°C)	Molecular weight, remarks, and property data	References
1	$Be_4O_m(CH_3COO)_{8-2m}$ [63]	Be(II)	C,1	—	—	—	Ethanol, methanol adducts, pyridine adduct	46, 49
2	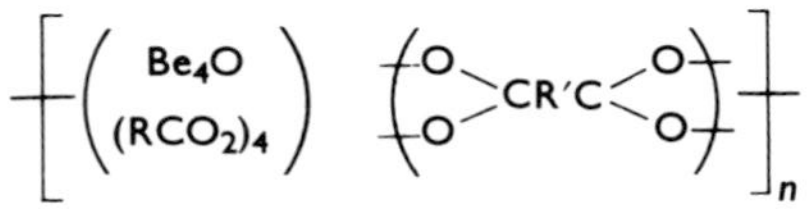 [57] R and R′ = Various groups (see text)	Be(II)	—	—	—	—		97, 100
3								
4		Th(IV)	C,3	—	—	405	—	131, 132
		U	C,3	—	—	<400 d	—	131, 132
5	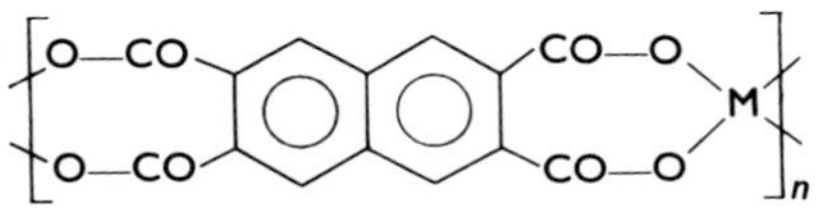	Th(IV)	C,3	—	—	360 d	—	131, 132

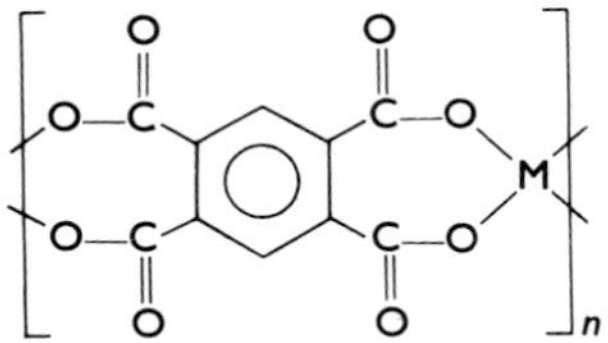

$$\left[OOC-R-COO-M(C_6H_5) \right]_n$$

No.		Metal	Code	Color	Solubility	Temp.	η / Note	Ref.
6	R = $-(CH_2)_4-$	Tl(III)	C,3	White	C_6H_5CHO, $C_6H_5NH_2$, C_6H_5OH	150–200d	η_{red} 0.09	70
7	R = $-(CH_2)_7-$	Tl(III)	C,3	White	C_5H_5N, DMF, $C_6H_5NO_2$	180–185	η_{red} 0.04	70
8	R = $-(CH_2)_8-$	Tl(III)	C,3	White	Cresol, CH_3CO_2H	140–188d	η_{red} 0.05	70
9 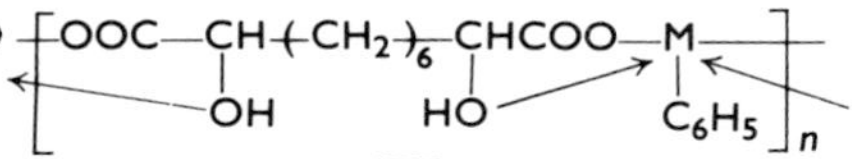	[71]	Tl(III)	C,2	—	CH_3CO_2H	105–110	—	70
10		Cd(II)	C,2	Blue	Insoluble	280–290d	292°C (Temp. of max. dimensional change)	73
11		Co(II)	C,2	Violet	Insoluble	250	351°C (Temp. of max. dimensional change)	73
12 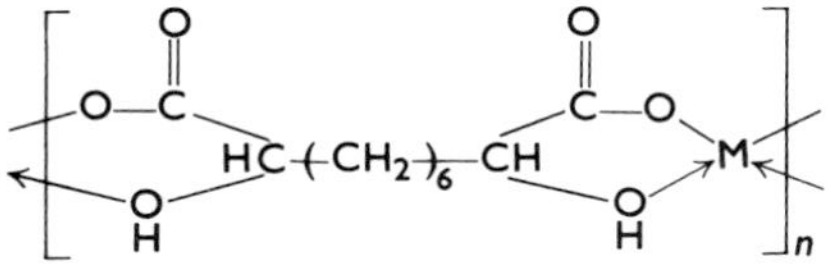	[68]	Cu(II)	C,2	Blue	Insoluble	330 d	341°C (Temp. of max. dimensional change)	73
13		Ni(II)	C,2	Green	Insoluble	300 d	365°C (Temp. of max. dimensional change)	73
14		Zn(II)	C,2	Blue	Insoluble	280–350d	327°C (Temp. of max. dimensional change)	73

Structure [71]:

$$\left[OOC-CH-(CH_2)_6-CHCOO-M \right]_n$$

Structure [68]: complex with $HC-(CH_2)_6-CH$ and M.

TABLE IX.3—*continued*

Polymeric Metal Carboxylates

No.	Structure	Metal (M)	Method	Color	Solubility	T_m (°C)	Molecular weight, remarks, and property data	References
15 R = —C_2H_5		Sn(IV)	C,2	—	Acetic acid, cresol	204	—	71
16 R = —C_4H_9		Sn(IV)	C,2	—	Acetic acid	140–146 d	—	71
17 R = —C_8H_{17}		Sn(IV)	C,2	—	Pyridine	148–150	η_{red} 0.02	71
18 R = —C_6H_5		Sn(IV)	C,2	—	Insoluble	300 d	—	71
19	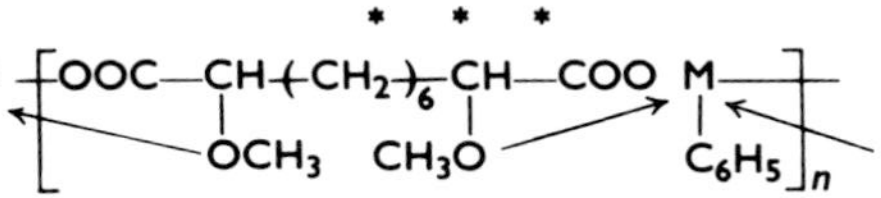	Tl(III)	C,2	—	C_5H_5N, DMF, cresol	—	—	70
20	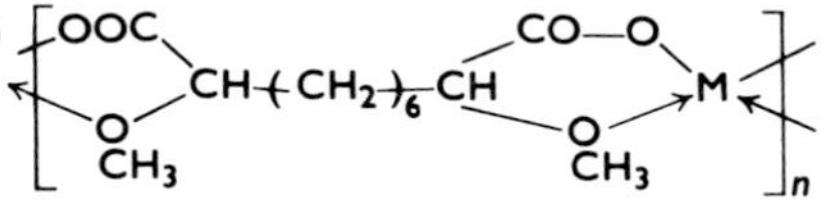	Co(II)	C,2	Violet	Insoluble	300 d	243°C (Temp. of max. dimensional change)	73
21		Zn(II)	C,2	Yellow	Insoluble	140–220	157°C (Temp. of max. dimensional change)	73

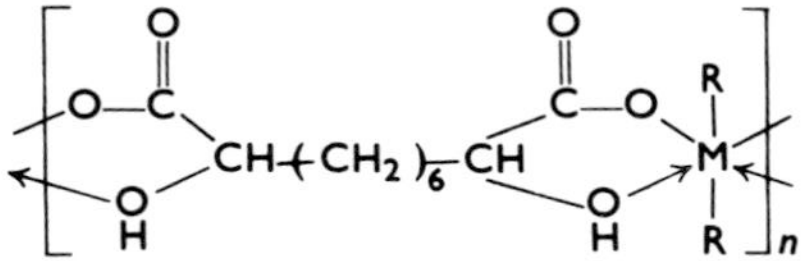

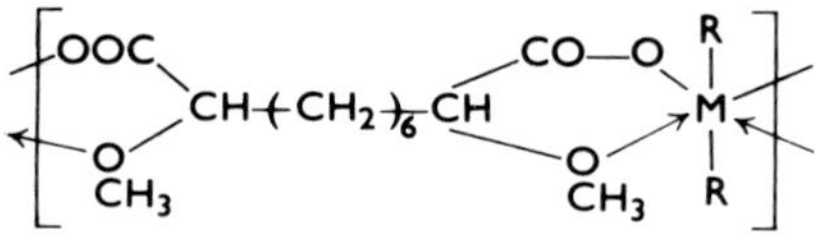

Compound	M		Color	Solubility	m.p./decomp.	η / Temp.	Ref.
22 R = —C₂H₅	Sn(IV)	C,2	—	C₆H₅CHO, C₆H₅NO₂, C₆H₅OCH₃	Resinous	η_{red} 0.04	71
23 R = —C₄H₉	Sn(IV)	C,2	—	C₆H₅CHO, C₆H₅NO₂, C₆H₅OCH₃	Resinous	η_{red} 0.02	71
24 R = —C₈H₁₇	Sn(IV)	C,2	—	Cresol	Resinous	—	71
25 R = —C₆H₅	Sn(IV)	C,2	—	C₆H₆, DMF, C₂H₄Cl₂	300 d	—	71
26	Cu(II)	C,2	Brown	—	—	253°C (Temp. of max. dimensional change)	72
27	Zn(II)	C,2	Yellow	—	—	359°C (Temp. of max. dimensional change)	72
28	Al(III)	C,2	—	Insoluble	—	—	131, 132
29	Fe(II)	C,2	—	Insoluble	180 d (TGA)	—	131, 132
30	Ni(II)	C,2	—	Insoluble	150 d (TGA)	—	131, 132
31	Zn(II)	C,2	—	Insoluble	240 d (TGA)	—	131, 132

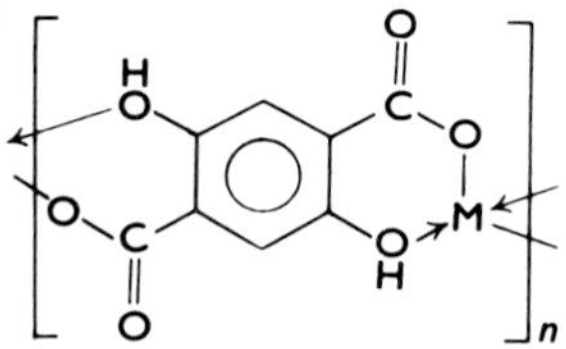

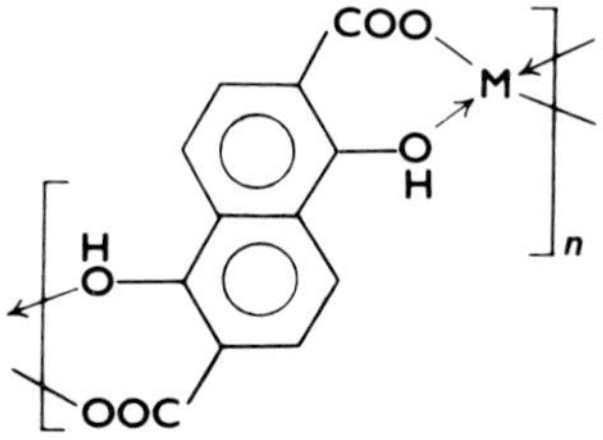

TABLE IX.3—*continued*

Polymeric Metal Carboxylates

No.	Structure	Metal (M)	Method	Color	Solubility	T_m (°C)	Molecular weight, remarks, and property data	References
32 R = —CH₂—; R′ = H		Cu(II), Ni(II), Zn(II)	C,2	—	—	—	Hygroscopic	99
33 R = —CH₂—; R′ = H		Si(IV)	C,2	—	—	<250 d	—	99
34 R = —C(CH₃)₂—; R′ = H [74]		Cu(II), Ni(II), Zn(II)	C,2	—	—	—	Hygroscopic	99
35 R = —C(CH₃)₂—; R′ = H [74]		Si(IV)	C,2	—	—	<250 d	—	99
36 R = —CH(C₆H₅)—; R′ = H		Cu(II)	C,2	Rose	—	>300 d	—	72
37 R = —CH(C₆H₅)—; R′ = H		Zn(II)	C,2	Brown	—	>350 d	—	72
38 R = —CH(C₆H₅)—; R′ = CH₃		Be(II)	C,2	Pink	—	—	317°C (Temp. of max. dimensional change)	72

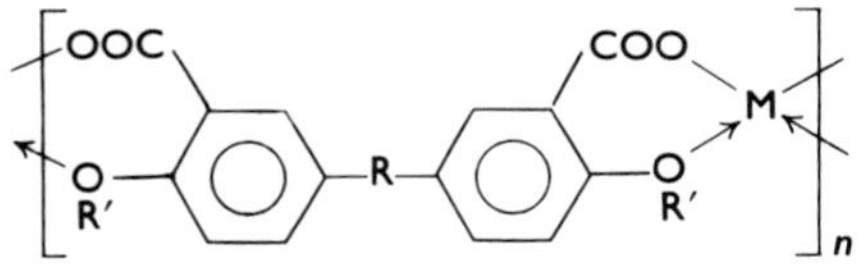

39 R = —CH(C_6H_5)—; R′ = CH_3	Cd(II)	C,2	White	—	—	—	290°C (Temp. of max. dimensional change)	72
40 R = —CH(C_6H_5)—; R′ = CH_3	Cu(II)	C,2	Brown	—	—	—	238°C (Temp. of max. dimensional change)	72
41 R = —CH(C_6H_5)—; R′ = CH_3	Zn(II)	C,2	White	—	—	—	310°C (Temp. of max. dimensional change)	72
42 R = ferrocenyl$(-N=N-)_2$; R′ = H [78]	—	—	—	—	—	—	—	9
43 R = —CH(C_6H_5)—	Co(II), Ni(II), Zn(II)	C,2	—	—	—	—	—	72

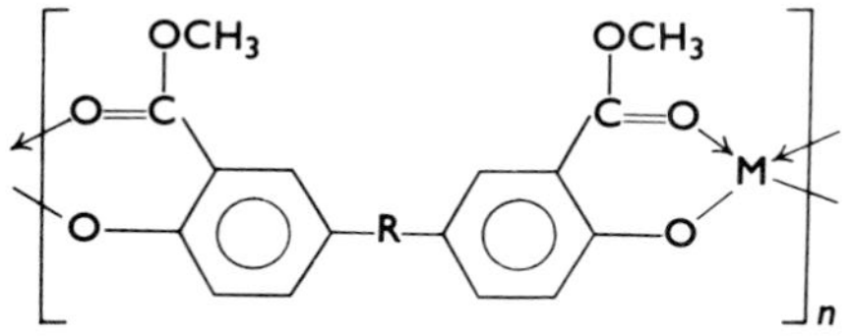

* * * *

* * *

TABLE IX.3—continued

Polymeric Metal Carboxylates

No.	Structure	Metal (M)	Method	Color	Solubility	T_m(°C)	Molecular weight, remarks, and property data	References
44		Cu(II)	C,3	Blue	DMF	—	Tough film prepared	3
45		Ni(II)	C,3	Green	DMF	—	—	3
46	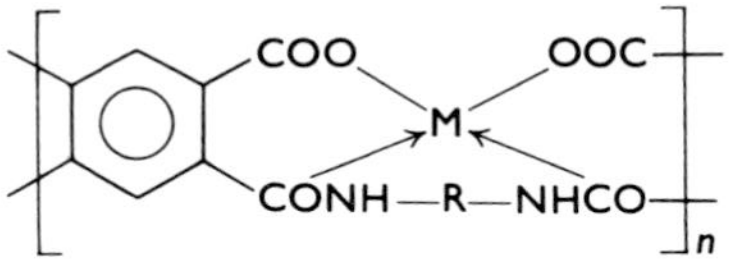	Fe(III)	C,3	Black	DMF	—	—	3
47		Co(II), Cr(III), Hg(II), Mg(II), Mn(II), Zn(II)	C,3	—	DMF	—	—	3

Structure:

$$\left[\begin{array}{c} COO \\ \nearrow M \swarrow \\ CONH-R-NHCO \end{array} \begin{array}{c} OOC \\ \end{array} \right]_n$$

$R = 4,4'—C_6H_4CH_2C_6H_4—$

Cu(II)	C,3	—	THF	—	Mol. wt. =1725 (VPO). Cyclic structure indicated by elemental analysis	130
Mn(II)	C,3	—	Cyclohexanone	—	Cyclic structure indicated by elemental analysis	130
Pb(II)	C,3	—	THF	—	Mol. wt. =1950 (VPO). Cyclic structure indicated by elemental analysis	130

48

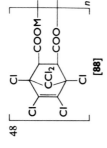

[88]

TABLE IX.4

Polymeric Metal Phosphinates and Arsinates

Structure:

$$\left[\begin{array}{c} R \quad R' \\ | \quad | \\ O \quad O \\ \diagdown P \diagdown \diagup P \diagup \\ \diagup \quad \diagdown M \diagup \quad \diagdown \\ O \quad O \\ | \quad | \\ R \quad R' \end{array}\right]_n$$

No.	Structure	Metal (M)	Method	Color	Solubility	Molecular weight	T_m (°C)	Remarks and property data	References
1	R = R′ = —CH₃	Co(II)	D,4	Blue	H_2O	—	342–343	Crystalline. 445°C d (TGA)	29, 112
2	R = R′ = —CH₃	Zn(II)	D,4	White	H_2O	—	340	Crystalline. 440°C d (TGA)	18, 44, 111
3	R = —CH₃; R′ = —C₆H₅	Co(II)	D,4	Blue	H_2O, pyridine	>10,000	210, 226	Crystalline. 445°C d (TGA)	29, 112
4	R = —CH₃; R′ = —C₆H₅	Zn(II)	D,4	White	H_2O, C_6H_6, $CHCl_3$	5600; >10,000 (ebullioscopy)	200	Crystalline. 415°C d (TGA)	14, 18, 44, 106, 111
5	R = R′ = —C₄H₉	Co(II)	D,4	—	H_2O, CCl_4	—	—	—	30, 43
6	R = R′ = —C₄H₉	Zn(II)	D,4	—	$CHCl_3$, CCl_4	[η] 0.70; >10,000	250	Crystalline. Oriented fibers	13, 30, 43, 44, 110
7	R = R′ = —C₆H₁₃	Zn(II)	D,4	—	$CHCl_3$	[η] 0.60; >10,000	250–275	Crystalline	13, 43, 44
8	R = R′ = —C₈H₁₇	Zn(II)	D,4	—	$CHCl_3$	[η] 0.60; >10,000	220 d	Crystalline	13, 110
9	R = R′ = —C₁₀H₂₁	Zn(II)	D,4	—	$CHCl_3$	[η] 0.30	200 d	Crystalline	13, 43, 44

No.	R, R'	M		Color	Solubility	[η]	Dec. temp (°C)	Physical state	Refs.
10	R = R' = —C₁₄H₂₉	Zn(II)	D,4	—	CHCl₃	[η] 0.30	200	Crystalline	13
11	R = R' = —C₆H₅	Be(II)	D,4	White	Insoluble	>10,000	—	530°C d (TGA)	14, 16, 18
12	R = R' = —C₆H₅	Co(II)	D,4	Blue	H₂O, C₆H₆, pyridine	—	>450	Crystalline. 485°C d (TGA)	18, 29, 112
13	R = R' = —C₆H₅	Cu(II)	D,4	—	—	—	—	293°C d (TGA)	14
14	R = R' = —C₆H₅	Zn(II)	D,4	White	Insoluble	—	>450	Crystalline. 495°C d (TGA)	14, 18, 44, 111

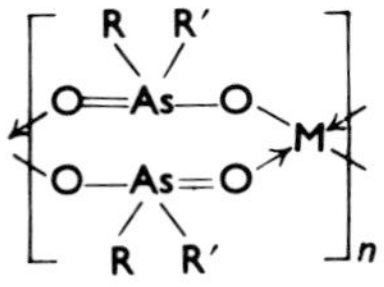

[124]

No.	R, R'	M	Color	Solubility	Refs.
15	R = R' = —C₆H₅	Co(II)	Blue	Insoluble	29

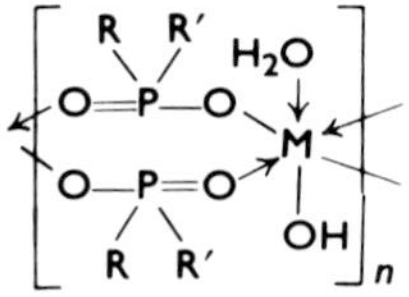

No.	R, R'	M		Solubility	[η]	Dec. temp	Physical state	Refs.
16	R = R' = CH₃	Cr(III)	D,3	H₂O, CHCl₃	[η] 0.13	—	—	118, 120
17	R = CH₃; R' = —C₆H₅	Cr(III)	D,3	CHCl₃	[η] 0.30	365 d (TGA)	Amorphous. Brittle films	18, 116–118, 120
18	R = R' = C₄H₉	Cr(III)	D,3	—	—	—	Amorphous. Flexible films	13

TABLE IX.4—*continued*

Polymeric Metal Phosphinates and Arsinates

No.	Structure	Metal (M)	Method	Color	Solubility	Molecular weight	T_m (°C)	Remarks and property data	References
19	R = R' = C$_8$H$_{17}$	Cr(III)	D,3	—	—	—	—	Amorphous. Flexible films	13
20	R = R' = C$_6$H$_5$ [127]	Cr(III)	D,3	—	C$_6$H$_6$, CHCl$_3$	[η] 0.70; >10,000	375 d (TGA)	Amorphous. Brittle films	13, 33, 116, 118, 120
21	R = —C$_6$H$_5$; R' = CO	Fe(III)	D,5	White	—	—	>300	—	107
22	R = —C$_6$H$_5$; R' = OPO(C$_6$H$_5$)$_2$	Cr(III)	D,5	Green	CHCl$_3$	7130	>360	—	107

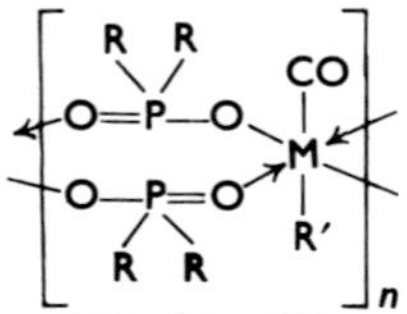

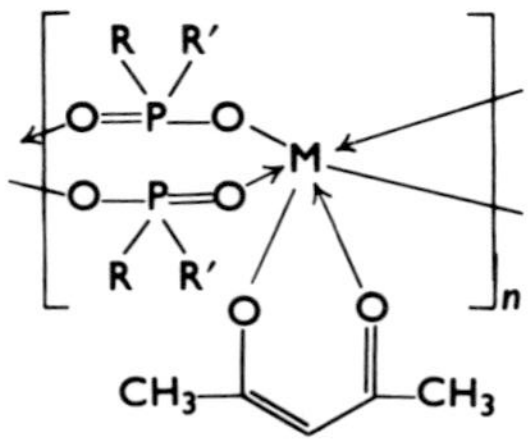

No.	Substituents	M	D,n	Solubility	Molecular weight	Decomposition		Reference
23	R = R′ = $-CH_3$	Cr(III)	D,2	—	—	—	—	11
24	R = CH_3; R′ = $-C_6H_5$	Cr(III)	D,1	—	—	—	—	11
25	R = CH_3; R′ = $-C_6H_5$	Fe(III)	D,1	Insoluble	—	—	—	11
26	R = R′ = $-C_6H_5$	Cr(III)	D,1	$CHCl_3$	5869; 10,870	290–330 d (TGA)	—	11,17,22
27	R = R′ = $-C_6H_5$	In(III)	D,1	Insoluble	—	—	—	11
28	R = R′ = $-C_6H_5$; ligand on M is $C_6H_5COCH_2COC_6H_5$	Co(III)	D,1	—	—	400 d	—	90
		Cr(III)	D,1	Partially in C_2H_5OH, C_6H_6, $CHCl_3$	Dimers and trimers	340 d (TGA)	—	90
		Fe(III)	D,1	—	Dimers and trimers	160–210 d	—	90
29	R = R′ = $-C_6H_5$; ligand on M is 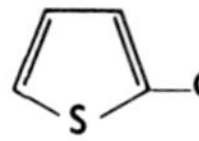 (thiophene)$-COCH_2COCF_3$	Cr(III)	D,1	Partially in C_2H_5OH, C_6H_6, $CHCl_3$	2200	350–450 d (TGA)	—	89
30	R = R′ = CH_3 [118]	Cr(III)	D,2	—	—	—	—	11
31	R = R′ = C_6H_5	Cr(III)	D,1	—	—	—	—	11

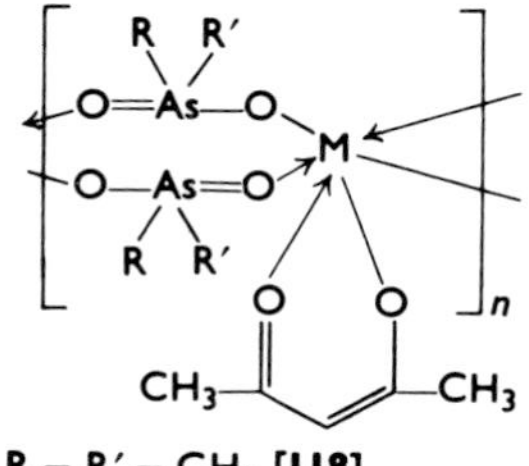

General structure (repeating unit):

$$\left[\ *\ \ *\ \ *\ \ \begin{array}{c} R\quad R' \\ O=As\quad As=O \\ R\quad R' \\ O\quad O \\ \searrow M \nearrow \\ O\quad O \\ CH_3\!-\!\!=\!\!-CH_3 \end{array}\ \right]_n$$

TABLE IX.4—continued

Polymeric Metal Phosphinates and Arsinates

No.	Structure	Metal (M)	Method	Color	Solubility	Molecular weight	T_m (°C)	Remarks and property data	References
32	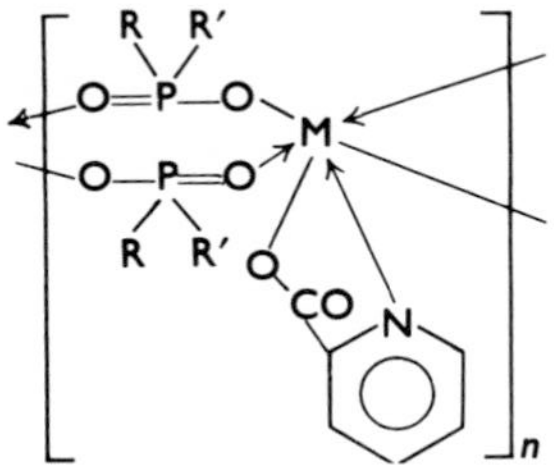 R = R′ = —C₆H₅ [107]	Cr(III)	D,1	—	CHCl₃	Dimer	—	—	11, 119
33	R = R′ = —C₆H₅	Al(III)	D,1	—	Insoluble	—	—	—	11
34	R = R′ = —C₆H₅	Cr(III)	D,1	—	—	—	—	—	11

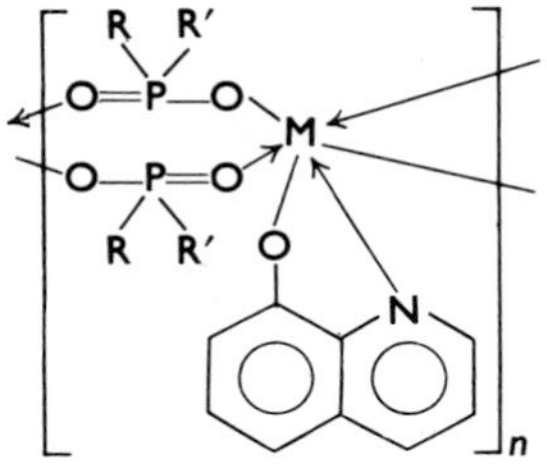

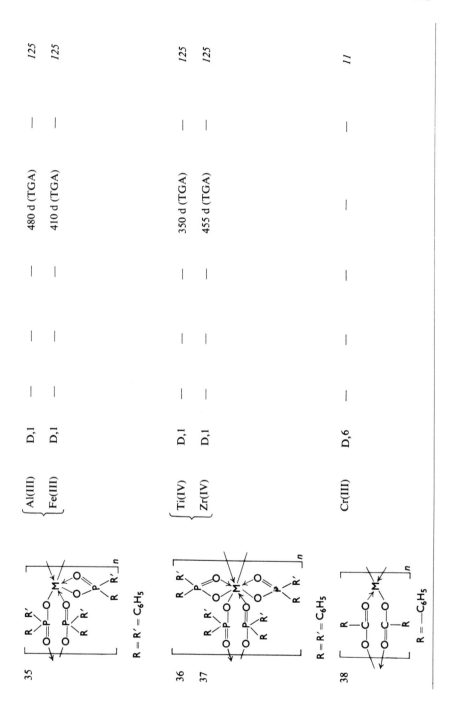

35	Al(III)	D,1	—	—	—	480 d (TGA)	—	125
	Fe(III)	D,1	—	—	—	410 d (TGA)	—	125
36	Ti(IV)	D,1	—	—	—	350 d (TGA)	—	125
37	Zr(IV)	D,1	—	—	—	455 d (TGA)	—	125
38	Cr(III)	D,6	—	—	—	—	—	11

$R = R' = C_6H_5$

$R = R' = C_6H_5$

$R = -C_6H_5$

TABLE IX.4—*continued*

Polymeric Metal Phosphinates and Arsinates

No.	Structure	Metal (M)	Method	Color	Solubility	Molecular weight	T_m (°C)	Remarks and property data	References
39	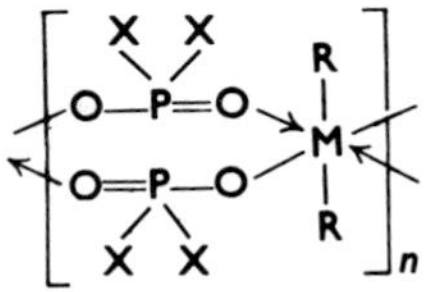 [138] X = Cl, Br; R = $CH_3COOC_2H_5$	Ca(II)	D,6	—	—	—	—	—	47
		Mg(II)	D,6	—	—	—	—	—	47
		Mn(II)	D,6	—	—	—	—	—	47
40	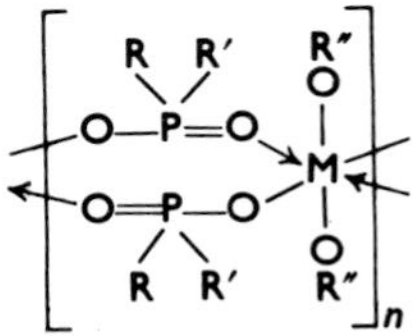 R = R′ = R″ = CH_3	Ti(IV)	D,1	—	—	943 (ebullioscopy)	—	—	31
41	R = R′ = CH_3; R″ = n-C_4H_9	Ti(IV)	D,1	—	$CHCl_3$	1735 (ebullioscopy)	—	—	31

42 R = CH$_3$; R' = C$_6$H$_5$; R'' = C$_2$H$_5$	Ti(IV)	D,1	—	—	—	—	31
43 R = R' = C$_6$H$_5$; R'' = C$_2$H$_5$	Ti(IV)	D,1	—	—	—	—	31
44 R = R' = C$_6$H$_5$; R'' = iso-C$_3$H$_7$	Ti(IV)	D,1	CHCl$_3$	1706 (ebullioscopy)	—	—	31

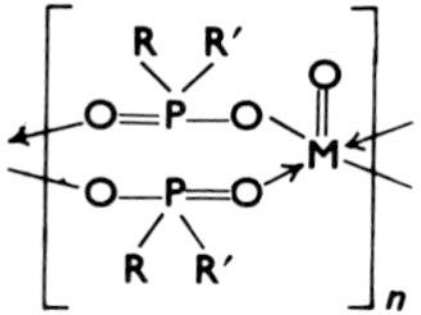

$$\left[\begin{array}{c} \text{O} \\ \| \\ \text{R} \quad \text{R}' \\ \text{P} \\ \text{O} \quad \text{O} \\ \diagdown \quad \diagup \\ \text{M} \\ \text{O} \quad \text{O} \\ \diagup \quad \diagdown \\ \text{P} \\ \text{R} \quad \text{R}' \end{array} \right]_n$$

45 R = R' = CH$_3$	Ti(IV)	D,1	Insoluble	—	450 d (TGA)	—	1, 2, 31
46 R = CH$_3$; R' = C$_6$H$_5$	Ti(IV)	D,1	—	4300 (ebullioscopy)	435 d (TGA)	—	31
47 R = R' = C$_6$H$_5$	Ti(IV)	D,1	—	7400→10,000 (ebullioscopy)	450 d (TGA)	—	31, 124

REFERENCES

1. Andrianov, K. A., and Kuznetsova, I. K., *Izv. Akad. Nauk SSSR, Otd. Khim. Nauk* p. 651 (1964).
2. Andrianov, K. A., and Kuznetsova, I. K., *Izv. Akad. Nauk SSSR, Otd. Khim. Nauk* p. 945 (1965).
3. Angelo, R. J., U.S. Patent 3,073,785 (E. I. duPont de Nemours & Co.) (1963); *Chem. Abstr.* **58**, 7006 (1963).
4. Bailar, J. C., Jr., Martin, K. V., Judd, M. L., and McLean, J. A., Jr., WADC Tech. Rept. No. 57-391, Part I (1957).
5. Bailar, J. C., Jr., Martin, K. V., Judd, M. L., and McLean, J. A., Jr., WADC Tech. Rept. No. 57-391, Part II (1958).
6. Bailes, R. H., and Calvin, M., *J. Am. Chem. Soc.* **69**, 1886 (1947).
7. Belskiĭ, N. K., and Tsikunov, V. N., *Vysokomolekul. Soedin.* **5**, 754 (1963); *Resins, Rubbers, Plastics* p. 2675 (1963).
8. Bennett, M. J., Cotton, F. A., Eiss, R., and Elder, R. C., *Nature* **213**, 174 (1967).
9. Berlin, A. A., and Kostroma, T. V., Russian Patent 129,018 (1960); *Chem. Abstr.* **55**, 3612 (1961).
10. Block, B. P., and Barth-Wehrenalp, G., *J. Inorg. & Nucl. Chem.* **24**, 365 (1962); *U.S. Dept. Comm. Office Tech. Serv.* AD 261,728 (1961); *Chem. Abstr.* **58**, 222 (1963).
11. Block, B. P., Ocone, L. R., and Simkin, J., U.S. Patent 3,197,436 (Pennsalt Chem. Corp.) (1965).
12. Block, B. P., Rose, S. H., Maguire, K. D., King, J. P., and Saraceno, A. J., *Am. Chem. Soc., Div. Org. Coatings Plastics Chem., Preprints* **25**, 294 (1965); *Chem. Abstr.* **66**, 2799, 29107p (1967).
13. Block, B. P., Rose, S. H., Maguire, K. D., King, J. P., and Saraceno, A. J., *Am. Chem. Soc., Div. Polymer Chem., Preprints* **6**, 1106 (1965).
14. Block, B. P., Rose, S. H., Schaumann, C. W., Roth, E. S., and Simkin, J., *J. Am. Chem. Soc.* **84**, 3200 (1962).
15. Block, B. P., Roth, E. S., Schaumann, C. W., and Ocone, L. R., *Inorg. Chem.* **1**, 860 (1962); *Resins, Rubbers, Plastics* p. 203 (1963).
16. Block, B. P., and Schaumann, C. W., U.S. Patent 3,245,953 (Pennsalt Chem. Corp) (1966); *Chem. Abstr.* **65**, 821 (1966).
17. Block, B. P., Simkin, J., and Ocone, L. R., *J. Am. Chem. Soc.* **84**, 1749 (1962).
18. Block, B. P., Simkin, J., Roth, E. S., and Rose, S. H., U.S. Patent 3,255,125 (Pennsalt Chem. Corp.) (1966); *Chem. Abstr.* **65**, 10688 (1966).
19. Boreskov, G. K., Keier, N. P., Rubtsova, L. F., and Rukhadze, E. G., *Dokl. Akad. Nauk SSSR* **144**, 1069 (1962); *Chem. Abstr.* **57**, 13959 (1962).
20. Bottei, R. S., and Gerace, P. L., *139th Meeting Am. Chem. Soc., St. Louis* p. 16M (1961).
21. British Patent 791,325 (issued to E. I. duPont de Nemours & Co.) (1958); *Chem. Abstr.* **52**, 14193 (1958).
22. British Patent 987,320 (issued to the Pennsalt Chem. Corp.) (1964); *Chem. Abstr.* **63**, 699 (1965).
23. Buckingham, D. A., Gorges, R. C., and Henry, J. T., *Australian J. Chem.* **20**, 281 (1967).
24. Chakravarty, D. N., and Drinkard, W. C., Jr., *J. Indian Chem. Soc.* **37**, 517 (1960); *Chem. Abstr.* **55**, 20752 (1961).
25. Charles, R. G., *J. Phys. Chem.* **64**, 1747 (1960); *Resins, Rubbers, Plastics* p. 2385 (1961).
26. Charles, R. G., *J. Polymer Sci.* A1, 267 (1963); *Resins, Rubbers, Plastics* p. 557 (1963).
27. Charles, R. G., Hickam, W. M., and von Hoene, J., *J. Phys. Chem.* **63**, 2084 (1959).
28. Charles, R. G., and Pawlikowski, M. A., *J. Phys. Chem.* **62**, 440 (1958).

29. Coates, G. E., and Golightly, D. S., *J. Chem. Soc.* p. 2523 (1962).
30. Crescenzi, V., Giancotti, V., and Ripamonti, A., *J. Am. Chem. Soc.* **87**, 391 (1965).
31. Dahl, G. H., and Block, B. P., *Inorg. Chem.* **6**, 1439 (1967).
32. Danielson, J., and Rasmussen, S. E., *Acta Chem. Scand.* **17**, 1971 (1963).
33. Delman, A. D., Kelly, J., Mironov, J., and Simms, B. B., *J. Polymer Sci.* **A-1, 4**, 1277 (1966).
34. Drinkard, W. C., Jr., and Chakravarty, D. N., WADC Tech. Rept. No. 59-761, p. 232 (1960).
35. Drinkard, W. C., Jr., Ross, D., and Wiesner, J., *J. Org. Chem.* **26**, 619 (1961).
36. Fernelius, W. C., WADC Tech. Rept. No. 56-203 (1956).
37. Fernelius, W. C., Shamma, M., Davis, L. A., Goldberg, D. E., Martin, B. B., Martin, D. F., and Thomas, F. D., III, WADC Tech. Rept. No. 56-203, Part III (1958).
38. Fernelius, W. C., Shamma, M., Garofano, N. R., Goldberg, D. E., Martin, D. F., and Thomas, F. D., III, WADC Tech. Rept. No. 56-203, Part II (1957).
39. Flumiani, G., and Bajic, V., *Monatsh. Chem.* **72**, 368 (1939); *Chem. Abstr.* **33**, 6831 (1939).
40. Flumiani, G., and Bajic, V., *Monatsh. Chem.* **74**, 92 (1942); *Chem. Abstr.* **38**, 351 (1944).
41. Frank, R. L., Clark, G. R., and Coker, J. N., *J. Am. Chem. Soc.* **72**, 1827 (1950).
42. Fujikawa, C. Y., *Dissertation Abstr.* **21**, 3621 (1961).
43. Giancotti, V., and Ripamonti, A., *Chim. Ind. (Milan)* **48**, 1065 (1966); *Chem. Abstr.* **66**, 2819, 29298b (1967).
44. Giordano, F., Randaccio, L., and Ripamonti, A., *Chem. Commun.* p. 19 (1967); *Chem. Abstr.* **66**, 5296, 55892k (1967).
45. Glukhov, N. A., Koton, M. M., and Mitin, Yu. V., *Vysokomolekul. Soedin.* **2**, 791 (1960); *Chem. Abstr.* **55**, 8920 (1961).
46. Grigoryev, A. I., Novoselova, A. V., and Semenenko, K. N., *Zh. Neorgan. Khim.* **2**, 2067 (1957); *Chem. Abstr.* **52**, 12639 (1958).
47. Grunze, H., *Z. Chem.* **6**, 266 (1966).
48. Guggiani, P. B., *Chem. Ber.* **45**, 2442 (1912).
49. Hardt, H. D., *Z. Anorg. Allgem. Chem.* **286**, 254 (1956); *Chem. Abstr.* **51**, 2447 (1956); *Z. Anorg. Allgem. Chem.* **292**, 53, 224, and 257 (1957); *Chem. Abstr.* **52**, 7002 (1958).
50. Hauserman, F. B., *Advan. Chem. Ser.* **23**, 338 (1959); *Chem. Abstr.* **54**, 4234 (1960).
51. Hofer, A., Kuckertz, H., and Sander, M., *Makromol. Chem.* **90**, 38 (1966).
52. Hoover, F. W., and Miller, H. C., British Patent 791,325 (E. I. duPont de Nemours & Co.) (1958); *Chem. Abstr.* **52**, 14193 (1958).
53. Hoover, F. W., and Miller, H. C., British Patent 807,198 (E. I. duPont de Nemours & Co.) (1959); *Chem. Abstr.* **53**, 11888 (1959).
54. Inoue, H., Hayashi, S., Takinchi, T., and Imoto, E., *Kogyo Kagaku Zasshi* **65**, 1622 (1962); *Resins, Rubbers, Plastics* p. 1487 (1963).
55. Jain, B. D., and Singhal, S. P., *J. Inorg. & Nucl. Chem.* **19**, 176 (1961).
56. Kanda, S., *Nippon Kagaku Zasshi* **81**, 1347 (1960); *Chem. Abstr.* **55**, 22994 (1961).
57. Kanda, S., and Saito, Y., *Bull. Chem. Soc. Japan* **30**, 192 (1957); *Chem. Abstr.* **51**, 17562 (1957).
58. Keier, N. P., *Nauchn. Osnovy Podbora i Proizv. Katalizatorov Akad. Nauk SSSR, Sibirsk. Otd.* p. 218 (1964); *Chem. Abstr.* **63**, 7681 (1965).
59. Keier, N. P., Boreskov, G. K., Rubtsova, L. F., and Rukhadze, E. G., *Kinetika i Kataliz* **3**, 680 (1962); *Chem. Abstr.* **58**, 7412 (1963).
60. Keier, N. P., Troitskaya, M. G., and Rukhadze, E. G., *Kinetika i Kataliz* **3**, 691 (1962); *Chem. Abstr.* **58**, 7413 (1963).
61. Kenney, C. N., *Chem. & Ind. (London)* p. 880 (1960).

62. Kluiber, R., and Lewis, J., *J. Am. Chem. Soc.* **82**, 5777 (1960).
63. Knobloch, F. W., *Dissertation Abstr.* **20**, 1171 (1959).
64. Knobloch, F. W., and Rauscher, W. H., *J. Polymer Sci.* **38**, 261 (1959).
65. Korshak, V. V., Krongauz, E. S., Gribkova, P. N., and Vasnev, V. A., *Vysokomolekul. Soedin.* **3**, 1203 (1961); *Chem. Abstr.* **56**, 8913 (1962); *Polymer Sci.* (*USSR*) (*English Transl.*) **3**, 883 (1962); *Resins, Rubbers, Plastics* p. 765 (1962).
66. Korshak, V. V., Krongauz, E. S., Gribkova, P. N., and Vasnev, V. A., *Vysokomolekul. Soedin.* **4**, 815 (1962); *Chem. Abstr.* **58**, 11475 (1963).
67. Korshak, V. V., Krongauz, E. S., and Sheina, V. E., *Vysokomolekul. Soedin.* **2**, 662 (1960); *Resins, Rubbers, Plastics* p. 1499 (1961).
68. Korshak, V. V., Krongauz, E. S., and Sheina, V. E., *Vysokomolekul. Soedin.* **3**, 1456 (1961); *Resins, Rubbers, Plastics* p. 1171 (1962).
69. Korshak, V. V., Krongauz, E. S., Sladkov, A. M., Sheina, V. E., and Luneva, L. K., *Vysokomolekul. Soedin.* **1**, 1764 (1959); *Chem. Abstr.* **54**, 20285 (1960); *Polymer Sci.* (*USSR*) (*English Transl.*) **2**, 148 (1961).
70. Korshak, V. V., Rogozhin, S. V., and Makarova, T. A., *Vysokomolekul. Soedin.* **4**, 1137 (1962); *Polymer Sci.* (*USSR*) (*English Transl.*) **4**, 326 (1963); *Resins, Rubbers, Plastics* p. 1261 (1963).
71. Korshak, V. V., Rogozhin, S. V., and Makarova, T. A., *Vysokomolekul. Soedin.* **4**, 1297 (1962); *Resins, Rubbers, Plastics* p. 1265 (1963).
72. Korshak, V. V., Rogozhin, S. V., and Volkov, V. I., *Vysokomolekul. Soedin.* **3**, 1808 (1961); *Chem. Abstr.* **56**, 14457 (1962); *Resins, Rubbers, Plastics* p. 1725 (1962).
73. Korshak, V. V., Rogozhin, S. V., and Volkov, V. I., *Vysokomolekul. Soedin.* **4**, 20 (1962); *Resins, Rubbers, Plastics* p. 1583 (1962).
74. Korshak, V. V., Sladkov, A. M., Luneva, L. K., and Bulgakova, I. A., *Vysokomolekul. Soedin.* **5**, 1288 (1963); *Polymer Sci.* (*USSR*) (*English Transl.*) **5**, 363 (1964).
75. Korshak, V. V., Slinkin, A. A., Vinogradova, S. V., and Babchinitser, T. M., *Vysokomolekul. Soedin.* **3**, 1624 (1961); *Chem. Abstr.* **56**, 14457 (1962).
76. Korshak, V. V., and Vinogradova, S. V., *Dokl. Akad. Nauk. SSSR* **138**, 1353 (1961); *Chem. Abstr.* **55**, 21646 (1961); *Proc. Acad. Sci. USSR, Chem. Sect.* (*English Transl.*) **138**, 612 (1961).
77. Korshak, V. V., Vinogradova, S. V., and Artemova, V. S., *Vysokomolekul. Soedin.* **2**, 492 (1960); *Chem. Abstr.* **55**, 3104 (1961).
78. Korshak, V. V., Vinogradova, S. V., and Artemova, V. S., *Vysokomolekul. Soedin.* **4**, 492 (1962); *Resins, Rubbers, Plastics* p. 2229 (1962).
79. Korshak, V. V., Vinogradova, S. V., Artemova, V. A., Babchinitser, T. M., and Pavlova, S. A., *Vysokomolekul. Soedin.* **3**, 1116 (1961); *Chem. Abstr.* **56**, 2562 (1962).
80. Korshak, V. V., Vinogradova, S. V., and Babchinitser, T. M., *Vysokomolekul. Soedin.* **2**, 498 (1960); *Chem. Abstr.* **55**, 3104 (1961).
81. Korshak, V. V., Vinogradova, S. V., and Morozova, D. T., *Vysokomolekul. Soedin.* **3**, 1500 (1961); *Chem. Abstr.* **56**, 13080 (1962).
82. Korshak, V. V., Vinogradova, S. V., and Vinogradov, M. G., *Vysokomolekul. Soedin.* **5**, 1771 (1963); *Polymer Sci.* (*USSR*) (*English Transl.*) **5**, 893 (1964); *Resins, Rubbers, Plastics* p. 2197 (1964).
83. Korshak, V. V., Vinogradova, S. V., and Vinogradov, M. G., *Vysokomolekul. Soedin* **6**, 729 (1964); *Chem. Abstr.* **61**, 4488 (1964); *Polymer Sci.* (*USSR*) (*English Transl.*) **6**, 802 (1965); *Resins, Rubbers, Plastics* p. 697 (1965).
84. Korshak, V. V., Vinogradova, S. V., and Vinogradov, M. G., *Dokl. Akad. Nauk SSSR* **155**, 1354 (1964); *Resins, Rubbers, Plastics* p. 699 (1965).
85. Korshak, V. V., Vinogradova, S. V., and Vinogradov, M. G., *Vysokomolekul. Soedin.* **6**, 1987 (1964); *Chem. Abstr.* **62**, 13253 (1965).

86. Korshak, V. V., Vinogradova, S. V., Vinogradov, M. G., and Davidovich, Y. A., *Vysokomolekul. Soedin.* **6**, 2149 (1964); *Chem. Abstr.* **62**, 13254 (1965); *Polymer Sci. (USSR) (English Transl.)* **6**, 2378 (1964); *Resins, Rubbers, Plastics* p. 1735 (1965).
87. Kubo, M., Kishita, M., and Kuroda, Y., *Intern. Symp. Macromol. Chem., Moscow,* 1960 Sect. I, pp. 185–90; *Chem. Abstr.* **55**, 12983 (1961).
88. Kuecker, J. F., *Dissertation Abstr.* **26**, 2496 (1965); *Chem. Abstr.* **64**, 6771 (1966).
89. LaGinestra, A., and Marucci, G., *Gazz. Chim. Ital.* **94**, 1464 (1964); *Chem. Abstr.* **64**, 19790 (1966).
90. LaGinestra, A., Marucci, G., and Monaci, A., *Gazz. Chim. Ital.* **94**, 1459 (1964); *Chem. Abstr.* **64**, 19790 (1966).
91. Langkammerer, C. M., U.S. Patent 2,489,651 (E. I. duPont de Nemours & Co.) (1949); *Chem. Abstr.* **44**, 1534 (1950).
92. Langkammerer, C. M., U.S. Patent 2,621,193 (E. I. duPont de Nemours & Co.) (1952); *Chem. Abstr.* **47**, 10549 (1953).
93. Ludke, W. O., Wiberley, S. E., Goldenson, J., and Bauer, W. H., *J. Phys. Chem.* **59**, 222 (1955).
94. Mangini, A., and Strata, R., *Gazz. Chim. Ital.* **62**, 686 (1932); *Chem. Abstr.* **27**, 285 (1933).
95. Martin, D. F., Shamma, M., and Fernelius, W. C., *J. Am. Chem. Soc.* **80**, 4891 and 5851 (1958).
96. Martin, D. F., Shamma, M., and Fernelius, W. C., *J. Am. Chem. Soc.* **81**, 130 (1959).
97. Marvel, C. S., and Martin, M. M., *J. Am. Chem. Soc.* **80**, 619 (1958).
98. Mattison, L. E., Phipps, M. S., Kazan, J., and Alfred, L., *J. Polymer Sci.* **54**, 117 (1961).
99. McLean, J. A., Jr., *Dissertation Abstr.* **20**, 3065 (1960).
100. Meyer, J., and Mantell, E., *Z. Anorg. Allgem. Chem.* **123**, 43 (1922); *Chem. Abstr.* **16**, 4153 (1922).
101. Nose, Y., Hatano, M., and Kambara, S., *Makromol. Chem.* **98**, 136 (1966).
102. O'Connell, J. J., U.S. Patent 3,192,236 (Monsanto Research Corp.) (1965); *Chem. Abstr.* **63**, 8517 (1965).
103. Oh, J. S., *Dissertation Abstr.* **22**, 61 (1961).
104. Olson, M. H., U.S. Patent 2,693,458 (Minnesota Mining and Manufacturing Co.) (1954); *Chem. Abstr.* **49**, 9962 (1955).
105. Patterson, T. R., Pavlik, F. J., Baldoni, A. A., and Frank, R. L., *J. Am. Chem. Soc.* **81**, 4213 (1959); *Resins, Rubbers, Plastics* p. 643 (1960).
106. Plazek, D. J., *Trans. Soc. Rheol.* **9**, 119 (1965); *Chem. Abstr.* **63**, 18283 (1965).
107. Podall, H. E., and Iapalucci, T. L., *J. Polymer Sci.* **B1**, 457 (1963).
108. Ramaswamy, K. K., and Sen, D. N., *Indian J. Chem.* **4**, 142 (1966); *Chem. Abstr.* **65**, 2094 (1966).
109. Reid, T. S., U.S. Patent 2,662,835 (Minnesota Mining and Manufacturing Co.) (1953); *Chem. Abstr.* **48**, 12791 (1954).
110. Rose, S. H., and Block, B. P., *J. Am. Chem. Soc.* **87**, 2076 (1965).
111. Rose, S. H., and Block, B. P., *J. Polymer Sci.* **A-1**, **4**, 573 (1966).
112. Rose, S. H., and Block, B. P., *J. Polymer Sci.* **A-1**, **4**, 583 (1966).
113. Rose, S. H., Block, B. P., and Davis, J. E., *Inorg. Chem.* **3**, 1258 (1964).
114. Saito, Y., and Kanda, S., Japanese Patent 7241 (1959); *Chem. Abstr.* **54**, 3890 (1960).
115. Sangal, S. P., *J. Prakt. Chem.* [4] **30**, 314 (1965).
116. Saraceno, A. J., U.S. Patent 3,275,574 (Pennsalt Chem. Corp.) (1966); *Chem. Abstr.* **66**, 2825, 29343h (1967).
117. Saraceno, A. J., U.S. Patent 3,328,296 (Pennsalt Chemical Corp.) (1967); *Chem. Abstr.* **67**, 6143, 65012h (1967).
118. Saraceno, A. J., and Block, B. P., *J. Am. Chem. Soc.* **85**, 2018 (1963).

119. Saraceno, A. J., and Block, B. P., *Inorg. Chem.* **2**, 864 (1963).
120. Saraceno, A. J., and Block, B. P., *Inorg. Chem.* **3**, 1699 (1964).
121. Schmeckenbecher, A., U.S. Patent 3,242,102 (Sperry Rand Corp.) (1966).
122. Slinkin, A. A., Dulov, A. A., and Rubinshtein, A. M., *Bull. Acad. Sci. USSR, Div. Chem. Sci. (English Transl.)* p. 1044 (1963).
123. Slinkin, A. A., Dulov, A. A., and Rubinshtein, A. M., *Izv. Akad. Nauk SSSR, Ser. Khim.* p. 1769 (1964); *Chem. Abstr.* **62**, 2838 (1965); *Bull. Acad. Sci. USSR, Div. Chem. Sci. (English Transl.)* p. 1679 (1964).
124. Sutton, R. A., British Patent 975,460 (1964).
125. Sutton, R. A., and Wood, J., British Patent 1,018,456 (Distiller's Co., Ltd.) (1966); *Chem. Abstr.* **64**, 17748 (1966).
126. Tanatar, S., and Kurovsky, E., *Zh. Russ. Fiz. Khim. Obshch.* **39**, 936 (1907); *Chem. Abstr.* **2**, 1128 (1908).
127. Terent'ev, A. P., Rode, V. V., and Rukhadze, E. G., *Vysokomolekul. Soedin.* **4**, 91 (1962); *Chem. Abstr.* **56**, 14455 (1962).
128. Terent'ev, A. P., Rode, V. V., and Rukhadze, E. G., *Vysokomolekul. Soedin.* **5**, 1666 (1963); *Chem. Abstr.* **60**, 15992 (1964).
129. Teyssie, P., *Chimia (Aarau)* **20**, 45 (1966); *Chem. Abstr.* **64**, 14292 (1966).
130. Tideswell, R. B., U.S. Patent 3,322,800 (Hooker Chemical Corp.) (1967); *Chem. Abstr.* **67**, 6130, 64891g (1967).
131. Tomic, E. A., *Am. Chem. Soc., Div. Polymer Chem., Preprints* **4**, 237 (1963); *Chem. Abstr.* **62**, 659 (1965).
132. Tomic, E. A., *J. Appl. Polymer Sci.* **9**, 3745 (1965); *Resins, Rubbers, Plastics* p. 899 (1966).
133. Tsuboyama, K., and Yanagita, M., *Sci. Papers Inst. Phys. Chem. Res. (Tokyo)* **61**, 20 (1967); *Chem. Abstr.* **67**, 4078, 43528d (1967).
134. Underwood, A. L., and Neuman, W. F., *Anal. Chem.* **21**, 1348 (1949).
135. Underwood, A. L., Toribara, T. Y., and Neuman, W. F., *J. Am. Chem. Soc.* **72**, 5597 (1950).
136. Vinogradov, M. G., Vinogradova, S. V., Davidovich, Y. A., and Korshak, V. V., *Izv. Akad. Nauk SSSR, Ser. Khim.* p. 2023 (1963); *Resins, Rubbers, Plastics* p. 1755 (1964).
137. Vinogradova, S. V., Vinogradov, M. G., and Korshak, V. V., *Kinetika i Kataliz* **5**, 247 (1964); *Resins, Rubbers, Plastics* p. 693 (1965).
138. von Hoene, J., Charles, R. G., and Hickam, W. M., *J. Phys. Chem.* **62**, 1098 (1958).
139. Wilkes, C. E., and Jacobson, R. A., *Inorg. Chem.* **4**, 99 (1965).
140. Wilkins, J. P., and Wittbecker, E. W., U.S. Patent 2,659,711 (E. I. duPont de Nemours & Co.) (1953); *Chem. Abstr.* **48**, 11109 (1954).

CHAPTER X

Metallorganic Ring Polymers from Sulfur Chelate Ligands

A. Polymeric Metal Mercaptides

METHOD 1. POLYMERIZATION OF MERCAPTANS WITH METAL SALTS

The earliest suggestion that monomercaptans yield polymers from reaction with metal salts was made by Mann and Purdie in 1935. The mercaptan was added to a chloroform solution of ammonium chloropalladite (*13*). Red-orange solids were obtained from aliphatic mercaptans. The polymeric structure was proposed because the products did not conduct electricity.

$$2n\,RSH + n\,(NH_4)_2PdCl_4 \longrightarrow \left[\begin{array}{c} R \\ S \\ Pd \\ S \\ R \end{array} \right]_n Pd + 2n\,HCl \qquad \text{(X-1)}$$

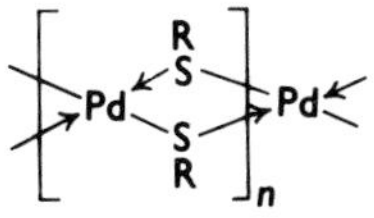

[1]   [2]   [3]   [4]

In 1944, Jensen proposed a similar structure for nickel mercaptides that he obtained from ammoniacal ethanolic solutions of mercaptans and nickel salts (*6*). These conditions (*2*), or the use of sodium hydroxide (*14, 15*) as the base, are generally useful for the synthesis of polymeric metal mercaptides. The nickel mercaptides prepared by Jensen were diamagnetic, which, in addition to other physical properties that he determined, were in accord with the polymeric structure [5]. The presence or absence of oxygen during the synthesis of metal mercaptides is another variable that has been investigated (*2, 15*).

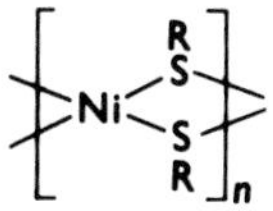

$$\left[\begin{array}{c} R \\ S \\ Ni \\ S \\ R \end{array} \right]_n \qquad \text{(X-2)}$$

[5]

301

The products prepared by this method can possess very high molecular weights. Co(III)–n-Hexyl mercaptan polymers are reported to possess intrinsic viscosities as high as 3.80 (14). More generally, the products possess soluble and insoluble fractions. The former are low molecular weight "mers", i.e., tetra, penta, or hexa. The insoluble materials are presumed to be of higher molecular weight of mostly unspecified structure. It has been noted in some cases that the soluble fractions became less soluble on standing at room temperature, a fact which is suggestive of further polymerization (2). The Co(III)–n-hexyl mercaptan polymers mentioned above were postulated to possess structure [6] and/or [7]. The high viscosities of their chloroform solutions was felt to favor the linear structure, whereas the cross-linked structure [7] could explain the different amount of soluble product that was obtained from the different reaction conditions (14).

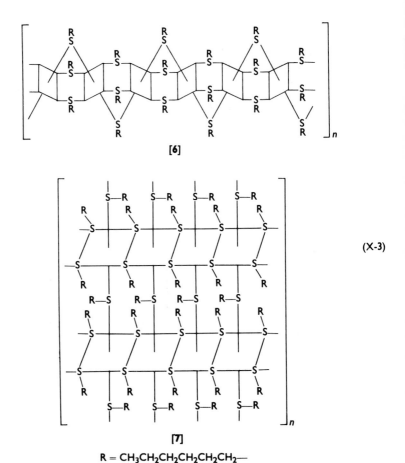

[6]

(X-3)

[7]

R = CH$_3$CH$_2$CH$_2$CH$_2$CH$_2$CH$_2$—

METHOD 2. POLYMERIZATION OF METAL CARBONYLS WITH DISULFIDES

Heating nickel carbonyl with dialkyl or diaryl disulfides yields polymeric metal mercaptides (5, 24).

$$n \ Ni(CO)_4 + n \ R_2S_2 \longrightarrow [Ni(SR)_2]_n \qquad (X-4)$$
$$[8] \qquad [9] \qquad [5]$$
$$R = CH_3, C_6H_5$$

Benzene or hexane under reflux in an inert atmosphere are suitable reaction conditions. The soluble fraction that was obtained possessed a molecular weight of 1177. X-Ray analysis of this product showed it to be a hexamer with a structure identical to the product that was obtained from the following method.

METHOD 3. POLYMERIZATION OF METAL SALTS WITH DI(ALKYLMERCAPTO) ORGANOTIN COMPOUNDS

Polymerization of dimethyldi(ethylthio)tin with nickel chloride in ethanol gives a purplish black, diamagnetic, crystalline compound in 53% yield (24).

$$NiCl_2 + (C_2H_5S)_2Sn(CH_3)_2 \longrightarrow \left[Ni(SC_2H_5)_2\right]_n \qquad (X-5)$$
$$[10] \qquad [11] \qquad [12]$$

The soluble portion of the product possessed a molecular weight of 1000 and was shown by X-ray analysis to be a hexamer. A cyclic structure containing the six nickel atoms in a planar hexagon was proposed. The nickel atoms are bridged with ethylthio groups above and below the plane of the nickel ring as shown in structure [13]. The authors also proposed this structure for the analogous palladium complexes. This structure, of course, has the same repeat units as that proposed in 1935 by Mann and Purdie [5].

METHOD 4. POLYMERIZATION OF DIMERCAPTANS WITH METAL SALTS

2,4-Dimethoxy-1,5-dimercaptobenzene [14] and metal acetylacetonates polymerize to chelate polymers containing a five-membered ring (X-7) (22). Reaction was carried out in dimethylformamide or quinoline at temperatures of 100°–200°C. Several of the soluble members of this class possessed intrinsic viscosities of 0.1 in acetic acid.

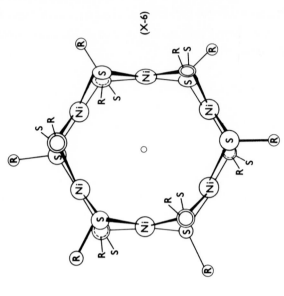

(X-6)

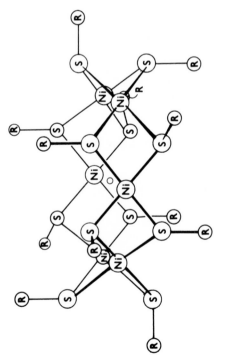

[13]

$$n \quad \underset{CH_3O}{\overset{HS}{\bigcirc}} \underset{OCH_3}{\overset{SH}{}} \quad + \quad n \, M(AcAc)_2 \quad \longrightarrow$$

[14]   [15]

$$\left[\underset{\underset{CH_3}{O}}{\overset{S}{\bigcirc}} \underset{\underset{CH_3}{O}}{\overset{S}{\bigcirc}} M \right]_n \quad + \quad 2n \, HAcAc \quad (X\text{-}7)$$

[16]   [17]

Although a cyclic structure was not considered for the product prepared from 2,9-*p*-menthane dithiol and cadmium acetate, it is included in this section and Table X.1 (pp. 308–312) (*23*).

B. Polymers from Bis(dithiocarbamates)

METHOD 1. POLYMERIZATION OF BIS(DITHIOCARBAMATES) WITH METAL SALTS

Polymeric metal bis(dithiocarbamates) have been prepared by polymerization of disodium salts of bis(dithiocarbamic acids) with metal acetates (*19*). Polymers prepared from nickel, zinc, and cobalt were prepared in aqueous media and were shown to possess structure [20].

$$n \, Na\overset{S}{\overset{\|}{S}}CNHRNHC\overset{S}{\overset{\|}{S}}Na + n \, Ni(C_2H_3O_2)_2 \quad \longrightarrow$$

[18]   [19]

$$\left[RNHC \overset{S}{\underset{S}{\diagdown}} Ni \overset{S}{\underset{S}{\diagdown}} CNH \right]_n \quad + \quad 2n \, Na(C_2H_3O_2) \quad (X\text{-}8)$$

[20]   [21]

On the other hand, analogous reaction with Cu(II) salts led to cross-linked structures. Reduction of Cu(II) to the monovalent state occurred with formation of sulfur and carbonyl sulfide. The copper polymer could also be obtained from aqueous ammoniacal copper chloride.

$$Na\overset{S}{\overset{\|}{S}}CNHRNHC\overset{S}{\overset{\|}{S}}Na + Cu(C_2H_3O_2)_2 \quad \longrightarrow \quad \begin{array}{c} \longleftarrow RNHCS \longrightarrow \\ | \\ S \\ | \\ Cu \\ \uparrow \\ S \\ \| \\ \longleftarrow C=SCuS-CNHR- \\ | \end{array} \quad + \; COS \; + \; S \quad (X\text{-}9)$$

[18]   [22]   [23]   [24]   [25]

High molecular weights were reported for some of the Ni(II) and Zn(II) polymers (*19*). They were determined on polymer samples prepared from metal salts of radioactive halides. The active halide in the polymer, presumably present solely as end groups, was counted and the molecular weights calculated from these data. It is surprising that no mechanical properties were reported for the polymers, if the reported values were accurate measures of their molecular weight (see Table X.2, pp. 313–314).

The poly[metal bis(dithiocarbamates)] are amorphous, as determined by X-ray diffraction analysis (*16*). Thermogravimetric data have been reported which show that the nickel derivatives are the most thermally stable. Also, those containing benzene rings possess added thermal stability. Appreciable decomposition began at 200°–300°C with the degradation mechanism the same in air or an inert atmosphere (*16*). Although early work was quite specific that linear structures were present in these polymers (except those containing copper), recent statements to the effect that two- and three-dimensional lattice structures are predominant have appeared (*17, 18*). In a fairly extensive study of the electrical conductivity of several classes of chelate polymers (*20, 21*), including the polymeric bis(dithiocarbamates) shown in Table X.2 (pp. 313–314), correlation of conductivity with molecular structure was attempted (*21*).

Certain of these polymers have been studied as catalysts for the decomposition of hydrazine (*1, 9, 10*) and the decomposition of hydrogen peroxide (*11*). The copper-containing polymers are the most active ones, whereas zinc and cadmium polymers were inactive (*1, 9*). The nature of the ligands attached to the metal atom was found to affect catalytic activity. The catalysis that was observed for the polymers was greater than for similar monomeric chelates or metal oxides. No correlation was observed between electrical conductivity of the chelate and its catalytic activity (*9*).

C. Polymers from Bis(xanthates)

METHOD 1. POLYMERIZATION OF BIS(XANTHATES) WITH METAL SALTS

Bis(xanthates) are a readily accessible class of bis(ligands), but surprisingly little research has been published about their coordination polymers with metals (*3, 7*). This could be due to the fact that thermal stability screening studies showed them to be inferior in this respect (*3*). A series of polymeric nickel bis(xanthates) have been prepared from reaction of bis(potassium xanthates) with nickel salts (*7*) (see Table X.3, p. 315). Only meager information about their properties has been published.

$$n\ \mathrm{KS\overset{S}{\overset{\|}{C}}OROC\overset{S}{\overset{\|}{C}}SK} + n\ \mathrm{NiX_2} \longrightarrow \left[\mathrm{OROC}\begin{smallmatrix}S\\ \diagup \diagdown \\ S\end{smallmatrix}\mathrm{Ni}\begin{smallmatrix}S\\ \diagup \diagdown \\ S\end{smallmatrix}C\right]_n + 2n\ \mathrm{KX} \quad (\text{X-10})$$

[26]   [27]   [28]   [29]

A series of reports describing the catalytic activity of a variety of chelates, including poly[metal bis(xanthates)], has appeared. Their utility as catalysts for the decomposition of hydrazine (*1*, *10*), isopropanol (*1*), formic acid (*1*), hydrogen peroxide (*11*), and the oxidation of cumene to cumene hydroperoxide (*8*) has been studied. These ligands, especially when linked to copper, were among the most active classes of polymeric chelates that were evaluated in these studies.

TABLE X.1

Polymeric Metal Mercaptides

No.	Mercaptan (RSH)	Metal	Method	Color	Solubility	Molecular weight	T_m (°C)	Remarks and property data	References
1	CH_3SH	Ni	A,1	—	Insoluble	—	180–200 d	—	2
2	CH_3SH	Ni	A,2	Brown	—	—	—	—	5
3	CH_3SH	Ni	A,3	—	—	—	—	—	24
4	C_2H_5SH	Co	A,1	Brown	Insoluble	—	—	—	2,15
5	C_2H_5SH	Ni [12]	A,1	—	$CHCl_3$, C_6H_{12}	DP = 5.4 (ebullioscopy)	180–200 d	Diamagnetic	2,6
6	C_2H_5SH	Ni	A,3	Purple	—	1006	—	Diamagnetic	24
7	C_2H_5SH	Pd	A,1	Orange	$CHCl_3$, C_6H_{12}	—	—	Crystalline	13,15
8	C_2H_5SH	Tl	A,1	—	$CHCl_3$, C_6H_{12}	—	—	—	15
9	$n\text{-}C_3H_7SH$	Co	A,1	Brown	Insoluble	—	—	—	2
10	$n\text{-}C_3H_7SH$	Ni	A,1	—	—	DP = 5.1 (ebullioscopy)	—	—	2
11	$n\text{-}C_3H_7SH$	Pd	A,2	—	—	—	—	—	5
12	$n\text{-}C_3H_7SH$	Pd	A,1	Orange	—	—	—	Crystalline	13
13	$iso\text{-}C_3H_7SH$	Co	A,1	Red	Insoluble	—	—	—	2

No.	Thiol	Metal	Method	Color	Solubility	DP / [η]	M.p./dec.	Stability	Ref.
14	iso-C_3H_7SH	Cu(I)	A,1	Yellow	Insoluble	—	—	Stable to 200°C/0.1 mm	2
15	iso-C_3H_7SH	Ni	A,1	—	—	DP = 4.0 (ebullioscopy)	180–200 d	—	2
16	iso-C_3H_7SH	Zn	A,1	White	Pyridine	—	—	Stable to 190°C/0.1 mm	2
17	$HSCH_2CH_2COOK$	Co	A,1	Red	—	[η] 0.20	—	—	14
18	$HSCH_2CHCOOK$ NH_2	Co	A,1	—	$CHCl_3$, C_6H_{12}	[η] 0.10	—	—	14
19	n-C_4H_9SH	Co	A,1	—	—	—	—	—	15
20	n-C_4H_9SH	Ni	A,1	—	—	DP = 5.4 (ebullioscopy)	180–200 d	—	2, 15
21	n-C_4H_9SH	Pd	A,1	Orange	—	—	—	Crystalline	13, 15
22	n-C_4H_9SH	Tl	A,1	—	$CHCl_3$, C_6H_{12}	—	—	—	15
23	iso-C_4H_9SH	Co	A,1	—	$CHCl_3$, C_6H_{12}	—	—	—	15
24	iso-C_4H_9SH	Ni	A,1	—	$CHCl_3$, C_6H_{12}	—	—	—	15
25	iso-C_4H_9SH	Pd	A,1	—	$CHCl_3$, C_6H_{12}	—	—	—	15
26	iso-C_4H_9SH	Tl	A,1	—	$CHCl_3$, C_6H_{12}	—	—	—	15
27	sec-C_4H_9SH	Co	A,1	—	$CHCl_3$, C_6H_{12}	—	—	—	15
28	sec-C_4H_9SH	Ni	A,1	—	$CHCl_3$, C_6H_{12}	—	—	—	15
29	sec-C_4H_9SH	Pd	A,1	—	$CHCl_3$, C_6H_{12}	—	—	—	15

TABLE X.1—*continued*

Polymeric Metal Mercaptides

No.	Mercaptan (RSH)	Metal	Method	Color	Solubility	Molecular weight	T_m (°C)	Remarks and property data	References
30	sec-C$_4$H$_9$SH	Tl	A,1	—	CHCl$_3$, C$_6$H$_{12}$	—	—	—	15
31	tert-C$_4$H$_9$SH	Co	A,1	Brown	—	—	—	—	2, 15
32	tert-C$_4$H$_9$SH	Ni	A,1	—	—	—	—	—	15
33	tert-C$_4$H$_9$SH	Pd	A,1	—	CHCl$_3$, C$_6$H$_{12}$	—	—	—	15
34	tert-C$_4$H$_9$SH	Tl	A,1	—	—	—	—	—	15
35	n-C$_5$H$_{11}$SH	Co	A,1	Green	—	—	—	—	2
36	n-C$_5$H$_{11}$SH	Cu(I)	A,1	Yellow	—	—	—	Stable to 200°C/0.1 mm	2
37	n-C$_5$H$_{11}$SH	Ni	A,1	—	—	DP = 6.3 (ebullioscopy)	180–200 d	—	2
38	n-C$_5$H$_{11}$SH	Pd	A,1	Orange	—	—	—	Crystalline. Stable to 190°C/0.1 mm	13
39	n-C$_5$H$_{11}$SH	Zn	A,1	White	Pyridine	—	—	—	2
40	n-C$_6$H$_{13}$SH	Co	A,1	Green	CHCl$_3$, CCl$_4$, C$_6$H$_6$	[η] 3.80	160–170 d	—	14, 15

No.	RSH	Metal	Method	Color	Solvent			Ref.
41	$n\text{-}C_6H_{13}SH$	Ni	A,1	—	$CHCl_3, C_6H_{12}$	—	—	15
42	$n\text{-}C_6H_{13}SH$	Pd	A,1	—	$CHCl_3, C_6H_{12}$	—	—	15
43	$n\text{-}C_6H_{13}SH$	Tl	A,1	—	$CHCl_3, C_6H_{12}$	—	—	15
44	$n\text{-}C_8H_{17}SH$	Co	A,1	—	$CHCl_3, C_6H_{12}$	—	—	15
45	$n\text{-}C_8H_{17}SH$	Ni	A,1	—	$CHCl_3, C_6H_{12}$	—	—	15
46	$n\text{-}C_8H_{17}SH$	Pd	A,1	—	$CHCl_3, C_6H_{12}$	—	—	15
47	$n\text{-}C_8H_{17}SH$	Tl	A,1	—	$CHCl_3, C_6H_{12}$	—	—	15
48	C_6H_5SH	Co	A,1	Brown	—	—	—	2, 15
49	C_6H_5SH	Ni	A,2	Brown	—	—	—	5
50	C_6H_5SH	Ni	A,1	—	—	—	—	6, 15
51	C_6H_5SH	Ni	A,3	—	—	—	—	24
52	C_6H_5SH	Pd	A,1	—	$CHCl_3, C_6H_{12}$	—	—	13, 15
53	C_6H_5SH	Pd	A,1	—	—	—	—	15
54	C_6H_5SH	Zn	A,1	White	—	—	—	2
55	C_6H_5SH	Tl	A,1	—	$CHCl_3, C_6H_{12}$	—	—	15
56	$p\text{-}CH_3C_6H_4SH$	Ni	A,1	—	—	—	—	6
57	$C_6H_5CH_2SH$	Co	A,1	—	$CHCl_3, C_6H_{12}$	—	—	15

TABLE X.1—continued

Polymeric Metal Mercaptides

No.	Mercaptan (RSH)	Metal	Method	Color	Solubility	Molecular weight	T_m (°C)	Remarks and property data	References
58	$C_6H_5CH_2SH$	Ni	A,1	—	$CHCl_3$, C_6H_{12}	—	—	—	15
59	$C_6H_5CH_2SH$	Pd	A,1	—	$CHCl_3$, C_6H_{12}	—	—	—	15
60	$C_6H_5CH_2SH$	Tl	A,1	—	$CHCl_3$, C_6H_{12}	—	—	—	15
61	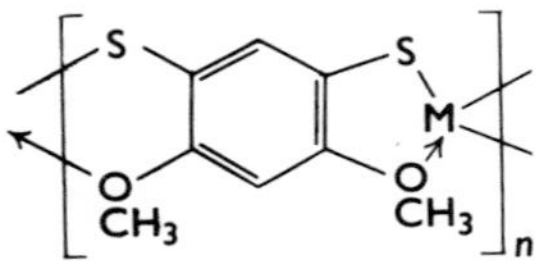	Ba	A,4	—	CH_3CO_2H	$[\eta]$ 0.1	—	—	22
62		Be	A,4	—	Insoluble	—	—	—	22
63		Ca	A,4	—	Insoluble	—	—	—	22
64		Cd	A,4	—	Insoluble	—	295 d (TGA)	—	22
65		Co	A,4	—	Insoluble	—	180 d (TGA)	—	22
66		Cu	A,4	—	Insoluble	—	270 d (TGA)	—	22
67		Mg	A,4	—	CH_3CO_2H	$[\eta]$ 0.1	—	—	22
68		Ni	A,4	—	Insoluble	—	200 d (TGA)	—	22
69		Si	A,4	—	CH_3CO_2H	$[\eta]$ 0.1	—	—	22
70		Zn	A,4	—	Insoluble	—	250 d (TGA)	—	22
71	2,9-p-Menthane dithiol	Cd	A,4	White	Insoluble	—	>300 d	—	23

[16]

TABLE X.2

Polymers from Bis(dithiocarbamates)

No.	Structure	Metal (M)	Method	Color	Solubility	Molecular weight	T_m (°C)	Remarks and property data	References
	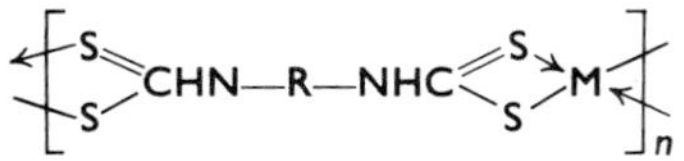								
1	R = $\text{+CH}_2\text{+}_2$	Co(II)	B,1	Brown	Insoluble	—	Infusible	Amorphous. Elec. conductivity data	*16, 21*
2	R = $\text{+CH}_2\text{+}_2$	Ni(II)	B,1	Brown	Insoluble	57,100 (analysis)	Infusible	Amorphous. Elec. conductivity data	*16, 19, 21*
3	R = $\text{+CH}_2\text{+}_2$	Zn(II)	B,1	White	Insoluble	59,300 (analysis)	Infusible	Amorphous. Elec. conductivity data	*16, 19, 21*
3a	R = —CH_2—$C(CH_3)_2$—	Zn(II)	—	—	—	—	—	Excellent fungicide	*12*
4	R = $\text{+CH}_2\text{+}_6$	Co(II)	—	Green	Insoluble	—	Infusible	Amorphous. Elec. conductivity data	*16, 21*
5	R = $\text{+CH}_2\text{+}_6$	Ni(II)	B,1	Green	Insoluble	64,000 (analysis)	Infusible	Amorphous. Elec. conductivity data	*16, 17, 19, 21*
6	R = $\text{+CH}_2\text{+}_6$	Zn(II)	B,1	White	Insoluble	53,500	Infusible	Amorphous. Elec. conductivity data	*16, 19, 21*
7	R = 1,4-C_6H_4	Co(II)	—	Brown	Insoluble	—	Infusible	Amorphous. Elec. conductivity data	*16, 21*
8	R = 1,4-C_6H_4	Zn(II)	B,1	White	Insoluble	64,000 (analysis)	Infusible	Amorphous. Elec. conductivity data	*16, 19, 21*
9	R = 4,4′-C_6H_4-C_6H_4	Co(II)	B,1	Green	Insoluble	—	Infusible	Amorphous. Elec. conductivity data	*16, 21*

TABLE X.2—*continued*
Polymers from Bis(dithiocarbamates)

No.	Structure	Metal (M)	Method	Color	Solubility	Molecular weight	T_m (°C)	Remarks and property data	References
10	R = 4,4'-C₆H₄—C₆H₄	Ni(II)	B,1	Brown	Insoluble	66,700 (analysis)	Infusible	Amorphous. Elec. conductivity data	16, 19, 21
11	R = 4,4'-C₆H₄—C₆H₄	Zn(II)	B,1	Yellow	Insoluble	61,500 (analysis)	Infusible	Amorphous. Elec. conductivity data	16, 19, 21
12	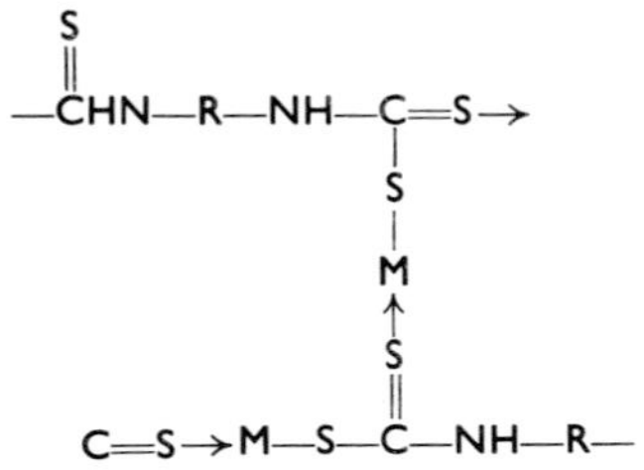 R = —(CH₂)₂—	Cu(I)	B,1	Brown	Insoluble	—	Infusible	Amorphous. Elec. conductivity data	4, 16, 19–21
13	R = —(CH₂)₆—	Cu(I)	B,1	Brown	Insoluble	—	Infusible	Amorphous. Elec. conductivity data	16–19
14	R = 1,4-C₆H₄	Cu(I)	B,1	Green	Insoluble	—	Infusible	Amorphous. Elec. conductivity data	16, 19
15	R = 4,4'-C₆H₄—C₆H₄	Cu(I)	B,1	Yellow	Insoluble	—	Infusible	Amorphous. Elec. conductivity data	16, 19

Structure (rows 10–11):

$$\ast\ \ast\ \ast$$

—CHN—R—NH—C=S →

S—M←S

C=S→M—S—C—NH—R—

TABLE X.3

Polymers from Bis(xanthates)

The structure for the polymers is:

$$\left[\begin{array}{c} S \\ \parallel \\ S \end{array} CO-R-OC \begin{array}{c} S \\ \diagdown \\ S \end{array} M \right]_n$$

[28]

No.	Structure	Metal (M)	Method	Remarks and property data	References
1	$R = +CH_2)_4$	Ni(II)	C,1	—	7
2	$R = +CH_2)_6$	Ni(II)	C,1	—	7
3	$R = +CH_2)_2-S+CH_2)_2$	N (II)	C,1	—	7
4	$R = +CH_2-O-CH_2)_n$	Ni(II)	C,1	—	7
5	$R = 1,3-C_6H_4$	Ni(II)	C,1	—	7
6	$R = 1,4-C_6H_4$	Ni(II)	C,1	Fiber-forming	7

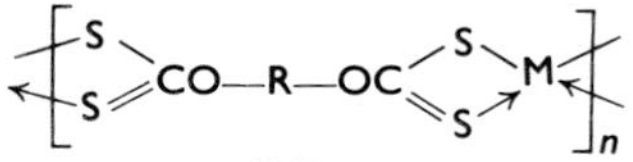

REFERENCES

1. Boreskov, G. K., Keier, N. P., Rubtsova, L. F., and Rukhadze, E. G., *Dokl. Akad Nauk SSSR* **144**, 1069 (1962); *Chem. Abstr.* **57**, 13959 (1962).
2. Bradley, D. C., and Marsh, C. H., *Chem. Ind. (London)* p. 361 (1967).
3. Fernelius, W. C., Shamma, M., Davis, L. A., Goldberg, D. E., Martin, B. B., Martin, D. F., and Thomas, F. D., III, WADC Tech. Rept. No. 56-203, Part III (1958).
4. German Patent 1,232,948 (issued to Roussel-Uclaf) (1967).
5. Hayter, R. G., and Humiec, F. S., *J. Inorg. & Nucl. Chem.* **26**, 807 (1964).
6. Jensen, K. A., *Z. Anorg. Chem.* **252**, 227 (1944); *Chem. Abstr.* **40**, 4352 (1946).
7. Karipides, D. G., *Dissertation Abstr.* **22**, 59 (1961).
8. Keier, N. P., *Nauchn. Osnovy Podbora i Proizv. Katalizatorov Akad. Nauk SSSR, Sibirsk. Otd.* p. 218 (1964); *Chem. Abstr.* **63**, 7681 (1965).
9. Keier, N. P., Boreskov, G. K., Rode, V. V., Terent'ev, A. P., and Rukhadze, E. G., *Kinetika i Kataliz* **2**, 509 (1961); *Chem. Abstr.* **58**, 5082 (1963).
10. Keier, N. P., Boreskov, G. K., Rubtsova, L. F., and Rukhadze, E. G., *Kinetika i Kataliz* **3**, 680 (1962); *Chem. Abstr.* **58**, 7412 (1963).
11. Keier, N. P., Troitskaya, M. G., and Rukhadze, E. G., *Kinetika i Kataliz* **3**, 691 (1962); *Chem. Abstr.* **58**, 7413 (1963).
12. Lehmann, H., Grewe, F., and Lautenschlager, W., U.S. Patent 3,294,829 (Farbenfabriken Bayer, A.G.) (1966).
13. Mann, F. G., and Purdie, D., *J. Chem. Soc.* p. 1549 (1935).
14. McCormick, B. J., and Gorin, G., *Inorg. Chem.* **2**, 928 (1963).
15. Swan, C. J., and Trimm, D. L., *Chem. & Ind. (London)* p. 1363 (1967).
16. Terent'ev, A. P., Rode, V. V., and Rukhadze, E. G., *Vysokomolekul. Soedin.* **4**, 1005 (1962); *Chem. Abstr.* **59**, 772 (1963).
17. Terent'ev, A. P., Rode, V. V., and Rukhadze, E. G., *Vysokomolekul. Soedin.* **5**, 1666 (1963); *Chem. Abstr.* **60**, 15992 (1964).
18. Terent'ev, A. P., Rukhadze, E. G., Kharakhorin, F. F., and Petrov, V. M., *Vysokomolekul. Soedin.* **B9**, 100 (1967); *Chem. Abstr.* **66**, 8972, 95538f (1967).
19. Terent'ev, A. P., Rukhadze, E. G., and Rode, V. V., *Vysokomolekul. Soedin.* **4**, 821 (1962); *Chem. Abstr.* **59**, 771 (1963); *Resins, Rubbers, Plastics* p. 565 (1963).
20. Terent'ev, A. P., Rukhadze, E. G., Vozzhennikov, V. M., Zvonkova, Z. V., Oboladze, N. S., and Mochalina, I. G., *Dokl. Akad. Nauk SSSR* **147**, 1094 (1962); *Chem. Abstr.* **58**, 10317 (1963).
21. Terent'ev, A. P., Vozzhennikov, V. M., Zvonkova, Z. V., and Badzhadze, L. I., *Proc. Acad. Sci. USSR, Chem. Sect. (English Transl.)* **140**, 1018 (1961); *Chem. Abstr.* **56**, 9556 (1962).
22. Vinogradova, S. V., Vasnev, V. A., and Korshak, V. V., *Vysokomolekul. Soedin.* **B9**, No. 7, 520 (1967); *Chem. Abstr.* **67**, 6985, 73915v (1967).
23. Warner, P. F., U.S. Patent 3,294,761 (Phillips Petroleum Co.) (1966).
24. Woodward, P., Dahl, L. F., Abel, E. W., and Crosse, B. C., *J. Am. Chem. Soc.* **87**, 5251 (1965).

CHAPTER XI

Polysiloxanes, Polysilazanes, and Polymetalloxanes from Ring-Forming Polymerizations

A. Polysiloxanes

METHOD 1. HYDROLYTIC POLYCONDENSATION OF MONOALKYL AND MONO-ARYL SILANES

The hydrolysis of monoalkyl or monoaryl silanes to poorly defined resins and gels was reported almost one hundred years ago. This type of reaction, which is sometimes known as a silsesquioxane polymerization, gave a quantitative yield of polymer when applied to silicochloroform (67). Hydrolysis in dilute ether solution yielded a crystalline, two-dimensional, sheetlike polymer. The product was insoluble in organic solvents. Heating it at 280°C in high vacuum causes evolution of hydrogen to yield the product shown in Eq. (XI-1).

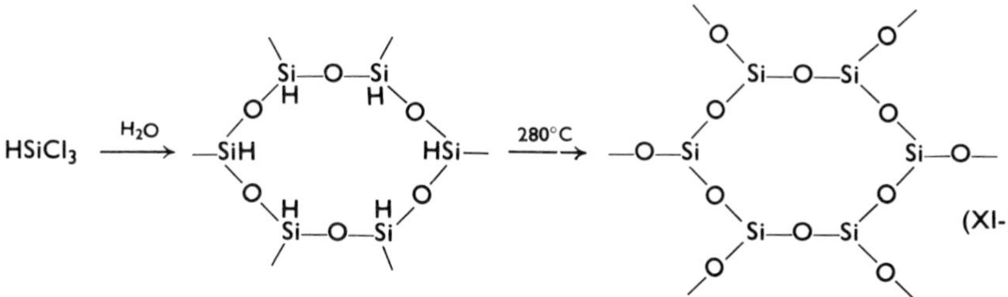

$$\text{HSiCl}_3 \xrightarrow{\text{H}_2\text{O}} \quad [1] \quad \xrightarrow{280°\text{C}} \quad [3] \quad \text{(XI-1)}$$

[1]　　　　　　　　[2]　　　　　　　　　[3]

Recently, an extensive study showed that the hydrolysis of several alkyl- and aryl-substituted trialkoxysilanes (60, 61) gave low molecular weight oligomers or gels. Hydrolytic polycondensation of the higher alkyl (C_6–C_9) trichlorosilanes yields similar oligomers [6] that are distillable to yield compounds possessing the cage-type structures [8] (2). These cyclic oligomers were postulated to form because of steric hindrance to further polymerization. This view was substantiated by the failure of a variety of nucleophiles and electrophiles to polymerize [8].

$$n \text{ RSiCl}_3 + 3n \text{ H}_2\text{O} \xrightarrow{25°C} \left[\begin{array}{c} R \\ | \\ -O-Si-O- \\ | \\ OH \end{array} \right]_n + 3n \text{ HCl} \longrightarrow$$

[4]   [5]   [6]   [7]

n = 6–8

(XI-2)

[8]

These results are in contrast to the fact that hydrolysis of phenyltriethoxysilane yields moderately high molecular weight, soluble polymers (61, 62). Reaction of phenyltriethoxysilane with water and a quaternary base in methyl isobutyl ketone under reflux resulted in precipitation of polymer over a period of days. It possessed intrinsic viscosities of 0.1–0.3 (62). This polymerization has received additional study since this original work and the "ladder" structure [10] shown in Eq. (XI-3) has been substantiated. Soluble "ladder" polymer [10] is prepared best by base-catalyzed equilibration of the initial hydrolysates obtained from either phenyltrichloro- or triethoxysilanes. At high concentrations (85–95%) at 250°C in solvents such as Dowtherm (24–26, 56), very high molecular weight ($\bar{M}_w > 10^6$), soluble polymer is obtained. Base-catalyzed, bulk equilibration generally gives a gel (18).

$$4n \text{ C}_6\text{H}_5\text{Si(OC}_2\text{H}_5)_3 \xrightarrow[\text{OH}^-]{\text{H}_2\text{O}}$$

(XI-3)

[9]   [10]

Equilibration of the phenyl silicone prepolymers in dilute solutions gives compounds with cagelike structures. These products, two of which are shown [11, 12], have been isolated as pure crystalline compounds (19, 20). Patents and other reports describe the preparation and polymerization of "T_8," octaphenylsilsesquioxane (5, 6, 35, 40) and "T_{12}," dodecaphenylsilsesquioxane (17) to the soluble ladder polymer [10].

(XI-4)

T_8	T_{12}	
[11]	[12]	[10]

(In the drawings, the vertices represent the locations of the C_6H_5Si groups, the lines the positions of the oxygens connecting them.)

A procedure for degrading the high molecular weight phenyl silicone polymers to hydroxyl-terminated oligomers employs amines as catalysts in pyridine solution (46). The use for these lower molecular weight products is in coatings applications (44). Solutions of the oligomers are advanced to polymers with intrinsic viscosities above 0.1 with the aid of ammonium and amine catalysts.

The polymerization of a trifunctional monomer to a linear, soluble, double-chain polymer is indeed remarkable. The methods that were used to prove the structure of the polymer are also of more than ordinary interest. Solution properties (37), X-ray diffraction studies, infrared and ultraviolet spectral data were all in agreement with the proposed structure. Bond angle calculations showed that the cis-syndiotactic double-chain arrangement was the only possible high polymer of phenyl silsesquioxane units that did not involve angular strain. In other words, the assigned structure represents the only strainless way in which the monomer units can join together. Hopefully, this example of stereoselective bond formation will be a prelude to further advances in double-chain and ordered network polymers (23). Another example has been reported that lends some credence to this hope (68). The bis(cyclotrisiloxane) [13] polymerizes to a brittle solid that has a melting point of 70°–80°C. A similar structure was postulated for the gelled product obtained from the m-tolyl analog of [13]. Proof for structure [14] was not presented, but the reaction has been included as an example of another possible route to double-chain polymers.

Since double-chain polymers of any structure have been an active goal of synthetic polymer chemists for some time, the properties of the double-chain phenyl silicone polymer is of high interest. Enhanced chemical and physical stability has been expected of double-chain polymers because the molecule cannot be degraded by cleavage of a single chemical bond. The phenyl silsesquioxane polymer is soluble in several common solvents, even at extremely high molecular weights, and can be cast into tough, transparent films.

[13]

(XI-5)

[14]

Oriented films obtained by stretching with the aid of solvent swelling were not crystalline but were shown to be laterally ordered by their X-ray patterns (*18*). The glass transition temperature of this amorphous polymer has been reported to be 300°C (*56, 57*), and in another instance greater than 400°C (*6*). Detailed studies of the solution properties of the polymer have shown the polymer to be rodlike at molecular weights of 10,000–50,000 whereas at 50,000–3,000,000 the molecules are coiled (*57, 65, 66*).

Tensile strengths for the polymer were 3500–6000 psi (*18, 24, 40*). Elongations ranged from 3% to 16%. At 250°C, the polymer possessed a tensile strength of 1090 psi and an elongation of 12%; this fact indicates that the glass transition temperature of the polymer must be at least greater than 250°C. A dielectric strength of 6.02 kV/mil was reported (*24*). The thermal stability of the polymer was outstanding, thereby lending some credence to the theory of improved properties from ladder polymers. Weight loss starts at about 500°C in air (*6, 18, 36*). It is also claimed that heating to temperatures of 900°C did not cause degradation of the backbone, but the weight losses that were encountered were due to losses of the organic part (phenyl ring) of the molecule (*6*).

Copolymers incorporating a poly(phenyl silsesquioxane) chain have been described. Careful, low-temperature hydrolysis of trichlorosilanes yields hydroxyl-terminated oligomers [15], (XI-6) (*21, 43*). Reaction of [15] with a variety of difunctional silicon-containing monomers has given soluble copolymers. Polymerization of dimethyldichlorosilane in the presence of a preformed silsesquioxane block gave products possessing intrinsic viscosities of 0.17–0.29 (*21, 43, 45, 47*). A variety of other dichlorosilanes have been copolymerized in a similar fashion (*43, 45, 47*).

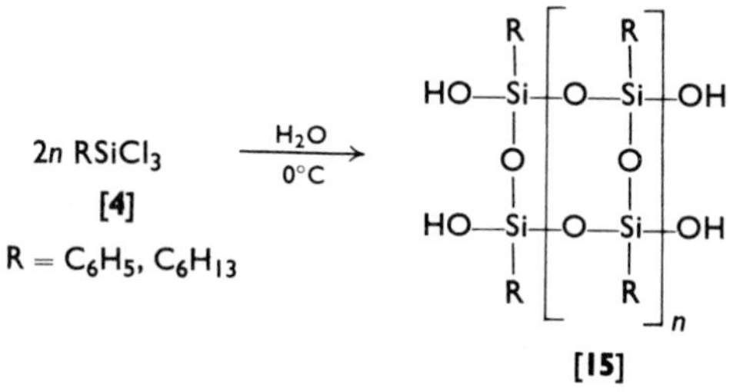

$$2n \ RSiCl_3 \quad \xrightarrow[0°C]{H_2O} \quad [15]$$

$$[4]$$

$$R = C_6H_5, C_6H_{13}$$

(XI-6)

Structural repeat units similar to that of the phenylsilsesquioxane polymer have been thought to be present, at least in part, in poly(aluminophenyl-siloxanes) and poly(titanomethylsiloxanes) (1, 12). Related products have been prepared by reaction of the prepolymeric phenyltrichlorosilane hydrolysate with a large number of metal salts (13).

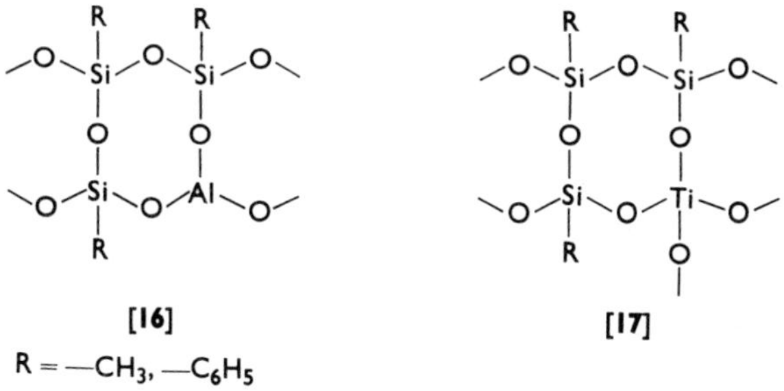

(XI-7)

[16]   [17]

$$R = -CH_3, -C_6H_5$$

METHOD 2. REEQUILIBRATION OF CYCLIC DIMETHYLSILOXANES

Recent evidence supports the presence of macrocyclic poly(dimethylsilox-anes) in dimethyl silicone polymers (22, 23, 31). In what is really a ring-opening followed by a ring-forming polymerization, octamethylcyclotetrasiloxane was heated with traces of potassium hydroxide with or without a diluent and chain-stopped with trimethylchlorosilane/pyridine.

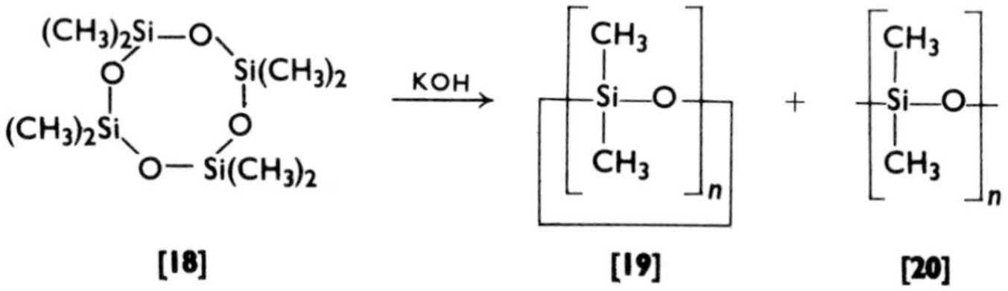

$$\xrightarrow{KOH}$$

(XI-8)

[18]   [19]   [20]

The individual cyclics were isolated by vapor-phase chromatography up to $n = 25$ [19]. Other evidence was obtained that indicates that they are part of a continuous population that extended to at least $n = 400$. Of course, these cyclics constitute only a minor part (2–3%) of the total polymer in commercial methyl silicone oils, gums, and rubbers. The stabilities of the lower cyclic siloxanes parallel those of alicyclic carbon rings containing one-half as many ring atoms. This fact was interpreted to mean that the geometrical character-istics of the $-CH_2-$ and $-O_{1/2}Si(CH_3)_2O_{1/2}-$ units are similar, and that this factor plays a key role in determining the stability relationships in a series of cyclic compounds.

B. Polysilazanes

METHOD 1. BASE-CATALYZED POLYMERIZATION OF SILAZANES AND DISILAZANES

Monomeric silazanes (*3*) and disilazanes (*4*) polymerize on treatment with catalytic amounts of potassium hydroxide at 250°–350°C. The type of ring structure thought to be present in the products is shown in Eq. (XI-9). The glass transition temperature of the polymer [**22**] is dependent on the reaction temperature employed, having varied from 35° to 150°C (*3*).

$$\text{[21]} \qquad \text{[22]} \qquad \text{[23]} \qquad \text{(XI-9)}$$

That these products are probably not homopolymers possessing a single repeat unit is shown by the product obtained from the disilazane [**24**] (*4*). These products [**25**] were described as possessing molecular weights from 21,000 to 300,000. However, their mechanical properties were not reported.

$$\text{[24]}$$

$$\text{[25]} \qquad \text{[26]} \qquad \text{(XI-10)}$$

METHOD 2. POLYMERIZATION OF DIAMINES WITH VARIOUS SILICON-CONTAINING MONOMERS

Reaction of the polysilazane derived from dimethyldichlorosilane and ethylenediamine with cupric chloride is thought to form a double-chain or "ladder" type of polymer (*52*). Although this has been carried out in two discrete steps, the conditions for each are such that it could probably be effected in one. The initial prepolymer [29] is an oil with a molecular weight of 1940 (ebullioscopy). The xylene-soluble ladder polymer [30] is a waxy material, whereas the xylene-insoluble product is a gel containing copper.

$$n(CH_3)_2SiCl_2 + n\ H_2NCH_2CH_2NH_2 \xrightarrow{50°C} \left[\begin{array}{c} CH_3 \\ | \\ -SiNHCH_2CH_2NH- \\ | \\ CH_3 \end{array} \right]_n + (2n\ HCl)$$

[27]　　　　　　　[28]　　　　　　　　　　　　　　[29]

$$Cu(en)_2Cl_2 +
\left[\begin{array}{ccc}
 & CH_3 & \\
 & | & \\
-N- & Si- & -N- \\
| & | & | \\
CH_2 & CH_3 & CH_2 \\
| & | & | \\
CH_2 & CH_3 & CH_2 \\
| & | & | \\
-N- & Si- & -N- \\
 & | & \\
 & CH_3 &
\end{array} \right]_{n/2}
\xleftarrow{\ \ \ \begin{array}{c} CuCl_2 \\ xylene, \\ 140°C \end{array}\ \ \ }
\qquad (XI\text{-}11)$$

[31]　　　　　　　[30]

Further heating with copper chloride causes cross-linking. It was theorized that the nitrogen atoms in the linear prepolymer coordinated with Cu(II) to form a square-planar intermediate in which each Cu(II) acts as a bridge between two chains. The fact that heating the same prepolymer with $BeCl_2$ did not cause rearrangement to a ladder polymer was interpreted to support this view (*53*). Apparently, the tetrahedral coordination of the Be(II) does not cause rearrangement, whereas the square-planar coordination of the Cu(II) is required. This polymer has been used as an additive for infusible silazane polymers to improve the flexibility of coatings derived therefrom (*27*).

Another method to synthesize ladder-type silazane polymers is to react diamines with hexamethylcyclotrisilazane [32] (*54*). Nuclear magnetic resonance studies on the polymers that are formed supported the presence of repeat units [34] and [35]. The products were of low molecular weight.

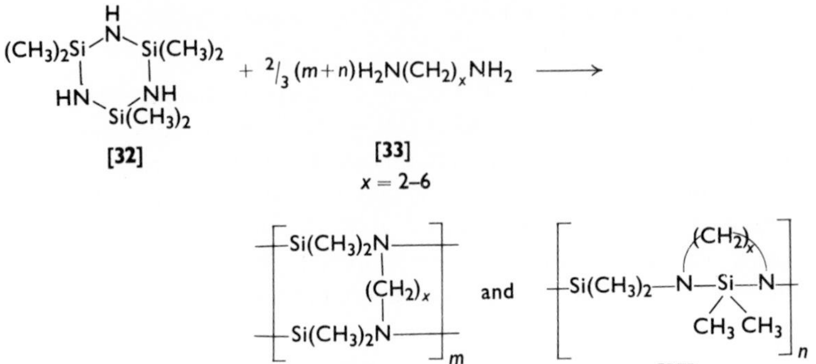

$$[32] \qquad [33]$$
$$x = 2\text{–}6$$

$$[34] \qquad \text{and} \qquad [35] \qquad (XI\text{-}12)$$

Polymers containing cyclodisilazane structures [38] have been prepared by a ring-forming polymerization (32). Benzidine and bis(ethylamino)diphenyl-silane react as shown in Eq. (XI-13).

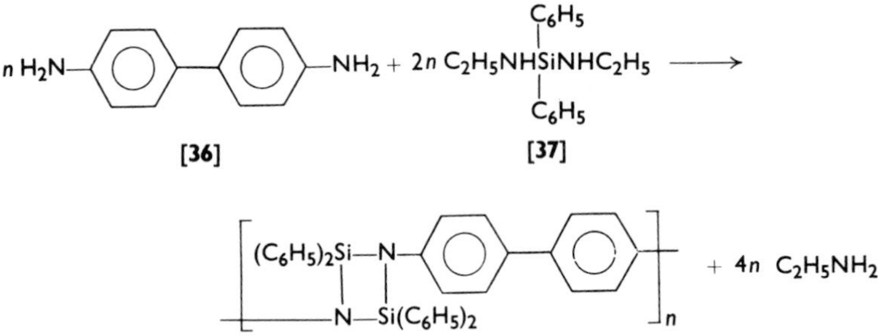

$$[36] \qquad [37]$$

$$+ \, 4n \, C_2H_5NH_2 \qquad (XI\text{-}13)$$

$$[38] \qquad\qquad [39]$$

Heating the reactants in bulk at temperatures of 190°–400°C for up to 59 hours gave a pale yellow solid that was insoluble in organic solvents and boiling water. An alternate route to this type of structure was also described (32). Two related examples are shown in Eq. (XI-14) and (XI-15) (30).

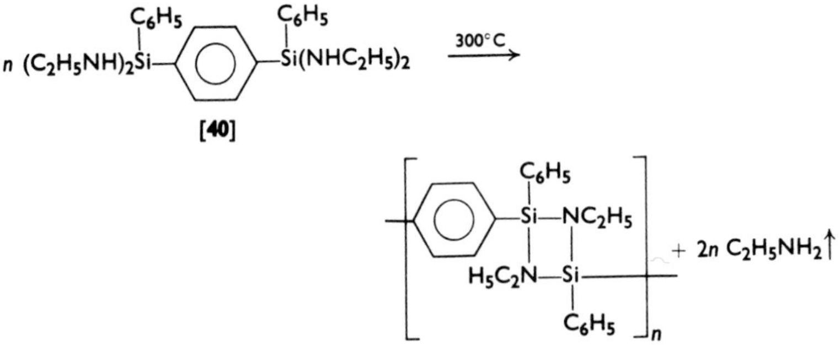

$$[40]$$

$$+ \, 2n \, C_2H_5NH_2\uparrow \qquad (XI\text{-}14)$$

$$[41]$$

$$n \ (C_2H_5NH)_2\overset{C_6H_5}{\underset{}{Si}}\!\!-\!\!\langle\bigcirc\rangle\!\!-\!\!\overset{C_6H_5}{\underset{}{Si}}(NHC_2H_5)_2 \ + \ \overset{NH_2}{\underset{}{\langle\bigcirc\rangle}} \xrightarrow{500°C}$$

[40]   [42]

$$C_2H_5NH_2 + C_6H_6 + \text{Cross-linked polymer, m.p.} > 1000 \ C \qquad (XI-15)$$

[43]

C. Polymetalloxanes

The polymerizations described in this section have been included primarily to broaden the scope of this book and make it more comprehensive. In many cases, the monomer contains a chelate ring on an atom at the site undergoing reaction; and it is conceivable that the ring does not remain intact throughout the polymerization. Rather, it could have opened at an intermediate stage and subsequently reformed. For this reason, they possibly proceed by a ring-forming polymerization.

METHOD 1. REACTION OF MONOMERIC METALLOXANES WITH WATER OR HYDROXYL COMPOUNDS

A polymerization reaction leading to a polymetalloxane that may involve ring-opening as well as ring-forming steps is shown in Eq. (XI-16).

$$n \ C_2H_5O\!-\!Al\!-\!OC_2H_5 + n \ H_2O \longrightarrow \left[-Al\!-\!O-\right]_n + 2n \ C_2H_5OH \qquad (XI-16)$$

[44]   [5]   [45]   [46]

Controlled hydrolysis of dialkoxy(or dichloro)-coordinated metals yields polymers of structure [45]. Polymers containing aluminum–oxygen (51, 55) and titanium–oxygen (41) backbones, and copolymers containing aluminum–oxygen: silicon–oxygen: titanium–oxygen backbones (10, 48) have been reported. Quinolinated (15) and phosphinated (16) aluminum (and titanium or zirconium)-to-oxygen; boron-to-oxygen copolymers form from polymerization of diorganometal monomers with boronic anhydrides. Some related phosphonate–phosphinate titanium copolymers have also been reported (14). Diethoxy and di(isopropoxy) metal derivatives are generally employed in this polymerization. Coordinating ligands that have been used include 8-hydroxy-quinoline, acetylacetone, ethyl acetoacetate, and benzoylacetone. Using pyridine as an acid acceptor for the polymerization of the dichloro metal derivatives is recommended (10). The soluble products obtained from this polymerization did not possess molecular weights in the plastic range. A molecular weight of 10,000 (ebullioscopy) was reported for the polymer from polymerization of diethoxydi(acetylacetonato)titanium (41).

Bis(chlorosilylpropyl) chelates were prepared from the beryllium and aluminum chelates of 4,4-diacetyl-1-butene. Subsequent hydrolysis and polymerization of the beryllium-containing monomers gave products with reduced viscosities of 0.43 (38, 39).

The aluminum-containing monomers give cross-linked powders. Certain copolymers containing both beryllium and aluminum were soluble and of moderately high molecular weights. Thermal decomposition of these polymers begins at 200°C with formation of methane by scission of the trimethylene chains (58).

Hydroxylic compounds of various types have been "polymerized" with uncoordinated and coordinated metalloidal monomers. Diols have also been used instead of water in polymerizations by this method (55). Hydroxyl-terminated dimethylsiloxanes polymerize with coordinated titanium compounds to yield high molecular weight elastomers (8, 11, 59). Bulk polymerization at 180°C in vacuo was effective for reaction (XI-18). The products are elastomeric and possess very high molecular weights. Tetrahydroxy compounds such as pentaerythritol, 2,5-dihydroxyhydroquinone, and 3,3'-

dihydroxybiphenol are reported to yield low molecular weight polymers when heated with silicon tetrachloride and chelated aluminum compounds (34).

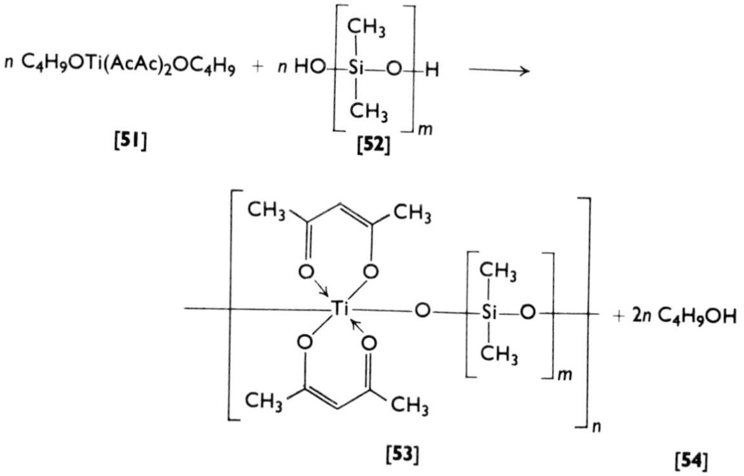

$$n \ C_4H_9OTi(AcAc)_2OC_4H_9 \ + \ n \ HO\left[\begin{array}{c} CH_3 \\ | \\ Si\text{—}O \\ | \\ CH_3 \end{array}\right]_m H \ \longrightarrow$$

[51] [52]

+ 2n C_4H_9OH   (XI-18)

[53]   [54]

A series of chelate polymers has been prepared from tetraalkoxy metals and N,N,N′,N′-tetrakis(2-hydroxyethyl)diamines (33). Dimethylacetamide is used as the solvent. The reactants that are used to introduce silicon and tin are their tetraethoxy derivatives, whereas tetraisopropoxytitanium was used to incorporate titanium. Polymers of different backbone and metal structure were prepared. From the scant data that are reported about the products, correlations of properties versus structure cannot be made. One point of interest is the much higher melting point that was found for the silicon-containing polymer ($R' = +CH_2+_6$ in [58]) as compared to the tin and titanium polymers.

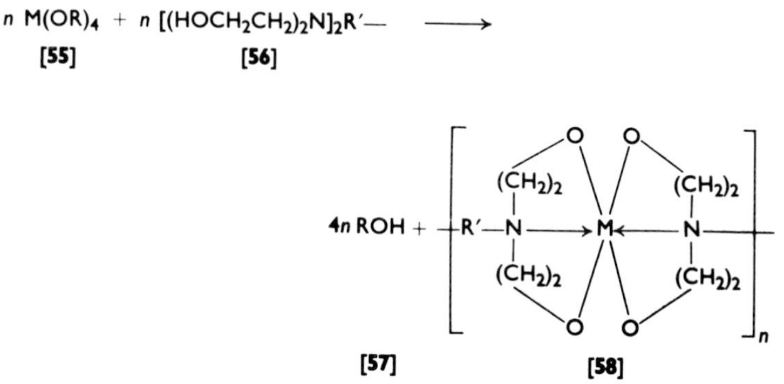

$$n \ M(OR)_4 \ + \ n \ [(HOCH_2CH_2)_2N]_2R'— \ \longrightarrow$$
[55]   [56]

4n ROH +   (XI-19)

[57]   [58]

METHOD 2. ESTER-INTERCHANGE TYPE POLYMERIZATIONS

Ester interchange between pentaerythritol tetraacetate and tetrabutyl titanate is catalyzed by p-toluenesulfonic acid (42). The product is a yellow powder ([**61**], $n = 3$) that melts above 250°C. An analogous silicon-containing polymer was prepared by the same route (42).

n Ti(OC$_4$H$_9$)$_4$ + n C(CH$_2$OOCCH$_3$)$_4$ $\longrightarrow$
  [59]   **[60]**

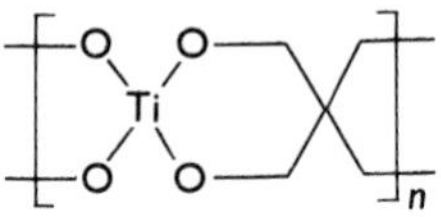

$+$ 4n C$_4$H$_9$OOCCH$_3$ (XI-20)

[61]   **[62]**

Copolymerization of dialkoxytitanium chelates with acyloxystannanes has been used to synthesize tin–titanium copolymers (64). Molecular weight data were not reported.

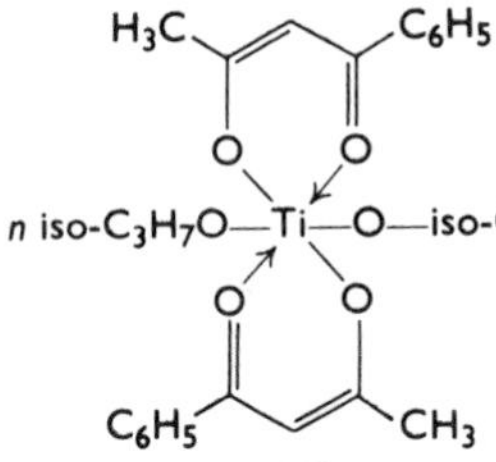

[63]   **[64]**

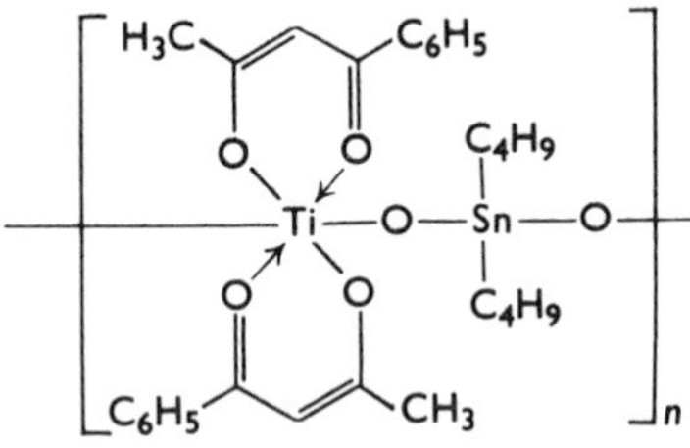

$+$ 2n iso-C$_3$H$_7$OOCCH$_3$ (XI-21)

[65]   **[66]**

A related polymerization is shown in Eq. (XI-22) (63).

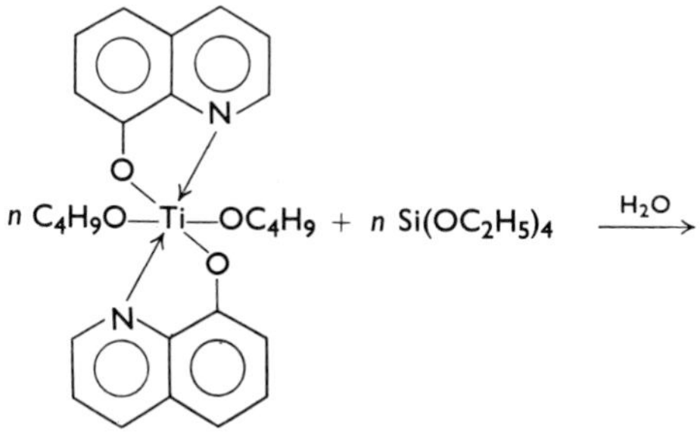

$$n \; C_4H_9O\!-\!\overset{}{Ti}\!-\!OC_4H_9 \; + \; n \; Si(OC_2H_5)_4 \xrightarrow{\; H_2O \;}$$

[67]   [68]

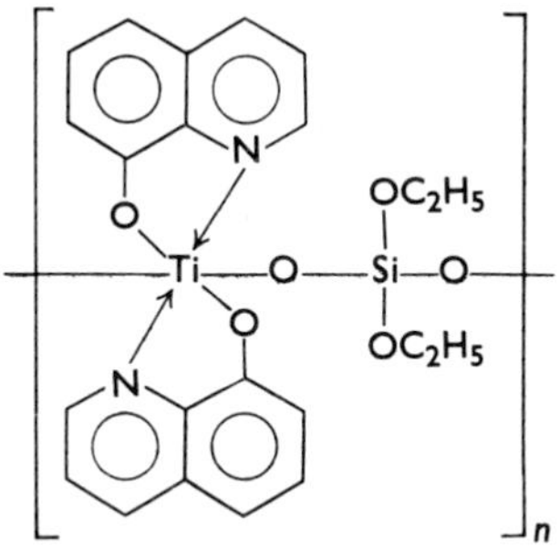

$$+ \; 2n \; C_2H_5OH \; + \; 2n \; C_4H_9OH \qquad \text{(XI-22)}$$

[69]

The polymerization of tetraketones with tetraalkoxy titanates has been described (*28, 29, 41*). Refluxing carbon tetrachloride or benzene is used as the reaction medium. Only low molecular weight materials were obtained from this reaction.

$$n \; Ti(OR)_4 \; + \; n \; (CH_3CO)_2CHR'CH(COCH_3)_2 \longrightarrow$$
$$\;\;\;\; [70] \qquad\qquad\qquad [71]$$

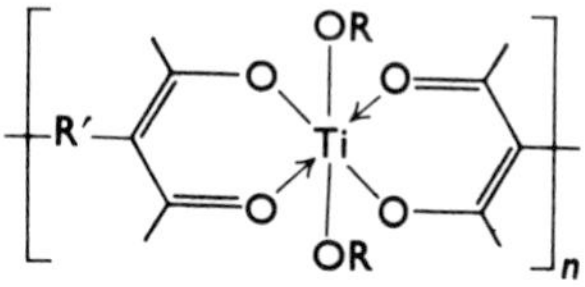

$$+ \; 2n \; ROH \qquad \text{(XI-23)}$$

[72]

A variant of this general polymerization is to employ a chelated metal reactant. Dialkoxyaluminum (*55*) or titanium acetylacetonates (*28, 29*) will react with tetraketones to yield polymers. As the molecular weight data in Table XI.2 (pp. 334–341) show, products with high molecular weights were not obtained from this method either.

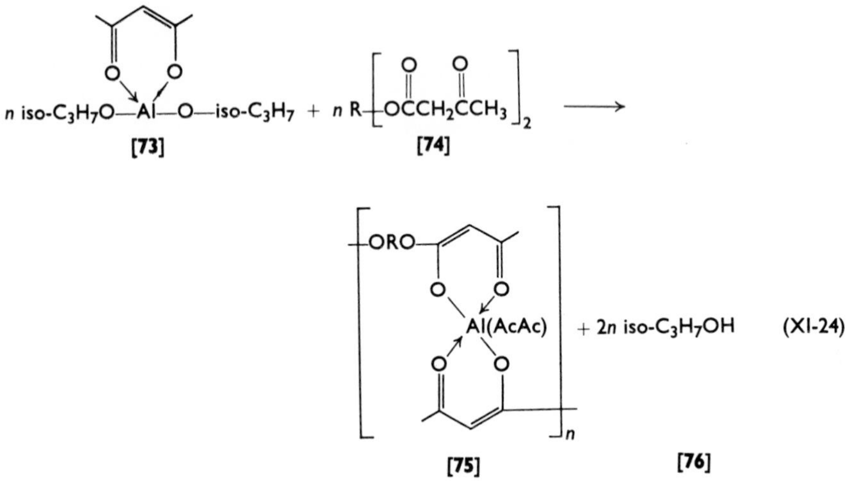

$$n \text{ iso-C}_3\text{H}_7\text{O—Al—O—iso-C}_3\text{H}_7 + n \text{ R} \left[\text{OCCH}_2\text{CCH}_3 \right]_2 \longrightarrow$$

[73]   [74]

$$\longrightarrow [75] + 2n \text{ iso-C}_3\text{H}_7\text{OH} \qquad \text{(XI-24)}$$

[75]   [76]

Another variation that was explored to prepare hexacoordinated aluminum polymers was to prepare a chelate-containing dicarboxylic ester and to submit it to ester exchange with a glycol (55). Initially, reaction was conducted in solution with a final advancing step in bulk *in vacuo* at temperatures to 200°C. However, molecular weights of only about 1000–2000 were obtained. The failure to obtain high molecular weight products from reaction (XI-25) could indicate a mobility of the chelated ligands that complicates the polymerization.

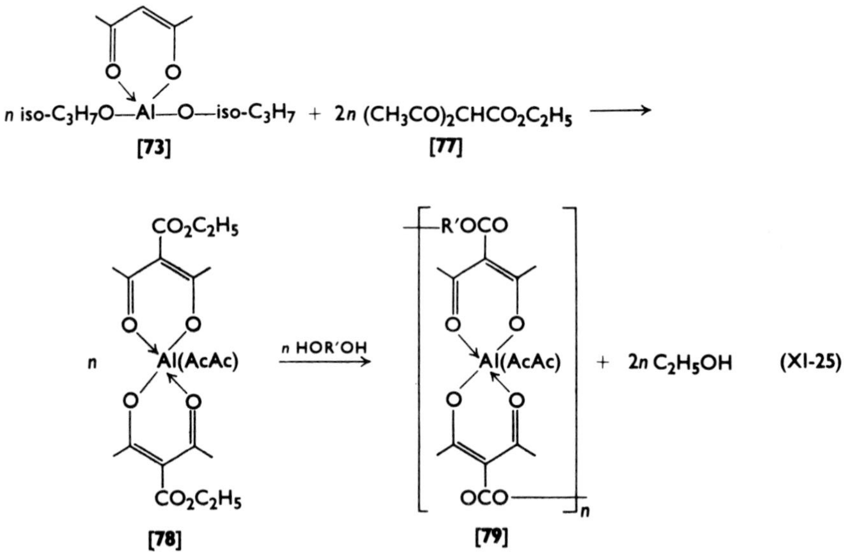

$$n \text{ iso-C}_3\text{H}_7\text{O—Al—O—iso-C}_3\text{H}_7 + 2n \text{ (CH}_3\text{CO)}_2\text{CHCO}_2\text{C}_2\text{H}_5 \longrightarrow$$

[73]   [77]

$$n [78] \xrightarrow{n \text{ HOR'OH}} [79] + 2n \text{ C}_2\text{H}_5\text{OH} \qquad \text{(XI-25)}$$

[78]   [79]

METHOD 3. ALUMINUM–NITROGEN POLYMERS

Heating ethylenediamine with aluminum isopropoxide in hydrocarbon solvents (benzene) gives products for which structure [81] was reported (49). Sodium and sodium methoxide are catalysts for this reaction.

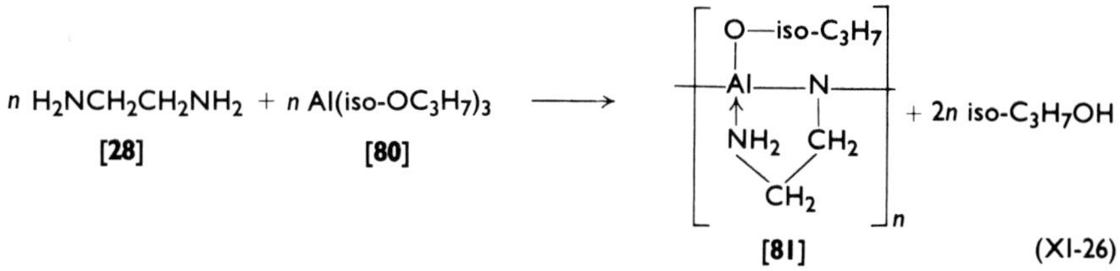

$$n\ H_2NCH_2CH_2NH_2\ +\ n\ Al(iso\text{-}OC_3H_7)_3\ \longrightarrow$$

[28]   [80]

[81]   (XI-26)

$+\ 2n$ iso-C_3H_7OH

The product decomposes as shown in Eq. (XI-27) at 300°C.

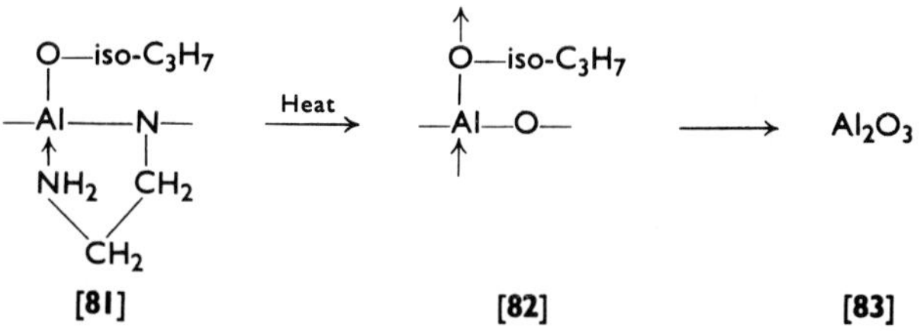

[81]   [82]   [83]   (XI-27)

Along related lines, triethylaluminum reacts with methylamine hydrochloride to yield a product that can be progressively converted to "imide" polymers by controlled pyrolysis (50). Postulated structures are as shown in Eq. (XI-28). Ultimately, aluminum nitride is obtained.

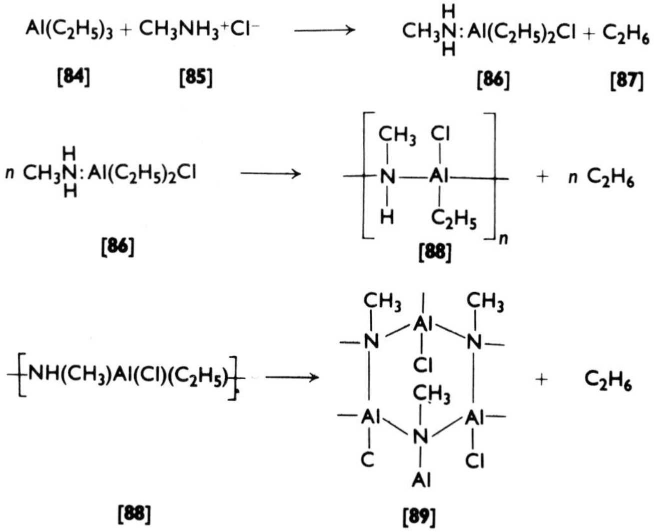

$$Al(C_2H_5)_3\ +\ CH_3NH_3^+Cl^-\ \longrightarrow\ CH_3\overset{H}{\underset{H}{N}}:Al(C_2H_5)_2Cl\ +\ C_2H_6$$

[84]   [85]   [86]   [87]

$$n\ CH_3\overset{H}{\underset{H}{N}}:Al(C_2H_5)_2Cl\ \longrightarrow$$

[86]

[88]   +\ $n\ C_2H_6$ (XI-28)

$$\left[NH(CH_3)Al(Cl)(C_2H_5)\right]\ \longrightarrow$$

[88]

[89]   +\ C_2H_6

TABLE XI.1

Polysiloxanes and Polysilazanes

No.	Structure	Method	Solubility	Molecular weight	Remarks and property data	References
1	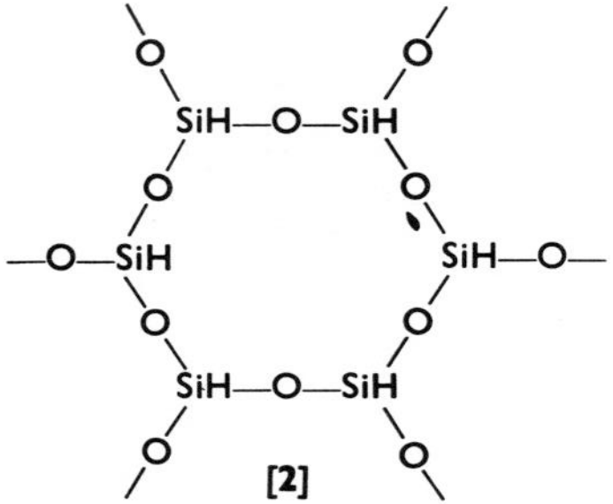 [2]	A, 1	Insoluble	—	Crystalline. $T_m = 280°C$ d	67
2	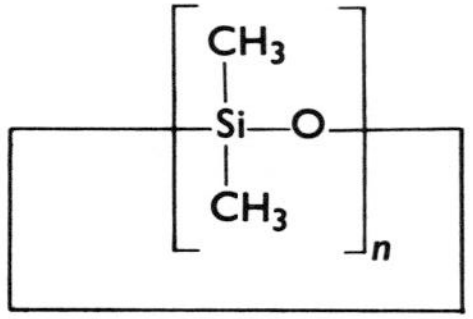 [19] 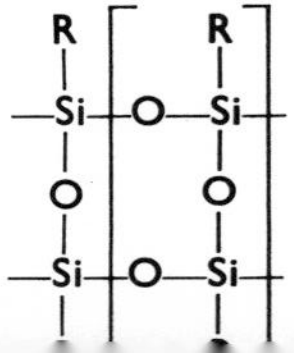	A, 2	—	$n \leqslant 400$	—	22, 31

No.	R	Method	Solubility	Molecular weight	Properties	References
3	R = CH_3	A,1	—	—	—	60
4	R = C_2H_5	A,1	—	—	—	60
5	R = C_5H_{11}	A,1	—	—	—	61
5a	R = C_6H_{13}	A,1	—	—	—	2
5b	R = C_7H_{15}	A,1	—	—	—	2
5c	R = C_8H_{17}	A,1	—	—	—	2
5d	R = C_9H_{19}	A,1	—	—	—	2
6	R = C_6H_5 [10]	A,1	C_6H_6, $CHCl_3$, THF, CH_2Cl_2	$[\eta]$ 6.0; $>10^6$	Not crystalline, but laterally ordered. Infusible. $T_m = 525°C$ d	18, 24–26, 35, 40
		A,1	—	2.6×10^4– 4.1×10^6	$T_g \cong 300°C$ Infusible. See text for additional properties	56, 57, 61, 62
7	R = $4,4'\text{-}C_6H_4\text{—}C_6H_4\text{—}$	A,1	—	—	—	24
8	R = $C_{10}H_7$	A,1	—	—	—	24
9	R = —CH_3 and —C_6H_5	A,1	—	—	—	24
10	[30]	B,2	—	—	Precursor polymer had mol. wt. = 1940	52
11	[38]	B,2	Insoluble	—	Yellow	32

Structure [10]: R = C_6H_5

Structure [30]:

$$\left[\begin{array}{c} * \; * \; * \\ N\text{—}Si(CH_3)_2\text{—}N\text{—}CH_2\text{—}CH_2\text{—}N\text{—}Si(CH_3)_2\text{—}N \\ \mid \qquad\qquad\qquad\qquad\qquad\qquad \mid \\ CH_2 \qquad\qquad\qquad\qquad\qquad\qquad CH_2 \\ \mid \qquad\qquad\qquad\qquad\qquad\qquad \mid \\ CH_2 \qquad\qquad\qquad\qquad\qquad\qquad CH_2 \end{array} \right]_n$$

[30]

Structure [38]:

$(C_6H_5)_2$ Si—N, N—$Si(C_6H_5)_2$, biphenyl unit, repeated n.

[38]

TABLE XI.2
Polymetalloxanes

No.	Structure	Metal (M)	Method	Color	Solubility	Molecular weight	T_m (°C), remarks, and property data	References
1	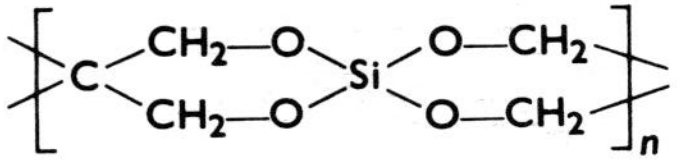	—	C,1	—	Insoluble	—	<300 d	34
2	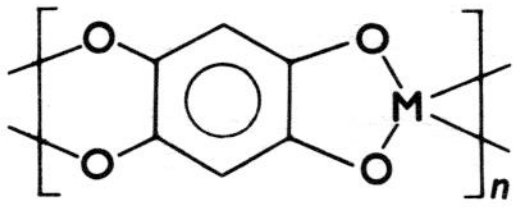	Al(III)	C,1	—	—	—	<300 d	34
3	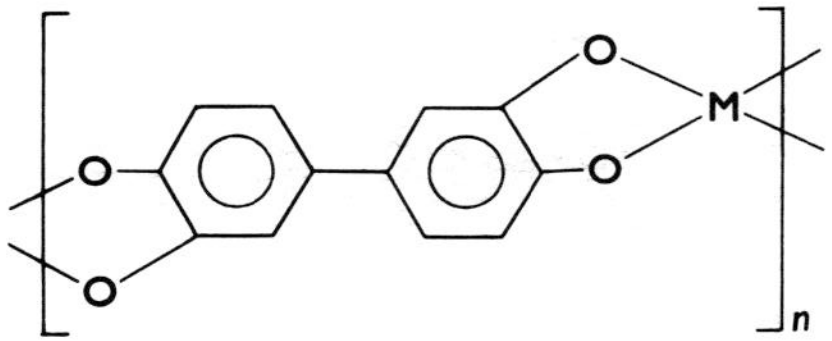	Al(III)	C,1	—	—	—	<300	34
4	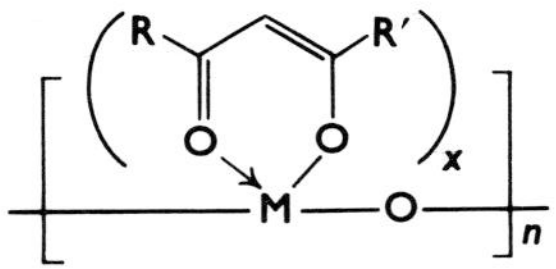 R = R' = CH$_3$; x = 1	Al(III)	C,1	—	—	—	Glassy solid	55
5	R = R' = CH$_3$; x = 2	Ti(IV)	C,1	—	—	12,000	~120	41

6	R = CH$_3$; R′ = OC$_2$H$_5$; x = 1	Al(III)	C,1	—	—	—	Glassy solid	55
7	R = CH$_3$; R′ = C$_6$H$_5$; x = 2	Ti(IV)	C,1	—	CH$_3$OH, C$_6$H$_6$, DMF, acetone	900	—	41
8	R = R′ = OC$_2$H$_5$; x = 1	Al(III)	C,1	—	—	—	Glassy solid	55
9	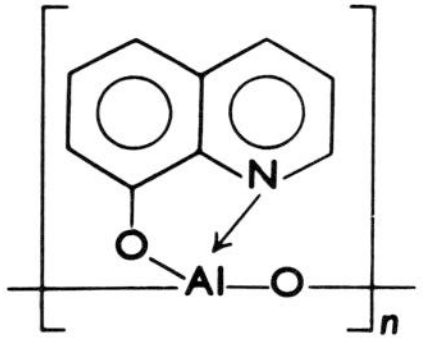	—	C,1	—	—	—	486–498 d	51

* * *

[structure: quinolinolato Al–O polymer]

[45]

[structure: metal acetylacetonate / siloxane polymer, R, R′, R$_2$, R$_3$, M, M′, x, n, m]

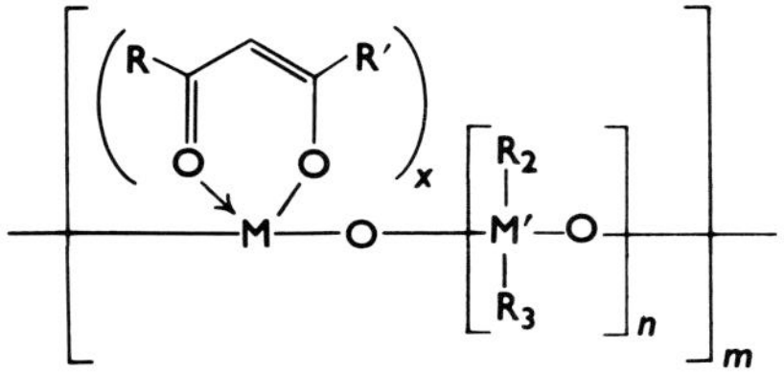

10	R = R$_2$ = R$_3$ = CH$_3$; R′ = OC$_2$H$_5$; x = n = 1; M′ = Si	Al(III)	C,1	Yellow	Aromatics	—	—	48
11	R = R′ = R$_2$ = R$_3$ = CH$_3$; M′ = Si; x = 2; n = 1	Ti(IV)	C,1	Yellow	—	—	—	10

TABLE XI.2—*continued*

Polymetalloxanes

No.	Structure	Metal (M)	Method	Color	Solubility	Molecular weight	T_m (°C), remarks, and property data	References
12	R = R' = CH₃; R₂ = R₃ = C₂H₅ x = 2; n = 1; M = Si	Ti(IV)	C,1	Yellow	—	—	—	10
13	R = R₂ = CH₃; R₃ = —CH=CH₂ x = 2; n = 1; M' = Si	Ti(IV)	C,1	Yellow	—	—	—	10
14	R = R₃ = CH₃; R₂ = C₆H₅ x = 2; n = 1; M' = Si	Ti(IV)	C,1	Yellow	—	—	—	10
15	R = CH₃; R' = C₆H₅; R₂ = R₃ = C₄H₉ x = 2; n = 1; M' = Sn	Ti(IV)	C,1	Amber	C_6H_6, $C_6H_5CH_3$	—	—	64
16	R = R' = R₂ = R₃ = CH₃; M' = Si x = 2; n ≡ Mol. wt. 4500 * * *	Ti(IV)	C,1	—	—	58,000	$T_g = -75°C$	7, 9, 11
17	R₂ = R₃ = CH₃; x = 2 n ≡ Mol. wt. 4500	Ti(IV)	C,1	—	—	97,000	$T_g = -110°C$	7–9, 11

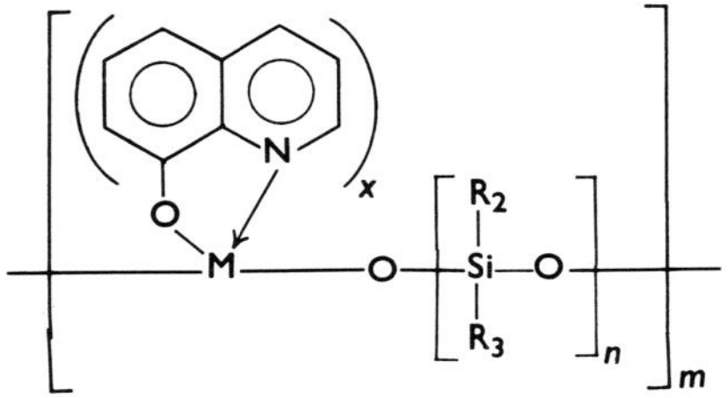

337

No.		M		Color	Solubility		Decomp.	Ref.
18	$R_2 = R_3 = CH_3$; $x = 2$; $n = 2$	Ti(IV)	—	—	—	—	200 d. Brittle to 100°C	38
19	$R_2 = R_3 = OC_2H_5$; $x = 2$; $n = 1$ [69]	Ti(IV)	C,1	—	C_6H_5Cl, $C_6H_5COCH_3$	—	350 d (TGA)	63
20	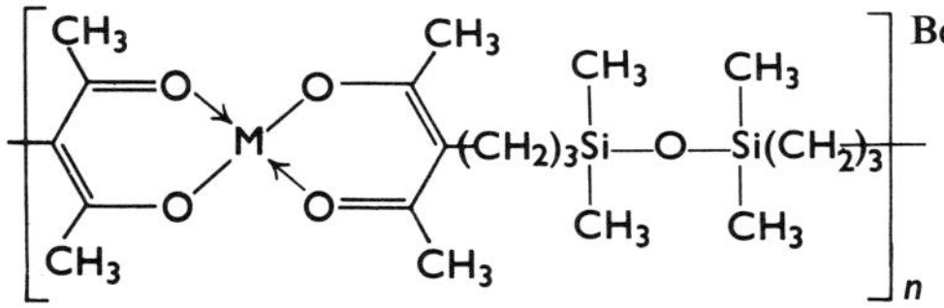 [50]	Be(II)	C,1	Yellow	C_6H_6	η_{red} 0.43	240	38, 39, 58
21	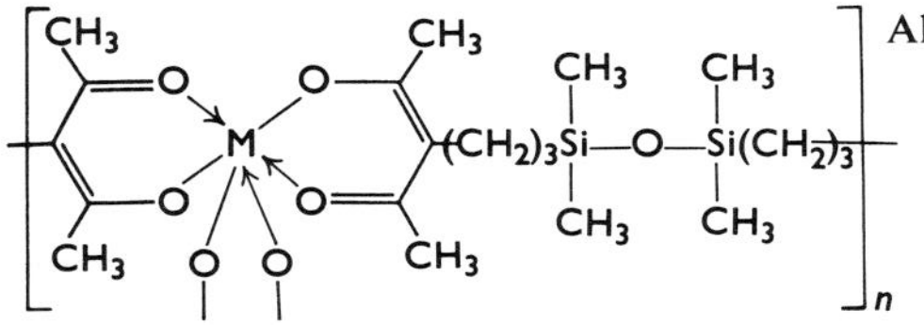	Al(III)	C,1	Orange	Insoluble	—	—	38, 39, 58
22	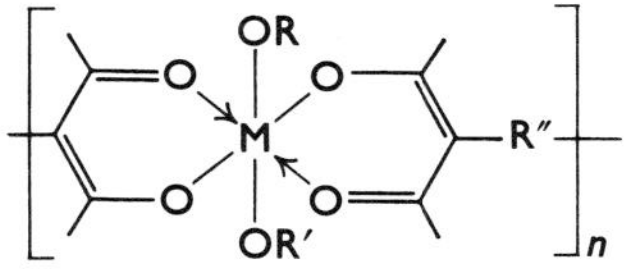 $R + R' = CH_3C{=}CHCOCH_3$; $R'' = $ —	Al(III)	C,2	White	—	—	>360	55

* * *

TABLE XI.2—continued

Polymetalloxanes

No.	Structure	Metal (M)	Method	Color	Solubility	Molecular weight	T_m (°C), remarks, and property data	References
23	R = R' = iso-C_3H_7; R" = —	Ti(IV)	C,2	Yellow	—	—	203 d	28, 29
24	R = R' = n-C_4H_9; R" = —	Ti(IV)	C,2	Yellow	Insoluble	—	170 d. Crystalline	28, 29, 41
25	R + R' = CH_3C=$CHCOCH_3$; R" = —CH_2— 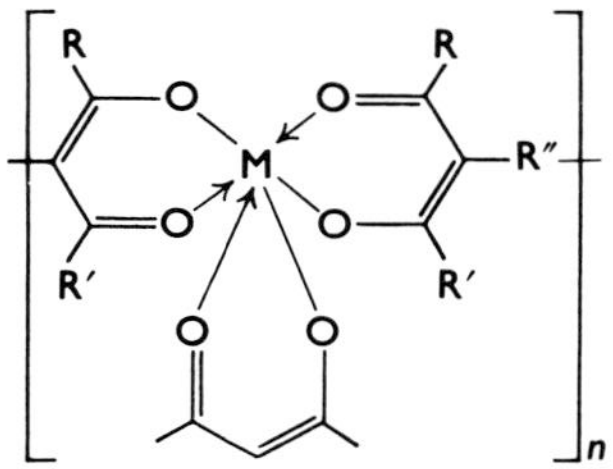	Al(III)	C,2	Red	C_6H_6	1070	90–150	55

* * * *

* * *

No.	Structure	Metal (M)	Method	Color	Solubility	Molecular weight	T_m (°C), remarks, and property data	References
26	R = CH_3; R' = OC_2H_5; R" = —	Al(III)	C,2	Tan	C_6H_6	1860	>360	55
27	R = CH_3; R' = OC_2H_5; R" = —CH_2—	Al(III)	C,2	Brown	C_6H_6	1275	110–130	55
28	R = R' = —C_6H_5; R" = —CH_2—	Al(III)	C,2	Amber	C_6H_6	920	130–145	55

29	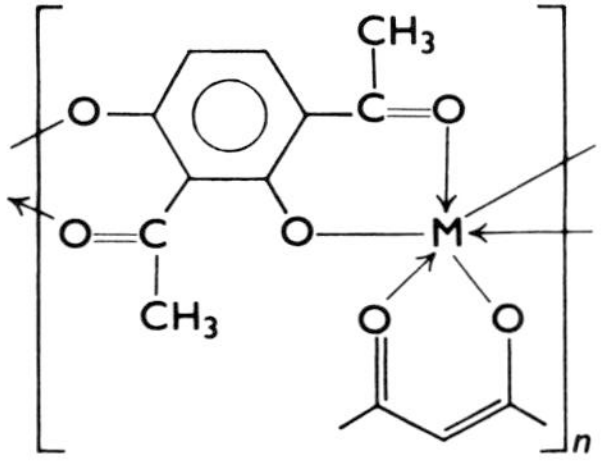 Al(III)		Tan	—	—	>360	55
30 R = $(CH_2)_2$	Al(III)	C,2	Yellow	C_6H_6	2020	105–150	55
31 R = $(CH_2)_4$	Al(III)	C,2	Yellow	C_6H_6	940	75–150	55
32 R = $(CH_2)_5$	Al(III)	C,2	Yellow	C_6H_6	1570	40–110	55
33 R = $-CH(CH_3)(CH_2)_2$	Al(III)	—	—	—	2620	100–110	55
34 R = $(CH_2)_2O(CH_2)_2$	Al(III)	C,2	Yellow	C_6H_6	980	80–150	55
35 R = $(CH_2)_2O(CH_2)_2O(CH_2)_2$	Al(III)	—	—	—	1100	75–130	55

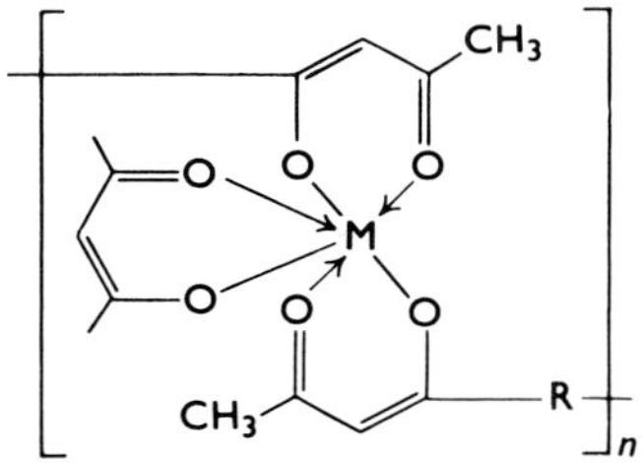

* * *

TABLE XI.2—*continued*

Polymetalloxanes

No.	Structure	Metal (M)	Method	Color	Solubility	Molecular weight	T_m(°C), remarks, and property data	References
36	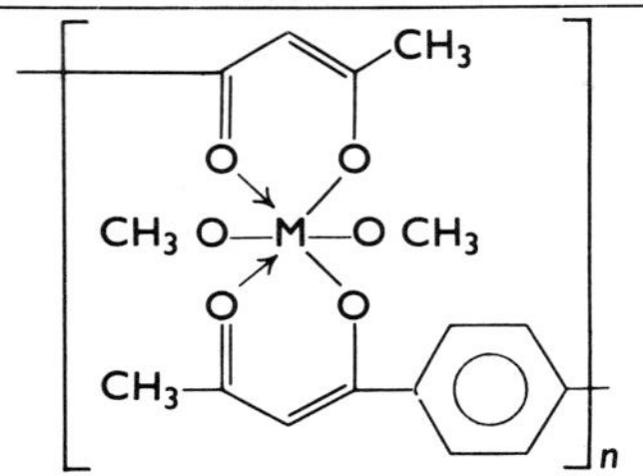	Ti(IV)	C,2	Yellow	Xylene, C_6H_6, DMF	800 (dimer)	—	*41*
37	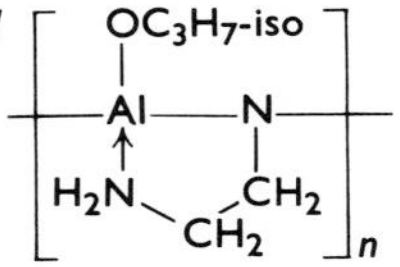 [81]	—	C,3	Various	—	—	300 d	*49*
38	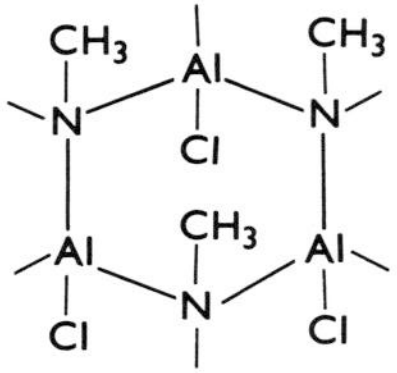 [89]	—	C,3	—	—	—	—	*50*

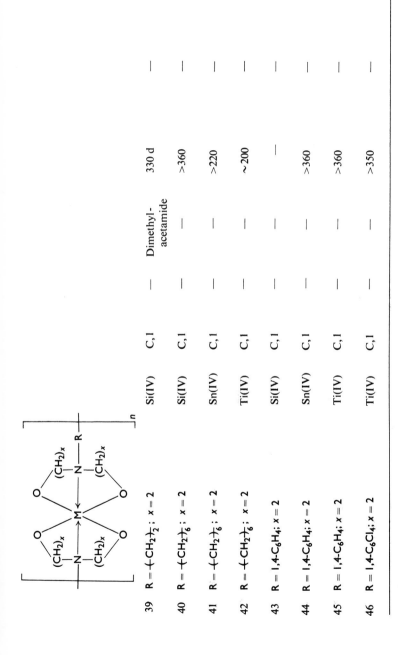

	R	M						Ref.
39	R = $+CH_2+_2$; x = 2	Si(IV)	C,1	—	Dimethyl-acetamide	330 d	—	33
40	R = $+CH_2+_6$; x = 2	Si(IV)	C,1	—	—	>360	—	33
41	R = $+CH_2+_6$; x = 2	Sn(IV)	C,1	—	—	>220	—	33
42	R = $+CH_2+_6$; x = 2	Ti(IV)	C,1	—	—	~200	—	33
43	R = $1,4\text{-}C_6H_4$; x = 2	Si(IV)	C,1	—	—	—	—	33
44	R = $1,4\text{-}C_6H_4$; x = 2	Sn(IV)	C,1	—	—	>360	—	33
45	R = $1,4\text{-}C_6H_4$; x = 2	Ti(IV)	C,1	—	—	>360	—	33
46	R = $1,4\text{-}C_6Cl_4$; x = 2	Ti(IV)	C,1	—	—	>350	—	33

REFERENCES

1. Andrianov, K. A., *J. Polymer Sci.* **52**, 257 (1961).
2. Andrianov, K. A., and Izmaylov, B. A., *J. Organometal. Chem.* (*Amsterdam*) **8**, 435 (1967).
3. Andrianov, K. A., Kononov, A. M., and Makarova, N. N., *Plasticheskie Massy* p. 19 (1966); *Chem. Abstr.* **66**, 5292, 55846y (1967).
4. Andrianov, K. A., Kononov, A. M., and Makarova, N. N., *Vysokomolekul. Soedin.* **A9**, 624 (1967); *Chem. Abstr.* **67**, 3148, 33045e (1967).
5. Andrianov, K. A., Kurakov, G. A., Shushentsova, F. F., Myagkov, V. A., and Avilov, V. A., *Vysokomolekul. Soedin.* **7**, 1477 (1965); *Chem. Abstr.* **63**, 18273 (1965); *Polymer Sci.* (*USSR*) (*English Transl.*) **7**, 1637 (1965).
6. Andrianov, K. A., Kurakov, G. A., Shushentsova, F. F., Myagkov, V. A., and Avilov V. A., *Dokl. Akad. Nauk SSSR* **166**, 855 (1966); *Chem. Abstr.* **64**, 14288 (1966); *Proc. Acad. Sci. USSR, Chem. Sect.* (*English Transl.*) **166**, 151 (1966).
7. Andrianov, K. A., and Lavygin, I. A., *Vysokomolekul. Soedin.* **7**, 1585 (1965); *Polymer Sci.* (*USSR*) (*English Transl.*) **7**, 1755 (1965).
8. Andrianov, K. A., and Lavygin, I. A., *Vysokomolekul. Soedin.* **7**, 1000 (1965); *Chem. Abstr.* **63**, 10122 (1965); *Polymer Sci.* (*USSR*) (*English Transl.*) **7**, 1105 (1965).
9. Andrianov, K. A., Lavygin, I. A., and Pertsova, N. V., *Izv. Akad. Nauk SSSR, Neorgan. Materialy* **1**, 1001 (1965); *Chem. Abstr.* **64**, 6761 (1966).
10. Andrianov, K. A., Pichkhadze, S. V., and Bochkareva, I. V., *Vysokomolekul. Soedin.* **3**, 1321 (1961); *Resins, Rubbers, Plastics* p. 1175 (1962).
11. Andrianov, K. A., Pichkhadze, S. V., and Komarova, V. V., *Bull. Acad. Sci. USSR, Div. Chem. Sci.* (*English Transl.*) p. 238 (1962).
12. Andrianov, K. A., Zhdanov, A. A., and Asnovich, E. Z., *Izv. Akad. Nauk SSSR, Otd. Khim. Nauk* p. 1760 (1959); *Resins, Rubbers, Plastics* p. 227 (1960).
13. Bartholin, M., and Guyot, A., *Compt. Rend.* **264**, 1694 (1967).
14. British Patent 1,016,821 (issued to Distiller's Co., Ltd.) (1966).
15. British Patent 1,025,157 (issued to Distiller's Co., Ltd.) (1966).
16. British Patent 1,043,679 (issued to Distiller's Co., Ltd.) (1966).
17. Brown, J. F., Jr., U.S. Patent 3,000,858 (General Electric Co.) (1961).
18. Brown, J. F., Jr., *J. Polymer Sci.* **C1**, 83 (1963); *Resins, Rubbers, Plastics* p. 1505 (1963).
19. Brown, J. F., Jr., *Am. Chem. Soc., Div. Org. Coatings Plastics Chem., Preprints* **25**, 311 (1965); *Chem. Abstr.* **66**, 2816, 29259q (1967).
20. Brown, J. F., Jr., *Am. Chem. Soc., Div. Polymer Chem., Preprints* **6**, 1123 (1965).
21. Brown, J. F., Jr., French Patent 1,437,889 (Compagnie Française Thomson-Houston) (1966); *Chem. Abstr.* **66**, 361, 3166z (1967).
22. Brown, J. F., Jr., and Slusarczuk, G. M. J., *J. Am. Chem. Soc.* **87**, 931 (1955); *Chem. Abstr.* **62**, 13246 (1965).
23. Brown, J. F., Jr., and Slusarczuk, G. M. J., *Am. Chem. Soc., Div. Polymer Chem., Preprints* **8**, 157 (1967).
24. Brown, J. F., Jr., and Vogt, L. H., Jr., U.S. Patent 3,017,386 (General Electric Co.) (1962).
25. Brown, J. F., Jr., Vogt, L. H., Jr., Katchman, A., Eustance, J. W., Kiser, K. M., and Krantz, K. W., *J. Am. Chem. Soc.* **82**, 6194 (1960).
26. Brown, J. F., Jr., Vogt, L. H., Jr., and Prescott, P. I., *J. Am. Chem. Soc.* **86**, 1120 (1964); *Resins, Rubbers, Plastics* p. 199 (1965).
27. Burks, R. E., Jr., Lacey, R. E., and Christy, C. L., Jr., U.S. Patent 3,311,571 (Southern Research Institute) (1967).

28. Fernelius, W. C., Shamma, M., Davis, L. A., Goldberg, D. E., Martin, B. B., Martin, D. F., and Thomas, F. D., III, WADC Tech. Rept. No. 56-203, Part III (1958).

29. Fernelius, W. C., Shamma, M., Garofano, N. R., Goldberg, D. E., Martin, D. F., and Thomas, F. D., III, WADC Tech. Rept. No. 56-203, Part II (1957).

30. Fink, W., U.S. Patent 3,297,592 (Monsanto Co.) (1967).

31. Flory, P. J., and Semlyen, J. A., *J. Am. Chem. Soc.* **88**, 3209 (1966).

32. French Patent 1,425,306 (issued to Monsanto Co.) (1966); *Chem. Abstr.* **65**, 12366 (1966); also British Patent 1,085,012 (1967).

33. Frühauf, E. J., and Bonsack, J. P., French Patent 1,386,077 (J. T. Baker Chem. Co.) (1965); *Chem. Abstr.* **62**, 14901 (1965).

34. Fujikawa, C. Y., *Dissertation Abstr.* **21**, 3621 (1961).

35. Guyot, A., and Cuidard, R., *Compt. Rend.* **C264**, 1585 (1967).

36. Guyot, A., Cuidard, R., and Bartholin, M., *Intern. Symp. Macromol. Chem., Brussels, 1966 Preprints*, p. 1 (4/32) (1967).

37. Helminiak, T. E., Benner, C. L., and Gibbs, W. E., *Am. Chem. Soc., Div. Polymer Chem., Preprints* **8**, 284 (1967).

38. Hofer, A., Kuckertz, H., and Sander, M., *Angew. Chem. Intern. Ed. Engl.* **4**, 530 (1965).

39. Hofer, A., Kuckertz, H., and Sander, M., *Makromol. Chem.* **90**, 49 (1966).

40. Katchman, A., U.S. Patent 3,162,614 (General Electric Co.) (1964); *Chem. Abstr.* **62**, 10554 (1965).

41. Korshak, V. V., Sladkov, A. M., Luneva, L. K., and Bulgakova, I. A., *Vysokomolekul. Soedin.* **5**, 1288 (1963); *Polymer Sci. (USSR) (English Transl.)* **5**, 363 (1964).

42. Koton, M. M., and Kiseleva, T. M., *Zh. Obshch. Khim.* **36**, 87 (1966); *Chem. Abstr.* **64**, 14086 (1966).

43. Krantz, K. W., French Patent 1,423,143 (Compagnie Française Thomson-Houston) (1966); *Chem. Abstr.* **65**, 12361 (1966).

44. Krantz, K. W., U.S. Patent 3,294,717 (General Electric Co.) (1966); *Chem. Abstr.* **66**, 3694, 38436x (1967).

45. Krantz, K. W., U.S. Patent, 3,294,737 (General Electric Co.) (1966); *Chem. Abstr.* **66**, 4459, 46908t (1967).

46. Krantz, K. W., U.S. Patent 3,294,738 (General Electric Co.) (1966); *Chem. Abstr.* **66**, 4458, 46907s (1967).

47. Krantz, K. W., U.S. Patent, 3,318,844 (General Electric Co.) (1967).

48. Kugler, V., Czech Patent 89,453 (1959); *Chem. Abstr.* **54**, 8154 (1960).

49. Lang, R. F., *Makromol. Chem.* **78**, 1 (1964).

50. Laubengayer, A. W., Smith, J. D., and Ehrlich, G. G., *J. Am. Chem. Soc.* **83**, 542 (1961); *Resins, Rubbers, Plastics* p. 2139 (1961).

51. McCloskey, A. L., Brotherton, R. J., Woods, W. G., English, W. D., Boone, J. L., Campbell, G. W., Jr., Goldsmith, H., Iverson, M. L., Newsom, H. C., Manasevit, H. M., and Petterson, L. L., WADC Tech. Rept. No. 59-761 (1960).

52. Minné, R., and Rochow, E. G., *J. Am. Chem. Soc.* **82**, 5625 (1960).

53. Minné, R., and Rochow, E. G., *J. Am. Chem. Soc.* **82**, 5628 (1960).

54. Morgunova, M. M., Zhuzhgov, E. L., Zaev, E. E., Zhinkin, D. Ya., and Bubnov, N. N., *Chem. Heterocyclic Compounds (USSR) (English Transl.)* **1**, 644 (1965).

55. Patterson, T. R., Pavlik, F. J., Baldoni, A. A., and Frank, R. L., *J. Am. Chem. Soc.* **81**, 4213 (1959); *Resins, Rubbers, Plastics* p. 643 (1960).

56. Pavlova, S. A., Pakhomov, V. I., and Tverdokhlebova, I. I., *Vysokomolekul. Soedin.* **6**, 1275 (1964); *Chem. Abstr.* **62**, 1751 (1965).

57. Pavlova, S. A., Pakhomov, V. I., and Tverdokhlebova, I. I., *Vysokomolekul. Soedin.* **6**, 1281 (1964); *Chem. Abstr.* **62**, 1751 (1965).

58. Sander, M., *Makromol. Chem.* **100**, 139 (1967).

59. Slonimskii, G. L., Andrianov, K. A., Zhdanov, A. A., and Levin, V. Yu., *Vysokomolekul. Soedin*. **A9**, 27 (1967).
60. Sprung, M. M., and Guenther, F. O., *J. Am. Chem. Soc.* **77**, 3990, 3996, 4173, and 6045 (1955).
61. Sprung, M. M., and Guenther, F. O., *J. Polymer Sci.* **28**, 17 (1958).
62. Sprung, M. M., and Guenther, F. O., U.S. Patent 3,017,385 (General Electric Co.) (1962).
63. Sutton, R. A., and Wood, J., British Patent 1,029,040 (Distiller's Co., Ltd) (1966); *Chem. Abstr.* **65**, 3999 (1966).
64. Takimoto, H., and Rust, J. B., U.S. Patent 3,244,645 (Hughes Aircraft Co.) (1966); *Chem. Abstr.* **65**, 822 (1966).
65. Tsvetkov, V. N., Andrianov, K. A., Vinogradov, E. L., Pakhomov, V. I., and Yakushkina S. E., *Vysokomolekul. Soedin.* **A9**, 3 (1967).
66. Tverdokhlebova, I. I., and Lesse, P., *Vysokomolekul. Soedin.* **B9**, 118 (1967); *Chem. Abstr.* **66**, 8078, 86101f (1967).
67. Wiberg, E., and Simmler, W., *Z. Anorg. Allgem. Chem.* **283**, 401 (1956).
68. Wu, T. C., U.S. Patent 3,296,197 (General Electric Co.) (1967); *Chem. Abstr.* **66**, 3701, 38497t (1967).

SUPPLEMENTARY REFERENCE LIST

The following references supplement the reference lists appearing at the end of each chapter. They are arranged by chapter and section or method when applicable.

INTRODUCTION

Gerrard, W., *Plastics Inst. (London) Trans. J.* **35** (117), 509 (1967); *Chem. Abstr.* **67**, 6981 and 73875g (1967).

CHAPTER I

METHOD 1 (p. 1).

Lebsadze, T. N., Tabidze, B. A., and Martirosova, I. A., *Soobshch. Akad. Nauk Gruz. SSR* **48**, 317 (1967); *Chem. Abstr.* **68**, 4877, 50165g (1968).

Kossmehl, G., and Manecke, G., *Makromol. Chem.* **113**, 182 (1968); *Chem. Abstr.* **68**, 11162, 115672s (1968).

Sartori, G., and Cameli, N., Italian Patent 725, 490 (Montecatini Societa Generale per l'Industria Mineraria e Chimica) (1966); *Chem. Abstr.* **69**, 2633, 28121p (1968).

Shopov, I., *Compt. Rend. Acad. Bulgare Sci.* **21** (3), 241 (1968); *Chem. Abstr.* **69**, 318, 3207h (1968).

Shopov, I., *Compt. Rend. Acad. Bulgare Sci.* **21** (5), 439 (1968); *Chem. Abstr.* **69**, 2610, 27859y (1968).

Smith, H. A., and Carrington, W. K., U.S. Patent 3,336,261 (Dow Chemical Co.) (1967); *Chem. Abstr.* **67**, 8612, 91255j (1967).

METHOD 2 (p. 5).

Bach, H. C., U.S. Patent 3,386,966 (Monsanto Co.) (1968); *Chem. Abstr.* **69**, 2631, 28096j (1968).

Bach, H. C., *Am. Chem. Soc., Div. Polymer Chem., Preprints* **9** (2), 1679 (1968).

Berlin, A. A., Liogon'kii, B. I., and Zelenetskii, A. N., *Dokl. Akad. Nauk SSSR* **178**, 1320 (1968); *Chem. Abstr.* **68**, 11103, 115039r (1968).

Liogon'kii, B. I., Zelenetskii, A. N., and Berlin, A. A., *J. Polymer Sci.* **C22**, 443 (1968).

METHOD 3 (p. 6).

Kanbe, M., and Okawara, M., *J. Polymer Sci., Part A-1* **6**, 1058 (1968); *Chem. Abstr.* **68**, 10220, 105721t (1968).

METHOD 5 (p. 9).

Lapitskii, G. A., Makin, S. M., and Berlin, A. A., *Polymer Sci. (USSR) (English Transl.)* **9**, 1423 (1967).

METHOD 6 (p. 11).

Ballester, M., Castaner, J., and Riera, J., U.S. Patent 3,360,574 (1967).

METHOD 8 (p. 13).

Ketley, A. D., U.S. Patent 3,367,902 (1968).

Pinazzi, C., Pleudeau A., and Brosse, J-C., *Compt. Rend.* **C266** (14), 1032 (1968).

Pinazzi, C., Pleudeau A., and Brosse, J-C., *Compt. Rend.* **C266** (17), 1278 (1968).

Takahashi, T., *J. Polymer Sci., Part A-1* **6** (2), 403 (1968); *Chem. Abstr.* **68**, 9298, 96210w (1968).

CHAPTER II

Aso, C., *Kogyo Kagaku Zasshi* **70**, 1920 (1967); *Chem. Abstr.* **68**, 10203, 105529m (1968).
Bardyshev, I. I., Gurich, N. A., and Komshilov, Yu. N., *Zh. Prikl. Khim.* **41** (2), 399 (1968); *Chem. Abstr.* **68**, 9294, 96177r (1968).
British Patent 1,098,536 (1968) issued to Rhone-Poulenc S.A.
Brown, D. W., and Wall, L. A., *Am. Chem. Soc., Div. Polymer Chem., Preprints* **9** (2), 1401 (1968).
Butler, G. B., and Joyce, K. C., *J. Polymer Sci.* **C22**, 45 (1968).
Duck, E. W., Locke, J. M., and Thomas, M. E., *Polymer* **9**, 60 (1968); *Chem. Abstr.* **68**, 5806, 59956y (1968).
Gaylord, N. G., Kössler, I., Matyska, B., and Mach, K., *J. Polymer Sci., Part A-1* **6**, 125 (1968).
Kawai, W., and Ichihashi, T., *Kogyo Kagaku Zasshi* **70**, 2004 (1967); *Chem. Abstr.* **68**, 11103, 115036n (1968).
Kennedy, J. P., and Makowski, H. S., *J. Polymer Sci.* **C22**, 247 (1968).
Kobayashi, S., Saegusa, T., and Furukawa, J., *Kogyo Kagaku Zasshi* **70**, 372 (1967); *Chem. Abstr.* **68**, 2948, 30163b (1968).
Matsoyan, S. G., and Akopyan, L. A., *Armyansk. Khim. Zh.* **20**, 719 (1967); *Chem. Abstr.* **68**, 4875, 50141w (1968).
Meyersen K., and Wang, J. Y. C., *J. Polymer Sci., Part A-1* **5**, 1845 (1967); *Chem. Abstr.* **68**, 4871, 50100g (1968).
Meyersen, K., and Wang, J. Y. C., *J. Polymer Sci., Part A-1* **6**, 2031 (1968).
Ramp, F. L., *J. Macromol. Sci.* **A1** (4), 603 (1967).
Tietz, R. F., U.S. Patent 3,366,616 (E. I. duPont de Nemours & Co.) (1968).
Trifan, D. S., Shelden, R. A., and Hoglen, J. J., *Am. Chem. Soc., Div. Polymer Chem., Preprints* **9**, 156 (1968).
Trifan, D. S., Shelden, R. A., and Hoglen, J. J., *J. Polymer Sci., Part A-1* **6** (6), 1605 (1968); *Chem. Abstr.* **69**, 317, 3191y (1968).
Yamaguchi, T., and Ono, T., *Chem. & Ind.* (*London*) p. 769 (1968).

CHAPTER III

Mikhailov, M., Budevska, Chr., Zabunova, O., and Berlin, A., *Compt. Rend. Acad. Bulgare Sci.* **19**, 803 (1966); *Chem. Abstr.* **66**, 1113, 11222n (1967).
Mukamal, H., Harris, F. W., and Stille, J. K., *J. Polymer Sci., Part A-1* **5**, 2721 (1967); *Chem. Abstr.* **68**, 3918, 40118e (1968).
Netherlands Patent Appl. 67,11057 (1968) issued to Ciba, Ltd.
Renner, A., and Widmer, F., *Chimia* **22** (5), 219 (1968); *Chem. Abstr.* **69**, 336, 3400r (1968).

CHAPTER IV

SECTION B (p. 124).

Armour, M., Davies, A. G., Upadhyay, J., and Wassermann, A., *J. Polymer Sci., Part A-1* **5**, 1527 (1967).
Chauser, M. G., Cherkashin, M. I., Kushnerev, M. Ya., Protsuk, T. I., and Berlin, A. A., *Vysokomolekul. Soedin.* **A10** (4), 916–924 (1968); *Chem. Abstr.* **69**, 1870, 19726n (1968).
Hasegawa, M., and Suzuki, Y., *J. Polymer Sci.* **B5**, 813 (1967).
Hasegawa, M., Suzuki, F., Nakanishi, H., and Suzuki, Y., *J. Polymer Sci.* **B6**, 293 (1968); *Chem. Abstr.* **68**, 11102, 115030f (1968).

Miura, M., Kitami, T., and Nagakubo, K., *J. Polymer Sci.* **B6**, 463 (1968); *Chem. Abstr.* **69**, 3423, 36501c (1968).
Neuse, E. W., and Quo, E., U.S. Patent 3,371,128 (McDonnell Douglas Corp.) (1968).
Slobodin, Ya. M., *Zh. Organ. Khim.* **4**, 179 (1968); *Chem. Abstr.* **68**, 7600, 78642j (1968).
Wojtczak, J., Weimann, L., and Konarski, J. M., *Monatsh. Chem.* **99**, 501 (1968).

CHAPTER V

METHOD 2 (p. 141).

Bennett, M. A., and Saxby, J. D., *Inorg. Chem.* **7**, 321 (1968).

CHAPTER VI

SECTION C (p. 150).

Mizushima, N., Naraba, K., Igarashi, Y., Noake, H., and Imamura, A., Japan. Patent 20,770 ('67) issued to Japan Telegram and Telephone Corp.; *Chem. Abstr.* **68**, 3006, 30747v (1968).
Naraba, T., Mizushima, Y., Noake, H., Nishioka, A., Igarashi, Y., Imamura, A., and Torihashi, Y., *Rev. Elec. Commun. Lab.* (*Tokyo*) **15**, 551 (1967); *Chem. Abstr.* **68**, 322, 3225s (1968).

SECTION D (p. 154).

Berezin, B. D., and Shormanova, L. P., *Vysokomolekul. Soedin.* **A10** (2), 384 (1968); *Chem. Abstr.* **68**, 9308, 96323k (1968).
Cherkashina, L. G., and Berlin, A. A., *Vysokomol. Soedin.* **B9** (5), 336 (1967); *Chem. Abstr.* **67**, 11083, 117424r (1967).
Inoue, H., Kida, Y., and Imoto, E., *Bull. Chem. Soc. Japan* **41**, 684 (1968).
Inoue, H., Kida, Y., and Imoto, E., *Bull. Chem. Soc. Japan* **41**, 692 (1968).
Novikov, G. F., and Frankevich, Ye. L., *Polymer Sci.* (*USSR*) (*English Transl.*), **9**, 659 (1967).

CHAPTER VII

SECTION A (p. 173).

Mikhant'ev, I., and Popova, T. K., *Tr. Probl. Lab. Khim. Vysokomol. Soedin., Voronezh. Gos. Univ.* **4**, 27 (1966); *Chem. Abstr.* **68**, 11103, 115037p (1968).

SECTION B (p. 175).

Sen, D. N., and Umapathy, P., *Indian J. Chem.* **5**, 209 (1967); *Chem. Abstr.* **67**, 7790, 82436s (1967).

SECTION C (p. 180).

O'Connell, J. J., U.S. Patent 3,373,077 (Monsanto Research Corp.) (1968); *Chem. Abstr.* **69**, 340, 3441e (1968).

SECTION E (p. 184).

Terent'ev, A. P., Il'ina, I. G., and Rukhadze, E. G., *Vysokomolekul. Soedin.* **B9** (10), 788 (1967); *Chem. Abstr.* **68**, 1307, 13464h (1968).

CHAPTER VIII

SECTION A (p. 211).

Akopdzhanov, R. G., Vainshtein, E. E., Kefeli, L. M., Keier, N. P., Rubtsova, L. F., Mamaeva, E. K., and Alikina, G. M., *Kinetika i Kataliz.* **8**, 340 (1967); *Chem. Abstr.* **67**, 11089, 117489r (1967).

SECTION C (p. 214).

Marcu, M. M., and Dima, M., *Rev. Roumaine Chim.* **12**, 1353 (1967); *Chem. Abstr.* **69**, 3422, 36496e (1968).

CHAPTER IX

SECTION A (p. 227).

Brown, J. F., Jr., U.S. Patent 3,390,163 (General Electric Co.) (1968).
Ginsberg, A. P., Martin, R. L., and Sherwood, R. C., *Chem. Commun.* p. 856 (1967).
Pearce, N. H., U.S. Patent 3,379,748 (The Distillers Co., Ltd.) (1968).

SECTION B (p. 237).

Cable, H. D., *Dissertation Abstr.* **B27** (10), 3446 (1967); *Chem. Abstr.* **67**, 7787, 82401b (1967).

SECTION C (p. 242).

British Patent 1,063,331 (1967) issued to W. G. Louden.
German Patent 1,255,005 (1967) issued to Minnesota Mining and Manufacturing Company.
Korshak, V. V., Polyakova, A. M., Vinogradova, O. V., Anusinov, K. N., Kolobova, N. E., and Kotova, M. N., *Izv. Akad. Nauk SSSR, Ser. Khim.* p. 440 (1968); *Chem. Abstr.* **68**, 8467, 87625h (1968).

SECTION D (p. 249).

Akiyama, K., Kihara, Y., Akita, M., and Mikogami, C., Japan. Patent 2916 (Tokyo Shibaura Electric Co.) ('67); *Chem. Abstr.* **67**, 8625, 91377a (1967).
Ciana, A., *Ric. Sci.* 37, 835 (1967); *Chem. Abstr.* **68**, 11103, 115042m (1968).
Gemiti, F., Giancotti, V., and Ripamonti, A., *J. Chem. Soc., A* p. 763 (1968); *Chem. Abstr.* **68**, 8473, 87686d (1968).
Giancotti, V., Giordano, V., Randaccio, L., and Ripamonti, A., *J. Chem. Soc., A* p. 757 (1968); *Chem. Abstr.* **68**, 8473, 87685c (1968).
Giordano, F., Randaccio, L., and Ripamonti, A., *Chem. Commun.* p. 1239 (1967); *Chem. Abstr.* **68**, 2962, 30305z (1968).
King, J. P., U.S. Patent 3,384,604 (Pennsalt Chemicals Corp.) (1968); *Chem. Abstr.* **69**, 2634, 28125t (1968).
Korshak, V. V., Krukovskii, S. P., Sheina, V. E., and Danilov, V. G., *Vysokomol. Soedin.* **B10**, 160 (1968); *Chem. Abstr.* **69**, 1043, 10820f (1968).
Korshak, V. V., Krukovskii, S. P., and Wang, J-H., *Vysokomolekul. Soedin.* **B9** (8), 583 (1967); *Chem. Abstr.* **67**, 9471, 100479g (1967).
Korshak, V. V., Krukovskii, S. P., Wang, J-H., and Lokshin, B. V., *Vysokomolekul. Soedin.* **B9** (8), 628 (1967); *Chem. Abstr.* **67**, 9471, 100480h (1967).
Korshak, V. V., Polyakova, A. M., Suchkova, M. D., Anisimov, K. N., and Kolobova, N. E., *Dokl. Akad. Nauk SSSR* **177**, 1348 (1967); *Chem. Abstr.* **68**, 5802, 59921h (1968).

Korshak, V. V., Polyakova, A. M., Vinogradova, O. V., Anisimov, K. N., Kolobova, N. E., and Kotova, M. N., *Izv. Akad. Nauk SSR, Ser. Khim.* No. 3 p. 642 (1968); *Chem. Abstr.* **68**, 10206, 105570t (1968).

Maguire, K. D., and Block, B. P., *J. Polymer Sci., Part A-1* **6**, 1397 (1968); *Chem. Abstr.* **69**, 315, 3174v (1968).

Pitts, J. J., and Hurley, T. J., U.S. Clearinghouse Fed. Sci. Tech. Inform., AD 660367 *Chem. Abstr.* **68**, 11104, 115049u (1968).

Podall, H. E., U.S. Patent 3,949,019 (Melpar, Inc.) (1967); *Chem. Abstr.* **68**, 340, 3403y (1968).

Radice, P. F., U.S. Patent 3,244,207 (Pennsalt Chemicals Corp.) (1967).

Radice, P. F., U.S. Patent 3,383,334 (Pennsalt Chemicals Corp.) (1968).

Radice, P. F., and Saraceno, A. J., U.S. Patent 3,383,334 (Pennsalt Chemicals Corp.) (1968); *Chem. Abstr.* **69**, 2631, 28101g (1968).

Saraceno, A. J., U.S. Patent 3,384,605 (Pennsalt Chemicals Corp.) (1968); *Chem. Abstr.* **69**, 1878, 19811m (1968).

Saraceno, A. J., King, J. P., and Block, B. P., *J. Polymer Sci.* **B6**, 15 (1968); *Chem. Abstr.* **68**, 4903, 50457d (1968).

Slota, P. J., Jr., Freeman, L. P., and Fetter, N. R., *J. Polymer Sci., Part A-1* **6**, 1975 (1968); *Chem. Abstr.* **69**, 2568, 27486z (1968).

Vdovenko, V. M., Skoblo, A. I., Suglobov, D. N., Shcherbakova, L. L., and Shcherbakov, V. A., *Zh. Neorgan. Khim.* **12** (10), 2863 (1967); *Chem. Abstr.* **68**, 9295, 96186t (1968).

CHAPTER X

SECTION B (p. 305).

Lyon, C. B., Nemec, J. W., and Unger, V. H., U.S. Patent 3,379,610 (Rohm & Haas Co.) (1968).

Netherlands Patent Appl. 67, 11775 (1968) issued to Soc. Italiana Resine.

CHAPTER XI

SECTION A (p. 317).

Andrianov, K. A., Khananashvili, L. M., and Zaval'nyi, V. G., *Plasticheskie Massy* No. 6, p. 48 (1967); *Chem. Abstr.* **68**, 6721, 69448y (1968).

Andrianov, K. A., and Makarova, N. N., *Bull. Acad. Sci. USSR, Div. Chem. Sci.* (*English Transl.*) p. 1339 (1967).

Andrianov, K. A., Petrashko, A. I., Bebchuk, T. S., Pashintseva, G. I., and Golubkov, G. E., *Vysokomolekul. Soedin.* **A9**, 2025 (1967).

British Parent 1,089,664 (1967) issued to General Electric Company.

Brown, J. F., Jr., U.S. Patent 3,378,575 (General Electric Co.) 1968).

Cekada, J., Jr., U.S. Patent 3,355,399 (Dow Corning Corp.) (1967).

Krantz, K. W., U.S. Patent 3,372,133 (General Electric Co.) (1968).

Laukevics, J., Tuten, A., Sprogis, J., Maijs, L., Steinbergs, O., and Vaivads, A., German Patent 1,244,782 (Central Construction Bureau for Administration of the Chemical and Silicate Ceramic Industries, Riga) (1967); *Chem. Abstr.* **67**, 7763, 82262g (1967).

Titkova, L. V., and Vinogradov, G. V., *Probl. Fiziol-Khim. Mekh. Voloknistykh Poristykh Dispersnykh Strukt Mater., Mater. Konf. Riga* p. 611 (1965).

Tkachuk, B. V., Bushin, V. V., Kolotyrkin, V. M., and Smetankina, N. P., *Vysokomolekul. Soedin.* **A9**, 2018 (1967).

Tsvetkov, V. N., Andrianov, K. A., Shtennikova, I. N., Okhrimenko, G. I., Andreeva, L. N., Fomin, G. A. and Pakhomov, V. I., *Vysokomolekul. Soedin.* **A10**, 547 (1968); *Chem. Abstr.* **69**, 1049, 10889k (1968).
Tsvetkov, V. N., Andrianov, K. A., Vinogradov, E. L., Shtennikova, I. N., Yakushkina, S. E., and Pakhomov, V. I., *J. Polymer Sci.* **C23** (1), 385 (1968).
Wu, T. C., U.S. Patent 3,354,119 (General Electric Co.) (1967).

SECTION B (p. 322).

Andrianov, K. A., and Kononov, A. M., *J. Macromol. Sci.* **A1**, 439 (1967).
Anonymous, *Chem. Week* **102** (25), 83 (1968).
Aylett, B. J., *Organometal. Chem. Rev.* **3**, 151 (1968).
Fink, W., *Helv. Chim. Acta* **51** (4), 954 (1968); *Chem. Abstr.* **69**, 2617, 27934u (1968).
French Patent 1,501,551 (Monsanto Co.) (1967).
French Patent 1,505,664 (1967) issued to Monsanto Co.

SECTION C (p. 325).

Cullingworth, A. R., Gosling, K., Smith, J. D., and Wharmby, D., U.S. Clearinghouse Fed. Sci. Tech. Inform., AD 655807; *Chem. Abstr.* **68**, 11104, 115050n (1968).
Giddings, S. A., U.S. Patent 3,347,887 (American Cyanamid Co.) (1967).
Kauder, O., U.S. Patent 3,384,649 (Argus Chemical Corp.) (1968); *Chem. Abstr.* **69**, 1876, 19796k (1968).
Sander, M., and Kuckertz, H., German Patent 1,242,877 (Fed. Republic of Germany) (1967); *Chem. Abstr.* **68**, 2996, 30646m (1968).

REVIEWS

Review on polysiloxanes and coordination polymers:
Delman, A. D., *Rev. Macromol. Chem.* **2**, 153 (1968); *Chem. Abstr.* **68**, 10203, 105535k (1968).

General review on coordination polymers:
Jones, R. D. G., and Power, L. F., *Proc. Roy. Australian Chem. Inst.* **35**, 43 (1968); *Chem. Abstr.* **68**, 11095, 114939x (1968).

Author Index

Numbers in parentheses are reference numbers and indicate that an author's work is referred to, although his name is not cited in the text. Numbers in italics show the page on which the complete reference is listed.

A

Abel, E. W., 139(1), 140(1), *144*, 303(24), 308(24), 311(24), *316*
Abdul-Karim, A., 53(41), 74(41), *93*
Abdulla-Zade, E. A., 185(10), *207*
Acres, G. J. K., 159(1), *169*
Adachi, J., 175(1), 190(1), *207*
Aftergut, S., 145(20), 160(20), *169*
Aitken, I. D., xxviii(1, 2), *xxxii*
Akopdzhanov, R. G., 183(72), *209*, 211(35), *226*
Alam, A., 176(9), 191(9), 192(9), *207*
Alder, K., 99(1, 2, 3), *119*
Alexander, R. J., 34(1), 55(1), *92*, 140(2), 143(2), *144*
Alfred, L., 174(53), *208*, 230(98), *299*
Alikina, J. M., 212(21), 216(21), *225*
Amon, W. F., 222(1), *225*
Andrianov, K. A., xxviii(3), *xxxii*, 254(1,2), 295(1,2), *296*, 317(2), 319(5,6), 320(6, 65), 321(1,12), 322(3,4), 325(10), 326(8, 10, 11, 59), 335(10), 336(7, 8, 9, 10, 11), *342, 344*
Angelo, R. J., 32(26), *92*, 248(3), 254(3), 286(3), *296*
Anufrienko, V. F., 211(12), 212(12), 216(12), 218(12), *225*
Anyos, T., 103(26), 116(26), 117(26), *119*
Arbuzova, I. A., 35(2), 69(2), *92*
Argabright, P. A., 100(18), 102(17), *119*
Artemova, V. A., 260(79), 261(79), *298*
Artemova, V. S., 229(78), 238(77), 239(77), 261(78), 277(77), 278(77), *298*
Aseev, Y. G., 153(64), 156(64), 163(64), *171*
Aseeva, R. M., 159(62), *170*
Aseyev, Yu. J., 156(11), 159(11), 164(11), 165(11), *169*
Asnovich, E. Z., 321(12), *342*
Aso, C., 31(4), 38(3, 6, 7), 49(5), 59(5, 6, 7), *92*
Aspey, S. A., 183(49), *208*
Atlas, S. M., xxviii(4), *xxxii*

Audrieth, L. F., xxviii(32), *xxxii*
Avetyan, M. G., 36(8, 9, 39, 102), 66(101), 67(9, 101), 68(9, 39), 77(102), 78(102), *92, 93, 95*
Avilov, V. A., 319(5, 6), 320(6), *342*

B

Babchinitser, T. M., 176(47), 179(46), 180(47), 192(42, 47), 193(46, 47), *208*, 237(75), 238(80), 242(75), 260(79), 261(75, 79), 278(75), *298*
Badzhadze, L. I., 183(68), *209*, 211(34), 216(34), 217(34), *226*, 306(21), 313(21), 314(21), *316*
Baenziger, N. C., 140(2, 3, 4), 143(2), *144*
Bailar, J. C., Jr., xxviii(5,6), *xxxii*, 154(4, 26), 155(4), 164(3, 4, 26), *169*, 173(2, 4, 5), 174(4, 5), 175(4, 5), 180(21), 181(4), 183(4), 188(2, 4), 189(4, 5), 192(4, 5), 193(2, 3, 4, 5), 194(4, 5), *207*, 211(2, 3, 4), 216(2, 3, 4), 219(2, 3, 4), *225*, 254(4, 5), 269(4, 5), 270(4, 5), *296*
Bailes, R. H., 237(6), 274(6), 277(6), *296*
Bailey, W. J., 99(4, 5), 100(6, 7), 102(6), 103(7), 106(5, 6), 107(4, 5, 6), 108(5, 6), 109(5, 6), 110(5, 6), 116(7), 117(7), *119*
Bajic, V., 238(39, 40), 278(39, 40), 279(39, 40), *297*
Baker, W. O., 1(1), *29*, 129(1), *136*
Balabanov, E. I., 156(23), 158(23), 159(5, 10, 23, 33), 164(10, 23), 165(10), 166(10), 167(10), *169, 170*
Balabanov, E. M., 156(11), 159(11), 164(11), 165(11), *169*
Baldoni, A. A., 233(105), 271(105), 272(105), 273(105), *299*, 325(55), 326(55), 329(55), 330(55), 334(55), 335(55), 337(55), 338(55), 339(55), *343*
Ball, L. E., 49(10), 70(10), *92*
Ballester, M., 11(2), 15(2), 16(2), 26(2), *29*

Subject Index

Numbers in italics refer to table entries.